Jamie Lawson

GCSE AQA

Biology

Complete Revision and Practice

Contents

How Science Works

Theories Come, Theories Go 1
Your Data's Got to Be Good 3
Bias and How to Spot It 5
Science Has Limits 6

Biology 1a — Human Biology

The Nervous System 8
Reflexes 9
Hormones 11
Hormonal and Nervous Responses 12
Warm-Up and Exam Questions 13
The Menstrual Cycle 14
Controlling Fertility 16
Homeostasis 17
Warm-Up and Exam Questions 19
Diet and Exercise 20
Weight Problems 21
Salt and Cholesterol 22
Cholesterol 23
Warm-Up and Exam Questions 24
Drugs 25
Tobacco 26
Alcohol and Tobacco 27
More About Drugs 28
Health Claims 29
Warm-Up and Exam Questions 31
Pathogens 32
Fighting Disease 33
Treating Disease — Past and Future 36
Warm-Up and Exam Questions 37
Revision Summary for Biology 1a 38

Biology 1b — Evolution and Environment

Adaptation 39
Populations and Competition 41
Warm-Up and Exam Questions 43
Variation in Plants and Animals 44
Genes, Chromosomes and DNA 45
Reproduction 46
Warm-Up and Exam Questions 48
Cloning 49
Genetic Engineering 51
Warm-Up and Exam Questions 53
Evolution 54
Warm-Up and Exam Questions 56
Human Impact on the Environment 57
The Greenhouse Effect 59
Climate Change 61
Sustainable Development 63
Warm-Up and Exam Questions 65
Exam Questions 66
Revision Summary for Biology 1b 67

Biology 2(i) — Life Processes

Cells 68
Cells, Tissues, Organs and Systems 69
Specialised Cells 70
Diffusion 72
Osmosis 73
Warm-Up and Exam Questions 75
Photosynthesis 76
The Rate of Photosynthesis 77
Warm-Up and Exam Questions 80
How Plants Use the Glucose 81
Minerals for Healthy Growth 82
Warm-Up and Exam Questions 83
Pyramids of Number and Biomass 84
Energy Transfer 85
Decay 86
Managing Food Production 87
The Carbon Cycle 89
Warm-Up and Exam Questions 90
Exam Questions 91
Revision Summary for Biology 2(i) 92

Contents

Biology 2(ii) — Enzymes and Homeostasis

Biological Catalysts — Enzymes ... 93
Enzymes and Respiration ... 95
Warm-Up and Exam Questions ... 96
Enzymes and Digestion ... 97
The Digestive System ... 98
Uses of Enzymes ... 99
Warm-Up and Exam Questions ... 100
Homeostasis ... 101
The Kidneys and Homeostasis ... 103
Warm-Up and Exam Questions ... 105
Controlling Blood Sugar ... 106
Insulin and Diabetes ... 108
Warm-Up and Exam Questions ... 110
Revision Summary for Biology 2(ii) ... 111

Biology 2(iii) — Genetics

DNA ... 112
DNA Fingerprinting ... 113
Mitosis ... 114
Meiosis ... 115
Warm-Up and Exam Questions ... 116
Stem Cells ... 117
X and Y Chromosomes ... 119
Warm-Up and Exam Questions ... 121
The Work of Mendel ... 122
Genetic Diagrams ... 123
Genetic Disorders ... 124
Screening for Genetic Disorders ... 125
More Genetic Diagrams ... 126
Warm-Up and Exam Questions ... 128
Exam Questions ... 129
Revision Summary for Biology 2(iii) ... 130

Biology 3(i) — Life Processes 2

Gas and Solute Exchange ... 131
The Respiratory System ... 133
Diffusion Through Cell Membranes ... 134
Active Transport ... 135
Warm-Up and Exam Questions ... 136
The Circulation System ... 137
Capillaries and Blood ... 138
Exercise ... 139
Exercise and Anaerobic Respiration ... 140
Warm-Up and Exam Questions ... 141
Kidneys ... 142
Kidney Failure ... 143
Warm-Up and Exam Questions ... 145
Revision Summary for Biology 3(i) ... 146

Biology 3(ii) — Microorganisms

The Theory of Biogenesis ... 147
Food and Drink from Microorganisms ... 148
Using Yeast ... 149
Microorganisms in Industry ... 150
Warm-Up and Exam Questions ... 152
Fuels from Microorganisms ... 153
Using Microorganisms Safely ... 156
Warm-Up and Exam Questions ... 157
Revision Summary for Biology 3(ii) ... 158

Exam Skills

Thinking in Exams ... 159
Answering Experiment Questions ... 160

Practice Exam Papers ... 165
Answers ... 222
Index ... 233

Published by Coordination Group Publications Ltd.

Editors:
Charlotte Burrows, Murray Hamilton and Karen Wells.

Contributors:
James Foster, Paddy Gannon, Gemma Hallam, Philip Rushworth and Adrian Schmit.

Proofreading:
Rosie Gillham.

ISBN: 978 1 84762 543 4

With thanks to Laura Jakubowski for copyright research.

Groovy website: www.cgpbooks.co.uk
Printed by Elanders Hindson Ltd, Newcastle upon Tyne.
Jolly bits of clipart from CorelDRAW®

Based on the classic CGP style created by Richard Parsons.

Theories Come, Theories Go

SCIENTISTS ARE ALWAYS RIGHT — OR ARE THEY?

Well it'd be nice if that were so, but it just ain't — never has been and never will be. Increasing scientific knowledge involves making mistakes along the way. Let me explain...

Scientists come up with **Hypotheses** — then **Test** them

1) Scientists try and explain things. Everything.

2) They start by observing or thinking about something they don't understand — it could be anything, e.g. planets in the sky, a person suffering from an illness, what matter is made of... anything.

3) Then, using what they already know (plus a bit of insight), they come up with a hypothesis (a theory) that could explain what they've observed.

Hundreds of years ago, we thought demons caused illness.

Remember, a hypothesis is just a theory, a belief. And believing something is true doesn't make it true — not even if you're a scientist.

4) So the next step is to try and convince other scientists that the hypothesis is right — which involves using evidence. First, the hypothesis has to fit the evidence already available — if it doesn't, it'll convince no one.

5) Next, the scientist might use the hypothesis to make a prediction — a crucial step. If the hypothesis predicts something, and then evidence from experiments backs that up, that's pretty convincing.

This doesn't mean the hypothesis is true (the 2nd prediction, or the 3rd, 4th or 25th one might turn out to be wrong) — but a hypothesis that correctly predicts something in the future deserves respect.

A hypothesis is a good place to start

You might have thought that science was all about facts... well, it's not as cut and dried as that — you also need to know about the process that theories go through to become accepted, and how those theories change over time. Remember, nothing is set in stone...

Theories Come, Theories Go

Other scientists will **Test** the hypotheses too

1) Now then... other scientists will want to use the hypothesis to make their own predictions, and they'll carry out their own experiments. (They'll also try to reproduce earlier results.) And if all the experiments in all the world back up the hypothesis, then scientists start to have a lot of faith in it.
2) However, if a scientist somewhere in the world does an experiment that doesn't fit with the hypothesis (and other scientists can reproduce these results), then the hypothesis is in trouble. When this happens, scientists have to come up with a new hypothesis (maybe a modification of the old theory, or maybe a completely new one).
3) This process of testing a hypothesis to destruction is a vital part of the scientific process. Without the 'healthy scepticism' of scientists everywhere, we'd still believe the first theories that people came up with — like thunder being the belchings of an angered god (or whatever).

Then we thought it was caused by 'bad blood' (and treated it with leeches).

If **Evidence** supports a hypothesis, it's **Accepted — For Now**

1) If pretty much every scientist in the world believes a hypothesis to be true because experiments back it up, then it usually goes in the textbooks for students to learn.

Now we know most illnesses are due to microorganisms.

2) Our currently accepted theories are the ones that have survived this 'trial by evidence' — they've been tested many, many times over the years and survived (while the less good ones have been ditched).
3) However... they never, never become hard and fast, totally indisputable fact.

You can never know... it'd only take one odd, totally inexplicable result, and the hypothesising and testing would start all over again.

You expect me to believe that — then show me the evidence

If scientists think something is true, they need to produce evidence to convince others — it's all part of testing a hypothesis. One hypothesis might survive these tests, while others won't — it's how things progress. And along the way some hypotheses will be disproved — i.e. shown not to be true. So, you see... not everything scientists say is true. It's how science works.

Your Data's Got to Be Good

Evidence is the key to science — but not all evidence is equally good.
The way that evidence is gathered can have a big effect on how trustworthy it is.

Lab Experiments are better than Rumour or Small Samples

1) Results from controlled experiments in laboratories are great. A lab is the easiest place to control variables so that they're all kept constant (except for the one you're investigating).

   This makes it easier to carry out a fair test.

   It's also the easiest way for different scientists around the world to carry out the same experiments. (There are things you can't study in a lab though, like climate.)

2) Old wives' tales, rumours, hearsay, 'what someone said', and so on, should be taken with a pinch of salt. They'd need to be tested in controlled conditions to be genuinely scientific.

3) Data based on samples that are too small don't have much more credibility that rumours do.

   A sample should be representative of the whole population (i.e. it should share as many of the various characteristics in the whole population as possible) — a small sample just can't do that.

Evidence is only Reliable if Other People can Repeat It

Scientific evidence needs to be reliable (or reproducible). If it isn't, then it doesn't really help.

RELIABLE means that the data can be reproduced by others.

Example: Cold fusion

In 1989, two scientists claimed that they'd produced 'cold fusion' (the energy source of the Sun — but without the enormous temperatures).

It was huge news — if true, this could have meant energy from sea water — the ideal energy solution for the world... forever.

However, other scientists just couldn't get the same results — i.e. the results weren't reliable. And until they are, 'cold fusion' isn't going to be generally accepted as fact.

Reliability is really important in science

The scientific community won't accept someone's data if it can't be repeated by anyone else. It may sound like a really fantastic new theory, but if there's no other support for it, it just isn't reliable.

Your Data's Got to Be Good

Evidence also needs to be *Valid*

To answer scientific questions scientists often try to link changes in one variable with changes in another. This is useful evidence, as long as it's valid.

VALID means that the data is reliable AND answers the original question.

Example: Do power lines cause cancer?

Some studies have found that children who live near overhead power lines are more likely to develop cancer. What they'd actually found was a correlation between the variables "presence of power lines" and "incidence of cancer" — they found that as one changed, so did the other.

But this evidence is not enough to say that the power lines cause cancer, as other explanations might be possible.

For example, power lines are often near busy roads, so the areas tested could contain different levels of pollution from traffic. Also, you need to look at types of neighbourhoods and lifestyles of people living in the tested areas (could diet be a factor... or something else you hadn't thought of...).

So these studies don't show a definite link and so don't answer the original question.

Controlling all the variables is *Really Hard*

In reality, it's very hard to control all the variables that might (just might) be having an effect.

You can do things to help — e.g. choose two groups of people (those near power lines and those far away) who are as similar as possible (same mix of ages, same mix of diets etc.).
But you can't easily rule out every possibility.

If you could do a properly controlled lab experiment, that'd be better — but you just can't do it without cloning people and exposing them to things that might cause cancer... hardly ethical.

Does the data really say that?

If it's so hard to be definite about anything, how does anybody ever get convinced about anything?
Well, what usually happens is that you get a load of evidence that all points the same way.
If one study can't rule out a particular possibility, then maybe another one can. So you gradually build up a whole body of evidence, and it's this (rather than any single study) that convinces people.

Bias and How to Spot It

Scientific results are often used to make a point, but results are sometimes presented in a biased way.

You don't need to Lie to make things Biased

1) For something to be misleading, it doesn't have to be untrue. We tend to read scientific facts and assume that they're the 'truth', but there are many different sides to the truth. Look at this headline...

1 in 2 people are of above average weight  *Sounds like we're a nation of fatties.*

2) But an average is a kind of 'middle value' of all your data. Some readings are higher than average (about half of them, usually). Others will be lower than average (the other half).

So the above headline could just as accurately say:  **1 in 2 people are of below average weight**

3) The point is... both headlines sound quite worrying, even though they're not. That's the thing... you can easily make something sound really good or really bad — even if it isn't. You can...

(1) ...use only some of the data, rather than all of it:	"Many people lost weight using the new SlimAway diet. Buy it now!!"	*"Many" could mean anything — e.g. 50 out of 5000 (i.e. 1%). But that could be ignoring most of the data.*
(2) ...phrase things in a 'leading' way:	90% fat free!	*Would you buy it if it were "90% cyanide free"? That 10% is the important bit, probably.*
(3) ...use a statistic that supports your point of view:	The amount of energy wasted is increasing. / Energy wasted per person is decreasing. / The rate at which energy waste is increasing is slowing down.	*These describe the same data. But two sound positive and one negative.*

Think about Why things Might be Biased

1) People who want to make a point can sometimes present data in a biased way to suit their own purposes (sometimes without knowing they're doing it).
2) And there are all sorts of reasons why people might want to do this — for example...

- Governments might want to persuade voters, other governments, journalists, etc. Evidence might be ignored if it could create political problems, or emphasised if it helps their cause.
- Companies might want to 'big up' their products. Or make impressive safety claims, maybe.
- Environmental campaigners might want to persuade people to behave differently.

3) People do it all the time. This is why any scientific evidence has to be looked at carefully. Are there any reasons for thinking the evidence is biased in some way?

- Does the experimenter (or the person writing about it) stand to gain (or lose) anything?
- Might someone have ignored some of the data for political or commercial reasons?
- Is someone using their reputation rather than evidence to help make their case?

Scientific data's not always misleading, you just need to be careful. The most credible argument will be the one that describes all the data that was found, and gives the most balanced view of it.

Science Has Limits

Science can give us amazing things — cures for diseases, space travel, heated toilet seats...
But science has its limitations — there are questions that it just can't answer.

Some questions are **Unanswered** by science — so far

1) We don't understand everything. And we never will. We'll find out more, for sure — as more hypotheses are suggested, and more experiments are done. But there'll always be stuff we don't know.

> For example, today we don't know as much as we'd like about climate change (global warming). Is climate change definitely happening? And to what extent is it caused by humans?

2) These are complicated questions, and at the moment scientists don't all agree on the answers. But eventually, we probably will be able to answer these questions once and for all.

3) But by then there'll be loads of new questions to answer.

Other questions are **Unanswerable** by science

1) Then there's the other type... questions that all the experiments in the world won't help us to answer — the "Should we be doing this at all?" type questions. There are always two sides...

> The question of whether something is morally or ethically right or wrong can't be answered by more experiments — there is no "right" or "wrong" answer.

2) The best we can do is get a consensus from society — a judgement that most people are more or less happy to live by. Science can provide more information to help people make this judgement, and the judgement might change over time. But in the end it's up to people and their conscience.

To answer or not to answer, that is the question

It's official — no one knows everything. Your teacher/mum/annoying older sister (delete as applicable) might think and act as if they know it all, but sadly they don't. So in reality you know one thing they don't — which clearly makes you more intelligent and generally far superior in every way. Possibly.

Science Has Limits

People have **Different Opinions** about **Ethical Questions**

1) Take embryo screening (which allows you to choose an embryo with particular characteristics). It's possible to do it — but does that mean we should?

2) Different people have different opinions. For example...

Some people say it's good... couples whose existing child needs a bone marrow transplant, but who can't find a donor, will be able to have another child selected for its matching bone marrow. This would save the life of their first child — and if they want another child anyway... where's the harm?

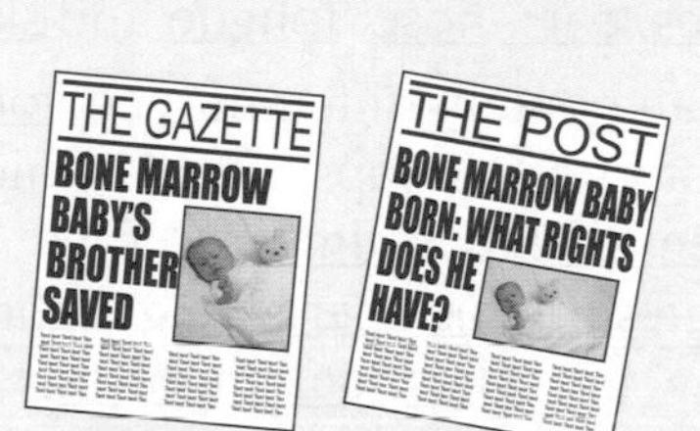

Other people say it's bad... they say it could have serious effects on the child. In the above example the new child might feel unwanted — thinking they were only brought into the world to help someone else. And would they have the right to refuse to donate their bone marrow (as anyone else would)?

Loads of other **Factors** can **Influence Decisions** too

Here are some other factors that can influence decisions about science, and the way science is used:

Economic factors

- Companies very often won't pay for research unless there's likely to be a profit in it.
- Society can't always afford to do things scientists recommend without cutting back elsewhere (e.g. investing heavily in alternative energy sources).

Social factors

- Decisions based on scientific evidence affect people — e.g. should fossil fuels be taxed more highly (to invest in alternative energy)? Should alcohol be banned (to prevent health problems)? Would the effect on people's lifestyles be acceptable...

Environmental factors

- Genetically modified crops may help us produce more food — but some people say they could cause environmental problems (see page 52).

Science is a "real-world" subject

Science isn't just done by people in white coats in labs who have no effect on the outside world. Science has a massive effect on the real world every day, and so real-life things like money, morals and how people might react need to be considered. It's why a lot of issues are so difficult to solve.

The Nervous System

Welcome to AQA Biology. First thing on the menu is a page about the nervous system. The nervous system is what lets you react to what goes on around you, so you'd find life tough without it.

Sense Organs Detect Stimuli

A stimulus is a change in your environment which you may need to react to (e.g. a recently pounced tiger). You need to be constantly monitoring what's going on so you can respond if you need to.

1) You have five different sense organs — eyes, ears, nose, tongue and skin.
2) They all contain different receptors. Receptors are groups of cells which are sensitive to a stimulus. They change stimulus energy (e.g. light energy) into electrical impulses.
3) A stimulus can be light, sound, touch, pressure, chemical, or a change in position or temperature.

Sense organs and Receptors
Don't get them mixed up:
The eye is a sense organ — it contains light receptors.
The ear is a sense organ — it contains sound receptors.

The Five Sense Organs and the receptors that each contains:

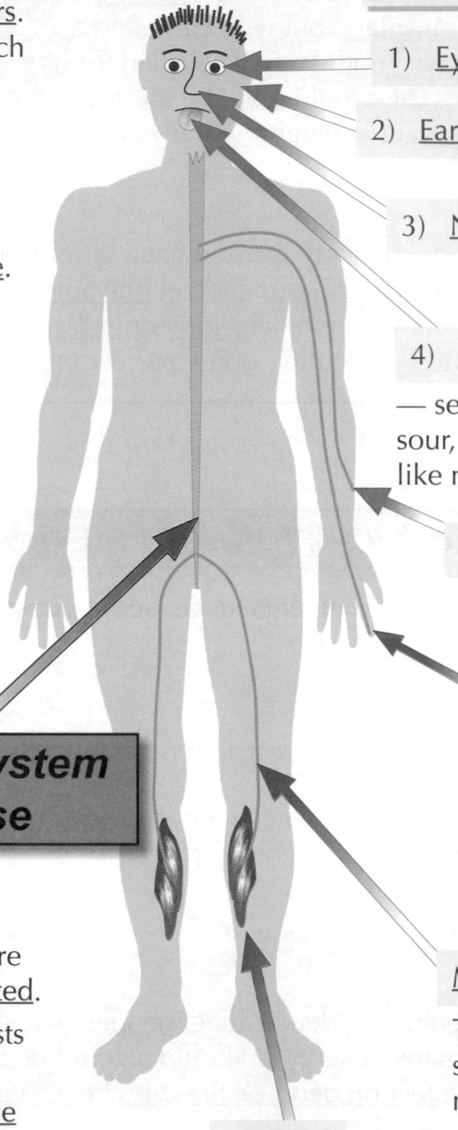

1) Eyes — Light receptors.
2) Ears — Sound and "balance" receptors.
3) Nose — Smell receptors — sensitive to chemical stimuli.
4) Tongue — Taste receptors: — sensitive to bitter, salt, sweet and sour, plus the taste of savoury things like monosodium glutamate (MSG) — chemical stimuli.
5) Skin — Sensitive to touch, pressure and temperature change.

Sensory Neurones
The nerve cells that carry signals as electrical impulses from the receptors in the sense organs to the central nervous system.

Motor Neurones
The nerve cells that carry signals to the effector muscles or glands.

Effectors
Muscles and glands are known as effectors — they respond in different ways.
Muscles contract in response to a nervous impulse, whereas glands secrete hormones.

The Central Nervous System Coordinates a Response

1) The central nervous system (CNS) is where all the information from the sense organs is sent, and where reflexes and actions are coordinated.
   The central nervous system consists of the brain and spinal cord only.
2) Neurones (nerve cells) transmit the information (as electrical impulses) very quickly to and from the CNS.
3) "Instructions" from the CNS are sent to the effectors (muscles and glands), which respond accordingly.

Nervous System = 5 sense organs + neurones + brain + spinal cord

In the exam, you might have to take what you know about a human and apply it to a horse (easy... sound receptors in its ears, light receptors in its eyes, etc.), or to a snake (so if you're told that certain types of snakes have heat receptors in nostril-like pits on their head, you should know what type of stimulus those pits are sensitive to).

Reflexes

Your brain can decide how to respond to a stimulus pretty quickly.
But sometimes, waiting for your brain to make a decision is just too slow. That's why you have reflexes.

Reflexes Help Prevent Injury

1) Reflexes are automatic responses to certain stimuli — they can reduce the chances of being injured.
2) For example, if someone shines a bright light in your eyes, your pupils automatically get smaller so that less light gets into the eye — this stops it getting damaged.
3) Or if you get a shock, your body releases the hormone adrenaline automatically — it doesn't wait for you to decide that you're shocked.
4) The passage of information in a reflex (from receptor to effector) is called a reflex arc.

The Reflex Arc Goes Through the Central Nervous System

1) The neurones in reflex arcs go through the spinal cord (or an unconscious part of the brain).
2) When a stimulus (e.g. a painful bee sting) is detected by receptors, an impulse is sent along a sensory neurone to the spinal cord.
3) In the spinal cord the sensory neurone passes on the message to another type of neurone — a relay neurone.
4) The relay neurone relays the impulse to a motor neurone.
5) The impulse then travels along the motor neurone to the effector (in the example below it's a muscle).
6) The muscle then contracts and moves your hand away from the bee.
7) Because you don't have to think about the response (which takes time) it's quicker than normal responses.

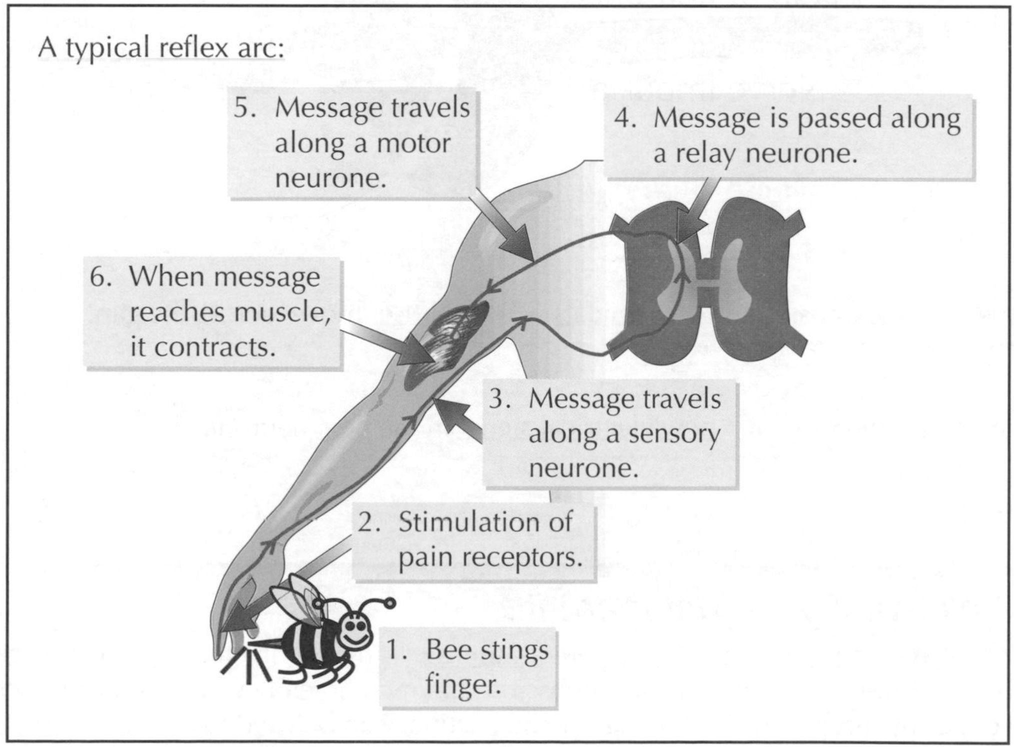

Reflexes

Make sure you've learnt the order of a reflex arc.

Stimulus, Receptor, Neurones, Effector, Response

Here's a block diagram of a reflex arc —
it shows what happens, from stimulus to response.

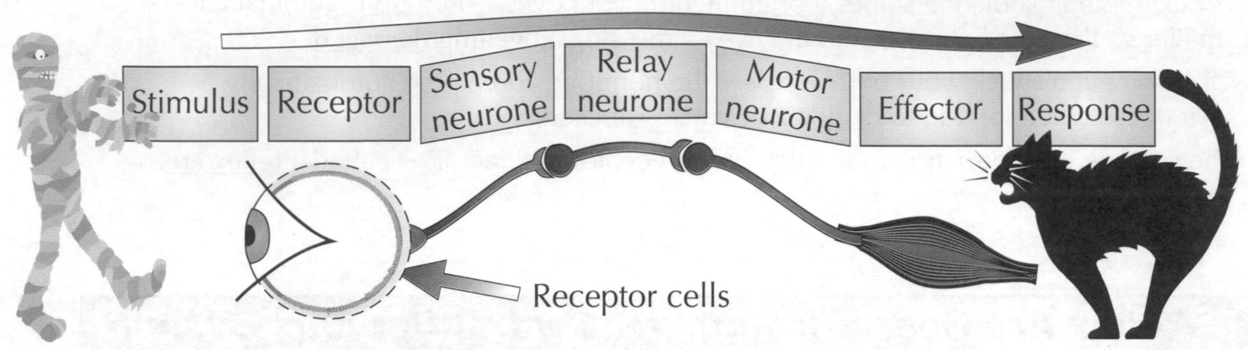

Synapses Connect Neurones

1) The connection between two neurones is called a synapse.

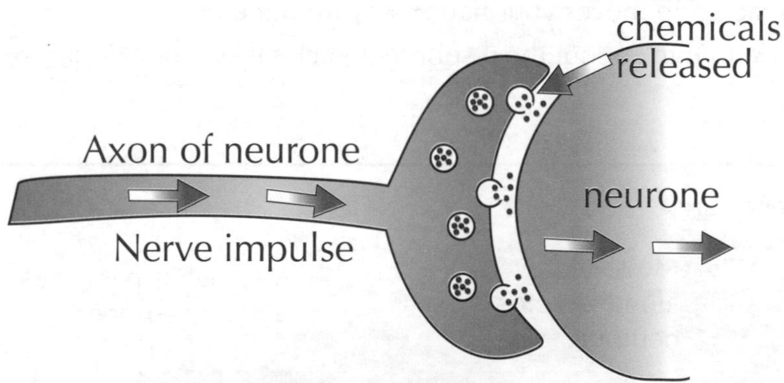

2) The nerve signal is transferred by chemicals which diffuse (move) across the gap.

3) These chemicals then set off a new electrical signal in the next neurone.

Don't get all twitchy — just learn it...

The difference between a reflex and a "considered response" is the involvement of the conscious part of your brain. Reflexes may bypass your conscious brain completely when a quick response is essential — your body just gets on with things. Reflex actions can be used to assess the condition of unconscious casualties (since the conscious brain isn't involved), or those with spinal injuries (an abnormal reflex could point to where a problem lies). So... if you're asked which bodily system doctors are examining when they tap your knee with a hammer and check that you kick, just work it out.

Hormones

The other way to send information around the body (apart from along nerves) is by using hormones.

Hormones Are Chemical Messengers Sent in the Blood

1) Hormones are chemicals released directly into the blood. They are carried in the blood plasma to other parts of the body, but only affect particular cells (called target cells) in particular places. Hormones control things in organs and cells that need constant adjustment.
2) Hormones are produced in various glands, as shown on the diagram. They travel through your body at "the speed of blood".
3) Hormones tend to have relatively long-lasting effects.

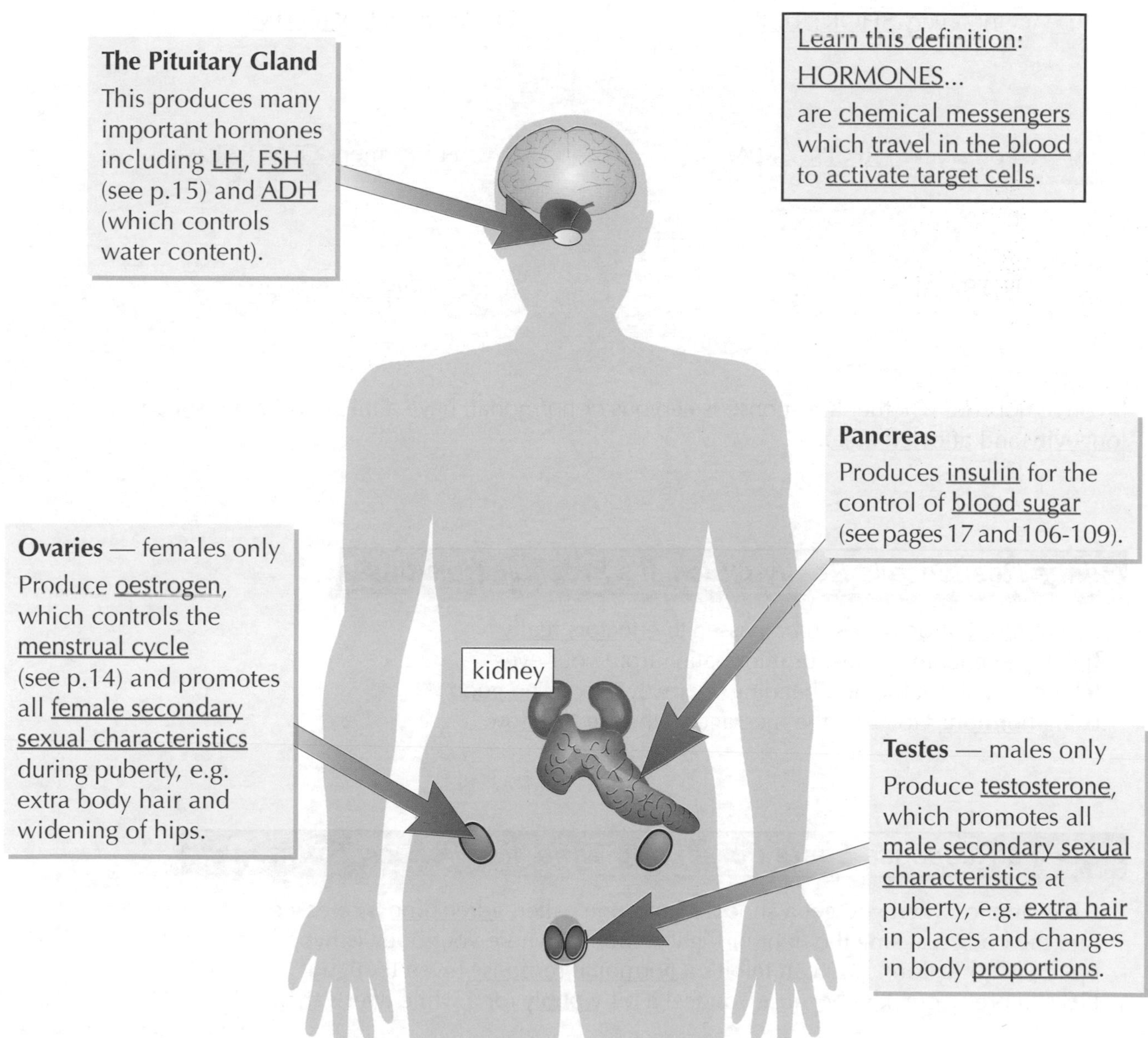

The Pituitary Gland
This produces many important hormones including LH, FSH (see p.15) and ADH (which controls water content).

Learn this definition:
HORMONES...
are chemical messengers which travel in the blood to activate target cells.

Pancreas
Produces insulin for the control of blood sugar (see pages 17 and 106-109).

Ovaries — females only
Produce oestrogen, which controls the menstrual cycle (see p.14) and promotes all female secondary sexual characteristics during puberty, e.g. extra body hair and widening of hips.

Testes — males only
Produce testosterone, which promotes all male secondary sexual characteristics at puberty, e.g. extra hair in places and changes in body proportions.

These are just examples — there are loads more hormones, each doing its own thing.

Hormonal and Nervous Responses

Now you know that there are two ways information can be sent round the body — via the nervous or hormonal systems — here's a recap of the differences between th

Hormones and Nerves Do Similar Jobs, but in Differen

Nerves	Hormones
1) Very FAST message.	1) SLOWER message.
2) Act for a very SHORT TIME.	2) Act for a LONG TIME.
3) Act on a very PRECISE AREA.	3) Act in a more GENERAL
4) ELECTRICAL message	4) CHEMICAL message.

If you're not sure whether a response is nervous or hormonal, have a think about the longevity and affected area...

If the Response is Really Quick, It's Probably Nervous

Some information needs to be passed to effectors really quickly (e.g. pain signals, or information from your eyes telling you about the lion heading your way), so it's no good using hormones to carry the message — they're too slow.

But if a Response Lasts For a Long Time, It's Probably Hormo

For example, when you get a shock, a hormone called adrenaline is released into the body (causing the fight-or-flight response, where your body is hyped up ready for action). You can tell it's a hormonal response (even though it kicks in pretty quickly) because you feel a bit wobbly for a while afterwards.

Learn the differences between nervous and hormona

Hormones control various organs and cells in the body, though they tend to co immediately life-threatening. For example, they take care of all things to do wit pregnancy, birth, breast-feeding, blood sugar levels, water content... and so on.

Warm-Up and Exam Questions

Welcome to the first page of questions. I reckon you'll realise pretty soon how important these are.

Warm-Up Questions

1) What are the five sense organs in the human body?
2) What is the role of the central nervous system (CNS)?
3) In what form is information transmitted along nerve cells?
4) What name is given to the connection between two nerve cells?
5) Define the term hormone.
6) Which organ in the human body produces insulin?

Exam Questions

1 Gordon accidentally touches a hot object, causing his hand to immediately move away from it. The diagram below shows some of the parts involved in this response.

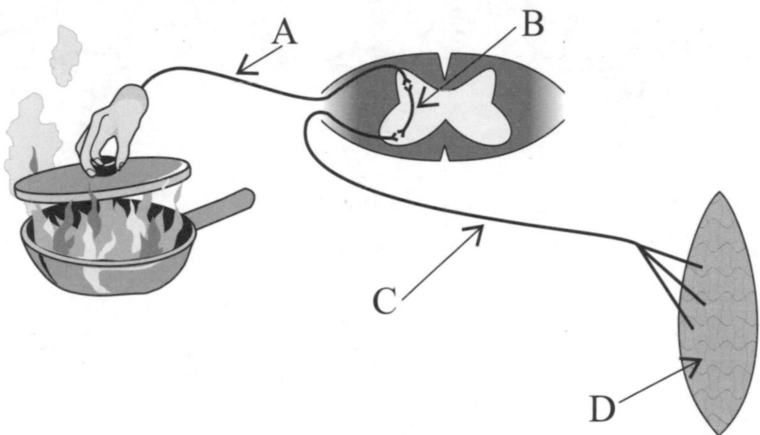

(a) What is the name of this type of automatic response?

(1 mark)

(b) On the diagram:

(i) Which letter points to a relay neurone?

(1 mark)

(ii) Which letter points to an effector?

(1 mark)

(c) Explain how an electrical impulse in one neurone is able to pass to the next neurone.

(2 marks)

(d) Give one physiological advantage, to the body, of these automatic responses.

(1 mark)

2 Which of the following statements about hormonal messages is **not** true?

A They're carried in the blood plasma.
B They act on a very precise area
C They're chemical messages.
D They act for a long time.

(1 mark)

The Menstrual Cycle

The monthly release of an egg from a woman's ovaries, and the build-up and breakdown of the protective lining in the uterus (womb), is called the menstrual cycle.

The Menstrual Cycle Has Four Stages

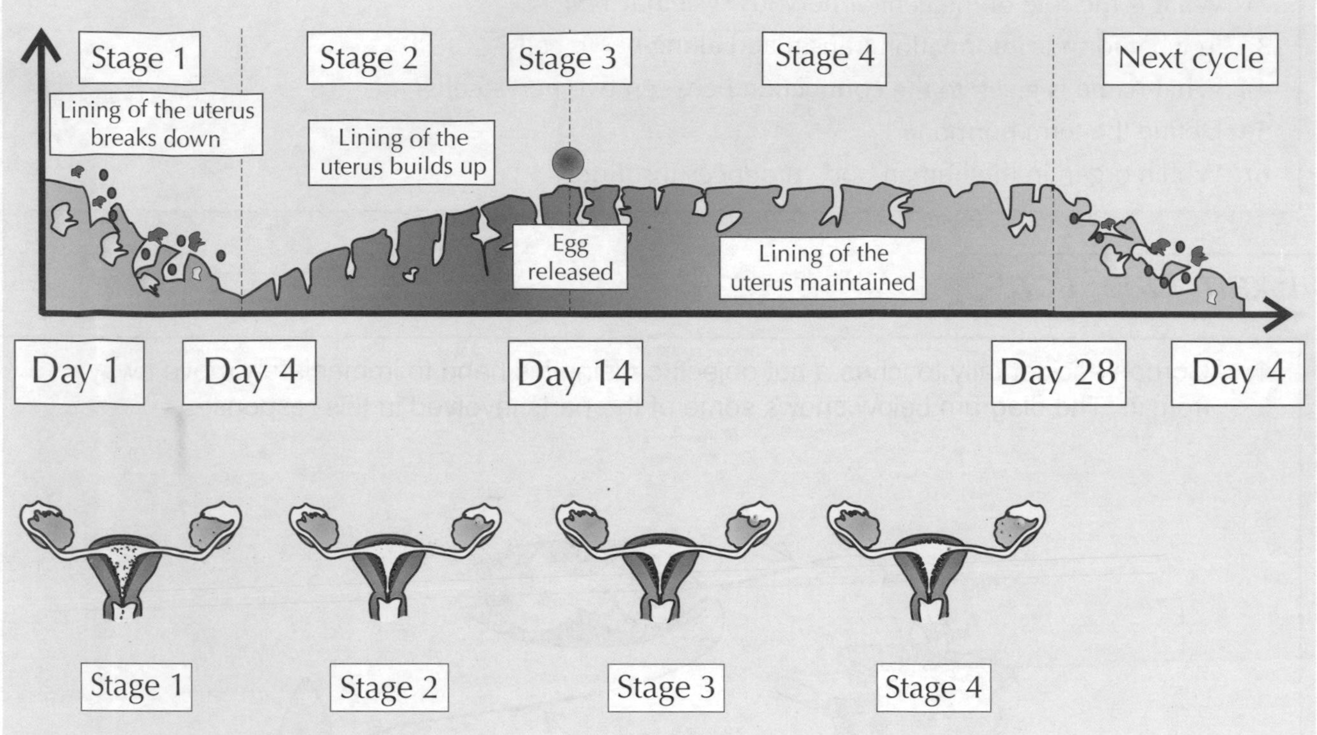

Stage 1

Day 1 is when the bleeding starts.
The uterus lining breaks down for about four days.

Stage 2

The lining of the uterus builds up again, from day 4 to day 14, into a thick spongy layer full of blood vessels, ready to receive a fertilised egg.

Stage 3

An egg is developed and then released from the ovary at day 14.

Stage 4

The wall is then maintained for about 14 days, until day 28. If no fertilised egg has landed on the uterus wall by day 28, the spongy lining starts to break down again and the whole cycle starts again.

The Menstrual Cycle

There are only a few hormones you need to know about in this section, and apart from insulin, they're all on this page...

Hormones Control the Different Stages

There are three main hormones involved:

1. FSH (Follicle-Stimulating Hormone)

1) Causes an egg to mature in one of the ovaries.
2) Stimulates the ovaries to produce oestrogen.

Produced by the pituitary gland.

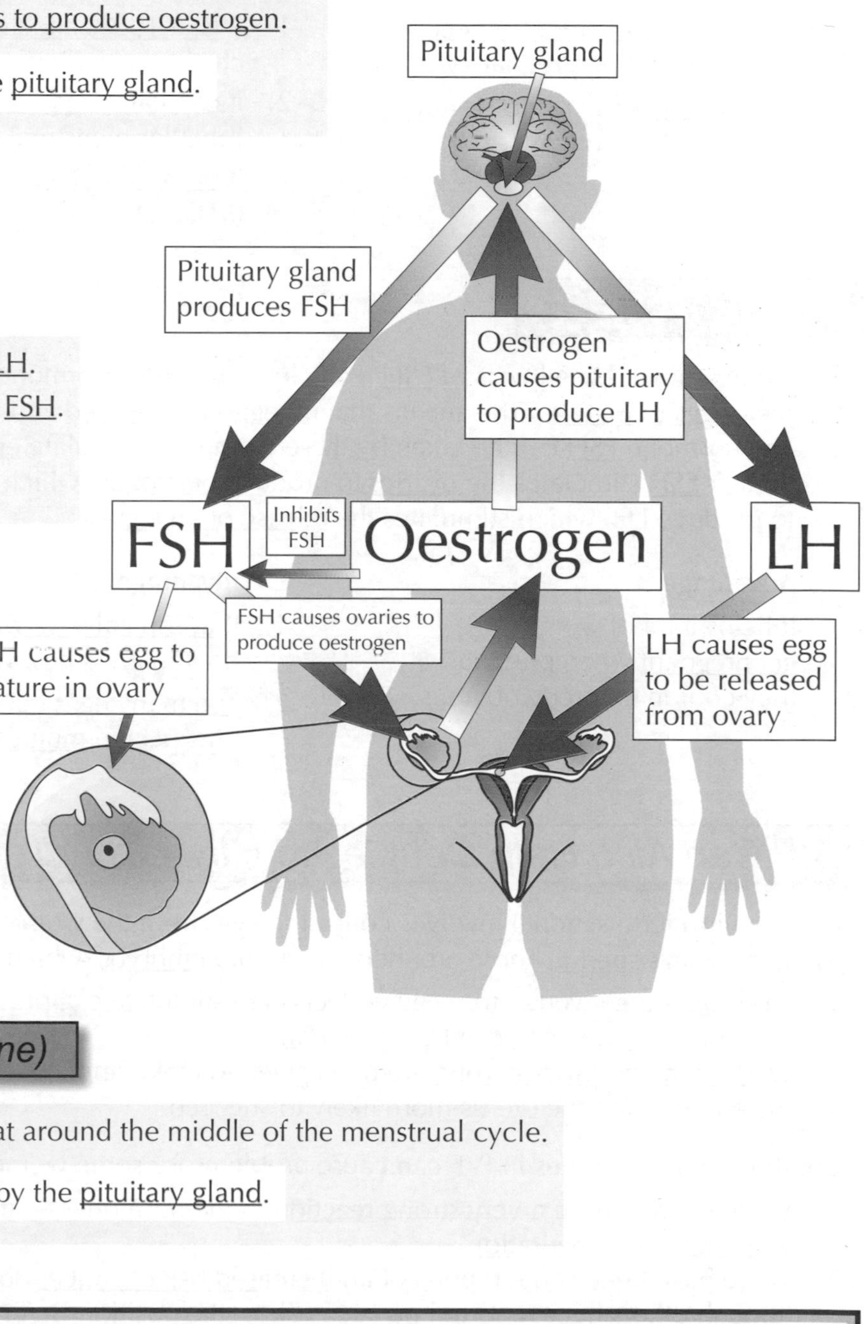

2. Oestrogen

1) Causes pituitary to produce LH.
2) Inhibits the further release of FSH.

Produced in the ovaries.

3. LH (Luteinising Hormone)

Stimulates the release of an egg at around the middle of the menstrual cycle.

Produced by the pituitary gland.

OK, I admit it — this is quite hard to get your head around

In the exam you could be given a completely new situation and have to answer questions about it. For example, say you're told that certain women with epilepsy suffer more seizures at certain points of the menstrual cycle and you have to suggest a reason why. Sounds scary, but the key is not to panic. You know that during the menstrual cycle, hormone levels change — so maybe it's these hormone changes that are triggering the seizures. There are no guarantees, but that'd be a pretty good answer.

Controlling Fertility

The hormones FSH, oestrogen and LH can be used to artificially change how fertile a woman is.

Hormones Can Be Used to *Reduce Fertility...*

1) The hormone oestrogen can be used to prevent the release of an egg — so oestrogen can be used as a method of contraception. The pill is an oral contraceptive that contains oestrogen.
2) This may seem kind of strange (since oestrogen naturally stimulates the release of eggs). But if oestrogen is taken every day to keep the level of it permanently high, it inhibits the production of FSH, and after a while egg development and production stops and stays stopped.

Advantages

1) The pill's over 99% effective at preventing pregnancy.
2) It reduces the risk of getting some types of cancer.

Disadvantages

1) It isn't 100% effective — there's still a very slight chance of getting pregnant.
2) It can cause side effects like headaches, nausea, irregular menstrual bleeding, and fluid retention.
3) It doesn't protect against sexually transmitted diseases (STDs).

...or *Increase It*

1) Some women have levels of FSH (Follicle-Stimulating Hormone) that are too low to cause their eggs to mature. This means that no eggs are released and the women can't get pregnant.
2) The hormone FSH can be taken by these women to stimulate egg production in their ovaries. (In fact FSH stimulates the ovaries to produce oestrogen, which stimulates the pituitary gland to produce LH, which stimulates the release of an egg.)

Advantage

It helps a lot of women to get pregnant when previously they couldn't... pretty obvious.

Disadvantages

1) It doesn't always work — some women may have to do it many times, which can be expensive.
2) Too many eggs could be stimulated, resulting in unexpected multiple pregnancies (twins, triplets etc.).

IVF Can Also Help Couples to *Have Children*

IVF ("in vitro fertilisation") involves collecting eggs from the woman's ovaries and fertilising them in a lab using the man's sperm. These are then grown into embryos, which are transferred to the woman's uterus.

1) Hormones are given before egg collection to stimulate egg production (so more than one egg can be collected).
2) Oestrogen and progesterone are often given to make implantation of the embryo into the uterus more likely to succeed.

But the use of hormones in IVF can cause problems for some women...

1) Some women have a very strong reaction to the hormones — including abdominal pain, vomiting and dehydration.
2) There have been some reports of an increased risk of cancer due to the hormonal treatment (though others have reported no such risk — the position isn't really clear at the moment).

The pill contains oestrogen to reduce fertility...

...and fertility drugs contain FSH to increase fertility — make sure you know the difference. Also, you need to be able to evaluate (weigh up the pros and cons) of in vitro fertilisation.

Homeostasis

Homeostasis is a fancy word, but it covers lots of things, so maybe that's fair enough.
It means all the functions of your body which try to maintain a "constant internal environment".

Your Body Needs Some Things to Be **Kept Constant**

1) All your body's cells are bathed in tissue fluid, which is just blood plasma which has leaked out of the capillaries (on purpose).
2) To keep all your cells working properly, this fluid must be just right — in other words, certain things must be kept at the right level — not too high, and not too low.
3) Bodily levels that need to be controlled include:

Ion content

Water content

Temperature

Sugar content

Ion Content Is **Regulated** by the **Kidneys**

1) Ions (e.g. sodium, Na^+) are taken into the body in food, then absorbed into the blood.
2) If the food contains too much of any kind of ion then the excess ions need to be removed. E.g. a salty meal will contain far too much Na^+.
3) Some ions are lost in sweat (which tastes salty, you'll have noticed).
4) The kidneys will remove the excess from the blood — this is then got rid of in urine.

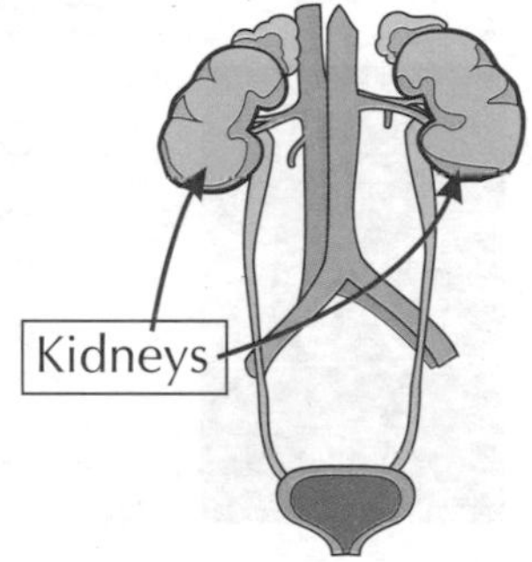

Blood Sugar Levels Need to Be Controlled Too

1) Eating foods containing carbohydrate puts glucose (a type of sugar) into the blood from the gut.
2) The normal metabolism of cells removes glucose from the blood. But if you do a lot of vigorous exercise, then much more glucose is removed.
3) To maintain the right level, you need a way to add or remove glucose to or from the blood — this is the role of the hormone insulin. Diabetes (Type I) is where your body doesn't produce enough insulin.

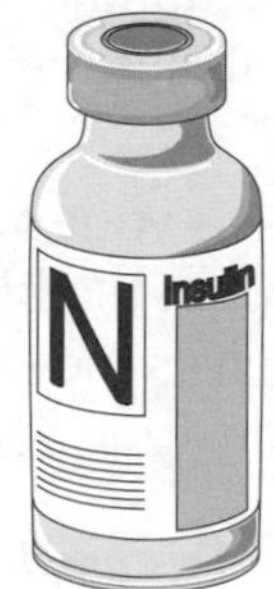

Adding insulin reduces blood sugar levels.

Levels of ions, sugar, water and your temperature must be constant

It's pretty handy that all of this homeostasis stuff goes on without you even having to think about it. Just imagine if we had to work out how much salt our bodies needed to lose in sweat... we'd probably get it wrong more often then not. Learn this page and test yourself by writing it all down again.

Homeostasis

You also need to know about how your body controls water level and temperature.

Water Is Lost from the Body in Various Ways

There's a need for the body to constantly balance the water coming in against the water going out. Water is taken into the body as food and drink and is lost from the body in these ways:

1) through the SKIN as SWEAT...
2) via the LUNGS in BREATH...
3) via the kidneys as URINE.

Some water is also lost in faeces.

The balance between sweat and urine can depend on what you're doing, or what the weather's like...

On a COLD DAY, or when you're NOT EXERCISING, you don't sweat much, so you'll produce more urine, which will be pale (since the waste carried in the urine is more diluted).

On a HOT DAY, or when you're EXERCISING, you sweat a lot, and so you will produce less urine, but this will be more concentrated (and hence a deeper colour). You will also lose more water through your breath when you exercise because you breathe faster.

Body Temperature Is Controlled by the Brain

1) All enzymes work best at a certain temperature. The enzymes within the human body work best at about 37 °C — and so this is the temperature your body tries to maintain.
2) A part of the brain acts as your own personal thermostat. It's sensitive to the blood temperature in the brain, and it receives messages from the skin that provide information about skin temperature.

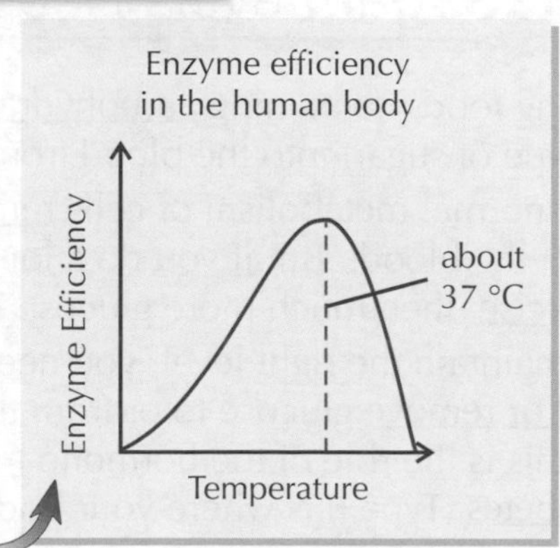

This graph shows that the enzymes within the human body are most efficient (work best) at about 37 °C.

Sweat and urine keep your water level balanced

Sports drinks (which usually contain electrolytes and carbohydrates) can help your body keep things in order. The electrolytes (e.g. sodium) replace those lost in sweat, while the carbohydrates can give a bit of an energy boost. But health claims like this need to be looked at carefully — see page 29.

Warm-Up and Exam Questions

You could skim through this page in a few minutes, but there's no point unless you check over any bits you don't know and make sure you understand everything. It's not quick but it's the only way.

Warm-Up Questions

1) Describe what happens at Day 1 in the menstrual cycle and why.
2) Briefly describe the process of in vitro fertilisation.
3) What is meant by the term homeostasis?
4) List four things that need to be kept constant within the body.
5) List three ways in which water is lost from the body.
6) Why is it important that human body temperature is kept at about 37 °C?

Exam Questions

1 Which of the following is controlled by the hormone FSH?

A Release of oestrogen from the pituitary.
B Production of oestrogen by the ovaries.
C Release of LH from the pituitary.
D Release of an egg from the ovary.

(1 mark)

2 The menstrual cycle is controlled by several different hormones.

(a) What effect does oestrogen have on the release of FSH?

(1 mark)

(b) Which hormone causes an egg to mature in an ovary?

(1 mark)

(c) On what day of the menstrual cycle is the egg released?

(1 mark)

3 Which of the following statements about the oestrogen-containing contraceptive pill is not true?

A It does not protect against sexually transmitted diseases.
B It is over 99% effective at preventing pregnancy.
C It is free from side effects.
D It reduces the risk of developing some forms of cancer.

(1 mark)

4 Give two potential side-effects associated with IVF.

(2 marks)

5 (a) Which organ is responsible for regulating the ion content of the blood?

(1 mark)

(b) Which organ is responsible for regulating body temperature?

(1 mark)

(c) Which hormone regulates blood sugar levels?

(1 mark)

Diet and Exercise

A balanced diet and exercise are the keys to being healthy — but you need both.

A **Balanced Diet** Does a Lot to Keep You Healthy

1) For good health, your diet must provide the energy you need (but not more) — see below.
2) But that's not all. Because the different food groups have different uses in the body, you need to have the right balance of foods as well.

   So you need: ...enough carbohydrates and fats to keep warm and provide energy,
   ...enough protein for growth, cell repair and cell replacement,
   ...enough fibre to keep everything moving smoothly through your digestive system,
   ...and tiny amounts of various vitamins and minerals to keep your skin, bones, blood and everything else generally healthy.
3) People whose diet is badly out of balance are said to be malnourished (not the same as starvation). Malnourished people can be fat or thin, or unhealthy in other ways. For example, a lack of vitamin C can cause scurvy, a deficiency disease which causes problems with the skin, joints and gums. Different deficiency diseases are caused by a lack of other nutrients.

People's Energy Needs Vary Because of **Who They Are...**

1) You need energy to fuel the chemical reactions in the body that keep you alive. These reactions are called your metabolism, and the speed at which they occur is your metabolic rate.
2) There are slight variations in the resting metabolic rate of different people. For example, muscle needs more energy than fatty tissue, which means (all other things being equal) people with a higher proportion of muscle to fat in their bodies will have a higher metabolic rate.
3) However, physically bigger people are likely to have a higher metabolic rate than smaller people — the bigger you are, the more energy your body needs to be supplied with (because you have more cells).
4) Men tend to have a slightly higher rate than women — they're slightly bigger and have a larger proportion of muscle. Other genetic factors may also have some effect.
5) And regular exercise can boost your resting metabolic rate because it builds muscle.

...and Because of **What They Do**

1) When you exercise, you obviously need more energy — so your metabolic rate goes up during exercise and stays high for some time after you finish (particularly if the exercise is strenuous).

Activity	kJ/min
Sleeping	4.5
Watching TV	7
Cycling (5 mph)	21
Jogging (5 mph)	40
Climbing stairs	77
Swimming	35
Rowing	58
Slow walking	14

2) So people who have more active jobs need more energy on a daily basis — builders require more energy per day than office workers, for instance. The table shows the average kilojoules burned per minute when doing different activities.
3) The temperature can also affect your metabolic rate. When it's cold, your body has to produce more heat (which requires energy) — this increases your metabolic rate.
4) All these factors have an effect on the amount of energy your diet should contain. If you do little exercise and it's hot outside, you're going to need less energy than if you're constantly on the go in a cold country.

Getting the right intake of nutrients is vital to health

Exercise is important as well as diet — people who exercise regularly are usually fitter than people who don't. However, you can be fit and slim, but also malnourished because your diet isn't balanced.

Weight Problems

Health problems due to the wrong kind of diet are different in different parts of the world. In some countries the problem is too much of the wrong kind of food, in others the problem is not having enough.

In Developed Countries the Problem Is Too Much Food

1) In developed countries, obesity is becoming a serious problem. In the UK, 1 in 5 adults are obese, with obesity contributing to the deaths of over 30 000 people each year in England alone.
2) Hormonal problems can lead to obesity, though the usual cause is a bad diet, overeating and a lack of exercise.
3) Health problems that can arise as a result of obesity include: arthritis (inflammation of the joints), diabetes (inability to control blood sugar levels), high blood pressure and heart disease. It's also a risk factor for some kinds of cancer.
4) The National Health Service spends loads each year treating obesity-related conditions. And more is lost to the economy generally due to absence from work.

In Developing Countries the Problem Is Often Too Little Food

1) In developing countries, some people suffer from lack of food.
2) This can be a lack of one or more specific types of food (malnutrition), or not enough food of any sort (starvation). Young children, the elderly and women tend to be the worst sufferers.
3) The effects of malnutrition vary depending on what foods are missing from the diet. But problems commonly include slow growth (in children), fatigue, poor resistance to infection, and irregular periods in women.

All the Above Claims Are Based on Data

1) If scientists are to decide on the best way to tackle these problems, they need to know as much as possible about them.
2) The first step is to collect some accurate data — but this is very rarely as easy as it sounds. The problem with getting data depends on what data you're trying to get...

Data on Malnutrition

1) People with malnutrition may not reach medical aid. If they do, and if records are being kept detailing causes of death, data can be collated fairly easily (and is usually pretty accurate).
2) However, sometimes medical staff may be dealing with a large-scale emergency, and so they may not have time to keep proper records.

Data on Obesity

1) With obesity the problems are different. The health problems caused by obesity are more long-term, and people don't necessarily seek medical assistance.
2) Surveys can be done and, provided the sample isn't biased, the data might be reliable. But it'll still depend on how you collect the data.
3) For example, not long ago people in the USA were asked to fill in a questionnaire asking about their weight — and obesity was reported in 20% of the population. A later scientific survey based on medical examinations revealed it to be 28% in men and 34% in women.

Too much or too little — it's a fine line to tread

Whenever you use data, you have to remember that the methods used to collect it are usually far from ideal, meaning the information is never perfect. This means the figures are often heavily argued about.

Salt and Cholesterol

You need some salt and some cholesterol in your body, but too much can put your health at risk. Most people have more salt than they need in their diet.

You Need to Watch Your **Salt Intake**

1) A risk factor (i.e. something that increases the risk) of heart disease is high blood pressure (hypertension).

2) Eating too much salt may cause hypertension. This is a particular problem for about 30% of the UK population, who are 'salt sensitive' and need to carefully monitor how much salt they eat.

However, it's not always easy to keep track of exactly how much salt you eat — most of the salt you eat is probably in processed foods (such as breakfast cereals, soups, sauces, ready meals, biscuits...).

The salt you sprinkle on your food makes up quite a small proportion.

And as if things weren't complicated enough... on food labels, salt is usually listed as sodium.

A **High Cholesterol Level** Is a Risk Factor for **Heart Disease**

1) Cholesterol is a fatty substance that's essential for good health. It's found in every cell in the body.

2) But you don't want too much of it because a high cholesterol level in the blood causes an increased risk of various problems — like coronary heart disease.

3) This is due to blood vessels getting clogged with fatty cholesterol deposits. This reduces blood flow to the heart, which can lead to angina (chest pain), or a heart attack (if the vessel is blocked completely).

4) The liver is really important in controlling the amount of cholesterol in the body. It makes new cholesterol and removes it from the blood so that it can be eliminated from the body.

5) The amount the liver makes depends on your diet and inherited factors.

Too much salt and cholesterol can damage your health

You need to understand exactly what "risk factor" actually means. If you have a risk factor, it means you're more likely to suffer from a disease, but not that you're guaranteed to. For example, a smoker with high cholesterol and high blood pressure is 30 times more likely to develop heart disease than someone without these risk factors. But it's not a guarantee... statistics don't do guarantees.

Cholesterol

To make sure your blood cholesterol level isn't too high, you need to eat the right amount and right type of fat.

Cholesterol is Carried Around the Body by HDLs and LDLs

1) Cholesterol is transported around the body in the blood by lipoproteins (i.e. fat attached to protein).

2) These can be high density lipoproteins (HDLs), or low density lipoproteins (LDLs).

3) LDLs carry cholesterol from the liver to the body cells — they're sometimes called 'bad cholesterol' as any excess can build up in the arteries.

4) HDLs carry cholesterol that isn't needed from the body cells back to the liver for removal from the body — so they're called 'good cholesterol'.

5) The LDL/HDL balance is very important. Ideally, you want more HDLs than LDLs in the blood.

6) A diet that's low in fat is important (and processed food contains quite a high proportion of fat) — but the types of fat you eat are even more crucial...

SATURATED FATS (with no C=C double bonds) raise cholesterol in the blood by increasing the amount the liver makes and decreasing the amount it gets rid of — so they should be eaten in moderation.

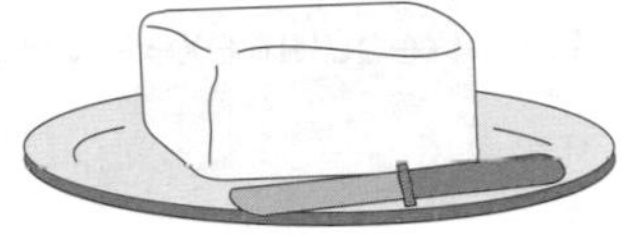

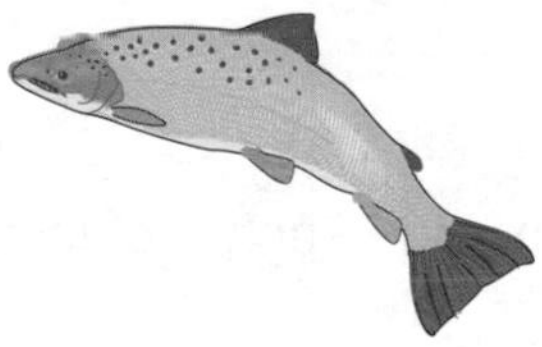

POLYUNSATURATED FATS (with more than one C=C double bond) tend to lower blood cholesterol by increasing its removal from the body and improve the LDI/HDL balance.

MONOUNSATURATED FATS (with exactly one C=C double bond) were long considered to be "neutral" as far as health is concerned.

But recent evidence suggests they may also help to lower blood cholesterol and improve the LDL/HDL balance.

People who have a diet high in monounsaturates tend to have lower levels of heart disease.

LDLs are bad, HDLs are good...

So there we go, there are genuine reasons why you shouldn't spread lard on your toast in the morning. A good LDL/HDL balance (i.e. more HDLs than LDLs) lowers the risk of heart disease. Poly- and monounsaturated fats lower blood cholesterol by improving the LDL/HDL balance.

Warm-Up and Exam Questions

By the time the big day comes you need to know all the facts in these warm-up questions and exam questions like the back of your hand. It's not a barrel of laughs, but it's the only way to get good marks.

Warm-Up Questions

1) Why is it important to eat enough fibre as part of a balanced diet?
2) List three possible causes of obesity.
3) Give three possible effects of malnutrition.
4) What health problem may be caused by eating too much salt?
5) Why does high blood cholesterol increase the risk of heart disease?
6) Which organ is responsible for controlling the amount of cholesterol in the body?

Exam Questions

1 Which of the following statements about metabolic rate is **not** true?

A People with a high proportion of muscle to fat tend to have a high metabolic rate.

B In general, men have a higher metabolic rate than women.

C Two people of the same size and weight will have the same metabolic rate.

D Regular exercise increases resting metabolic rate.

(1 mark)

2 The right amount of carbohydrates and vitamins are needed for a healthy, balanced diet.

(a) Name one other food group that is needed for a healthy, balanced diet.

(1 mark)

(b) Explain the difference between starvation and malnutrition.

(2 marks)

(c) Obesity increases the risk of various health problems. Name one such problem.

(1 mark)

3 Which of the following statements about energy is **not** true?

A When you exercise, your body needs more energy from your diet.

B Professional athletes need more energy from their diet than office workers.

C In cold temperatures, your body needs less energy from your diet.

D The bigger you are, the more energy you need from your diet.

(1 mark)

4 (a) What would be the likely effect on your blood cholesterol levels of eating:

(i) saturated fats?

(1 mark)

(ii) polyunsaturated fats?

(1 mark)

(b) Describe the difference between LDLs and HDLs.

(2 marks)

Drugs

Drugs alter what goes on in your body. Your body's essentially a mass of chemical reactions — drugs can interfere with these reactions, sometimes for the better, sometimes not.

Drugs Change Your Body Chemistry

1) Many drugs are derived from natural substances found in plants, and have been known and used for centuries. For example, heroin is derived from a chemical found in a species of poppy.
2) Some of the chemical changes caused by drugs can lead to the body becoming addicted to the drug. If the drug isn't taken, an addict can suffer physical withdrawal symptoms — and these are sometimes very unpleasant.
3) Heroin and cocaine are very addictive, so are nicotine and caffeine.

Medical Drugs Have to Be Thoroughly Tested

New drugs are constantly being developed. But before they can be given to the general public, they have to go through a thorough testing procedure. This is what usually happens...

1. Computer models are often used in the early stages — these simulate a human's response to a drug. This can identify promising drugs to be tested in the next stage (but sometimes it's not as accurate as actually seeing the effect on a live organism).

2. Drugs are then developed further by testing on human tissues in the lab. However, you can't use human tissue to test drugs that affect whole or multiple body systems, e.g. testing a drug for blood pressure must be done on a whole animal because it has an intact circulatory system.

3. The next step is to develop and test the drug using live animals. The law in Britain states that any new drug must be tested on two different live mammals. Some people think it's cruel to test on animals, but others believe this is the safest way to make sure a drug isn't dangerous before it's given to humans.

   But some people think that animals are so different from humans that testing on animals is pointless.

4. After the drug has been tested on animals it's tested on human volunteers in a clinical trial — this should determine whether there are any side effects.

Things Have Gone Wrong in the Past

An example of what can happen when drugs are not thoroughly tested is the case of thalidomide — a drug developed in the 1950s.

1) Thalidomide was intended as a sleeping pill, and was tested for that use. But later it was also found to be effective in relieving morning sickness in pregnant women.
2) Unfortunately, thalidomide hadn't been tested as a drug for morning sickness, and so it wasn't known that it could pass through the placenta and affect the fetus, causing stunted growth of the fetus's arms and legs. In some cases, babies were born with no arms or legs at all.
3) About 10 000 babies were affected by thalidomide, and only about half of them survived.
4) The drug was banned, and more rigorous testing procedures were introduced.
5) Thalidomide has recently been re-introduced — as a treatment for leprosy, AIDS and certain cancers. But it can't be used on pregnant women.

A little learning is a dangerous thing...

Thalidomide was an attempt to improve people's lives which then caused some pretty tragic knock-on effects. Could the same thing happen today? Well, maybe not the exact same thing, but there's no such thing as perfect knowledge — you can never eliminate risk completely.

Tobacco

Drugs are also used recreationally. Some of these are legal, others illegal. And some are more harmful than others. Here's one drug that has a massive impact on people and society, and is legal...

Smoking Tobacco Can Cause Quite a Few Problems

1) Tobacco smoke contains carbon monoxide — this combines irreversibly with haemoglobin in blood cells, meaning the blood can carry less oxygen. In pregnant women, this can deprive the fetus of oxygen, leading to the baby being born underweight.
2) Tobacco smoke also contains carcinogens — chemicals that can lead to cancer. Lung cancer is way more common among smokers than non-smokers (see below). It's estimated that 90% of lung cancers are associated with smoking (including passive smoking).
3) Disturbingly, the incidence rate (the number of people who get lung cancer) and the mortality rate (the number who die from it) aren't massively different. Put bluntly, this means lung cancer kills most of the people who get it.
4) Smoking also causes disease of the heart and blood vessels (leading to heart attacks and strokes), and damage to the lungs (leading to diseases like emphysema and bronchitis).

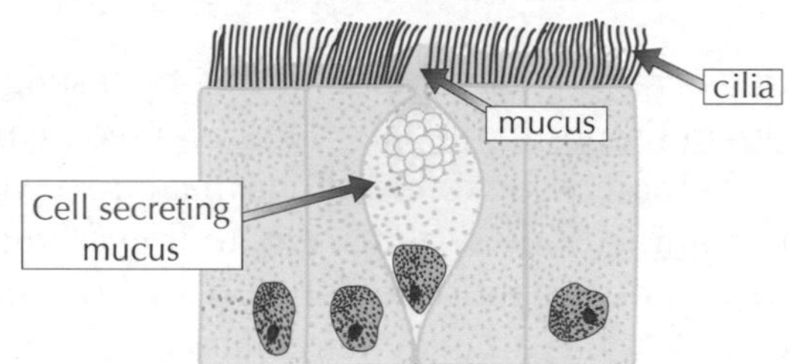

5) And the tar in cigarettes damages the cilia (little hairs) in your lungs and windpipe. These hairs, along with mucus, catch a load of dust and bacteria before they reach the lungs. When these cilia are damaged, it's harder for your body to eject stuff that shouldn't be there, which makes chest infections more likely.
6) And to top it all off, smoking tobacco is addictive — due to the nicotine in tobacco smoke.

Smoking and Lung Cancer Are Now Known to Be Linked

1) In the first half of the 20th century it was noticed that lung cancer and the popularity of smoking increased together. And studies found that far more smokers than non-smokers got lung cancer.
2) But it was just a statistical correlation at that time (see pages 163-164) — it didn't prove that smoking caused lung cancer. Some people (especially in the tobacco industry) argued that there was some other factor (e.g. a person's genes) which both caused lung cancer and also made people more likely to smoke.
3) Later research eventually disproved these claims. Now even the tobacco industry has had to admit that smoking does increase the risk of lung cancer.

Not surprisingly, the "stop-smoking industry" is now big business. The main products available are:

Nicotine gum and patches
These gradually decrease the dose of nicotine (the addictive chemical in tobacco). The success rate with these is about twice that of people using willpower alone.

Acupuncture
People report success with this method, but there is not yet scientific evidence that it works.

Hypnosis
Again, patients report success, but its effects are not scientifically proven.

If that wasn't enough, it also gives you yellow teeth

This page might make you think 'yeah yeah yeah heard it before', but there's no way you can make an informed decision about drug use without being informed. Whatever your take on this kind of thing, you need to know about it for your exam. So make sure you learn all the details.

Alcohol and Tobacco

Many people see drinking alcohol as more acceptable than smoking tobacco, but excessive drinking seems to be on the increase, and so are drink-related crimes and injuries.

Drinking Alcohol Can Do Its Share of Damage Too

1) The main effect of alcohol is to reduce the activity of the nervous system — slowing your reactions.

2) It can also make you feel less inhibited — which can help people to socialise and relax with each other.

3) However, too much leads to impaired judgement, poor balance and coordination, lack of self-control, unconsciousness and even coma.

4) Alcohol in excess also causes dehydration, which can damage brain cells, causing a noticeable drop in brain function. And too much drinking causes severe damage to the liver, leading to liver disease.

5) There are social costs too. Alcohol is linked with way more than half of murders, stabbings and domestic assaults. And alcohol misuse is also a factor in loads of divorces and cases of child abuse.

These Two Legal Drugs Have a Massive Impact

Alcohol and tobacco have a bigger impact in the UK than illegal drugs, as so many people take them.

Tobacco

The National Health Service spends loads on treating people with lung diseases caused by smoking (or passive smoking). Add to this the cost to businesses of people missing days from work, and the figures get pretty scary.

Alcohol

The same goes for alcohol. The costs to the NHS are huge, but are pretty small compared to the costs related to crime (police time, damage to people/property) and the economy (lost working days etc.).

And in addition to the financial costs, alcohol and tobacco cause sorrow and anguish to people affected by them, either directly or indirectly.

Learn all this stuff — not just for the exam

So it's legal drugs that have the most impact on the country as a whole — when you take everything into consideration. Should the government do more to reduce the number of people who smoke — or is it up to individual people what they do with their lives... there's no easy answer to that one.

More About Drugs

Tobacco and alcohol are legal drugs, but other drugs (e.g. heroin, cannabis, LSD, tranquillisers) are illegal. You need to know about illegal drugs and how soft drug use could lead to hard drug use...

Recreational Drugs Can Be Illegal or Legal

1) Illegal drugs are often divided into two main classes — soft and hard. Hard drugs (e.g. heroin and cocaine) are usually thought of as being seriously addictive and generally more harmful.
2) But the terms "soft" and "hard" are a bit vague — they're not scientific descriptions, and you can certainly have problems with soft drug use.

There Are Various Reasons Why People Use Recreational Drugs

So if all these recreational drugs are so dangerous, why do so many people use them...

1) When asked why they use cannabis, most users quote either simple enjoyment, relaxation or stress relief. Some say they do it to get stoned or for inspiration.
2) But very often this turns out to be not the whole story. There may be other factors in the user's background or personal life which influence them in choosing to use drugs. It's a personal thing, and often pretty complicated.

And some multiple sclerosis sufferers say cannabis can relieve pain.

Some Studies Link Cannabis and Hard Drug Use — Others Don't

Almost all users of hard drugs have tried cannabis first (though most users of cannabis do not go on to use hard drugs). The link between cannabis and hard drugs isn't clear, but three opinions are common...

Cannabis is a "stepping stone": The effects of cannabis create a desire to try harder drugs.

Cannabis is a "gateway drug": Cannabis use brings people into contact with drug dealers.

See page 30 for more info.

It's all down to genetics: Certain people are more likely to take drugs generally, so cannabis users will also try other drugs.

Illegal drugs are also harmful and addictive

Even though they're not scientific descriptions, make sure you know what the difference is between hard and soft drugs. Also, if you're asked to evaluate the link between hard and soft drugs in the exam make sure you give both sides of the argument.

Health Claims

It's sometimes hard to figure out if health claims or adverts are true or not.

New Day, New Food Claim — *It Can't All Be True*

1) To get you to buy a product, advertisers aren't allowed to make claims that are untrue — that's illegal.
2) But they do sometimes make claims that could be misleading or difficult to prove (or disprove).

   For example, some claims are just vague (calling a product "light" for instance — does that mean low calorie, low fat, something else...).

   Alternatively, they might call a breakfast cereal "low fat", and that'd be true. But that could suggest that other breakfast cereals are high in fat — when in fact they're not.
3) And every day there's a new food scare in the papers (eeek — we're all doomed). Or a new miracle food (phew — we're all saved).
4) It's not easy to decide what to believe and what to ignore. But these things are worth looking for:

   a) Is the report a scientific study, published in a reputable journal?
   b) Was it written by a qualified person (not connected with the food producers)?
   c) Was the sample of people asked/tested large enough to give reliable results?
   d) Have there been other studies which found similar results?
5) A "yes" to one or more of these is a good sign.

Not All Diets Are Scientifically Proven

With each new day comes a new celebrity-endorsed diet. It's a wonder anyone's overweight.

1) A common way to promote a new diet is to say, "Celebrity A has lost x pounds using it".
2) But effectiveness in one person doesn't mean much. Only a large survey can tell if a diet is more or less effective than just eating less and exercising more — and these aren't done often.

Example: The Atkins diet

The Atkins diet was high profile, and controversial — so it got investigated. People on the diet certainly lost weight. But the diet's effect on general health (especially long-term health) has been questioned. The jury's still out.

3) Weight loss is a complex process. But just like with food claims, the best thing to do is look at the evidence in a scientific way.

Health Claims

The same rules apply when looking into claims about drugs — look at all the evidence in a scientific way.

It's the Same When You Look at Claims About **Drugs**

Claims about the effects of drugs (both medical and illegal ones) also need to be looked at critically. But at least here the evidence is usually based on scientific research.

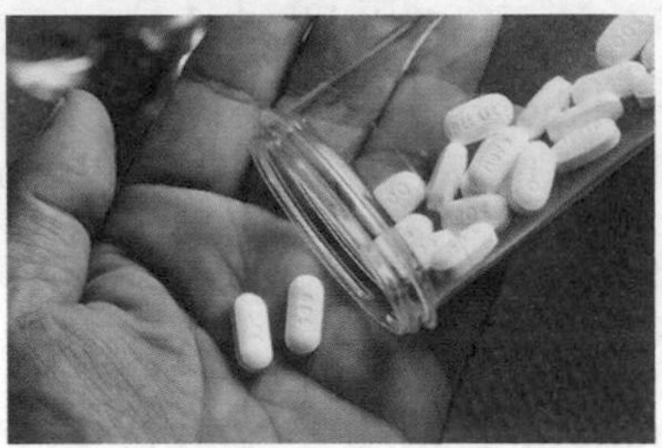

Statins

1) There's evidence that drugs called statins lower blood cholesterol and significantly lower the risk of heart disease in diabetic patients.

2) The original research was done by government scientists with no connection to the manufacturers. And the sample was big — 6000 patients.

So control groups were used. And the results were reproducible.

3) It compared two groups of patients — those who had taken statins and those who hadn't. Other studies have since backed up these findings.

But research findings are not always so clear cut...

Cannabis

1) Many scientists have looked at whether cannabis use causes brain damage and mental health problems or leads to further drug taking. The results vary, and are sometimes open to different interpretations.

2) Basically, until more definite scientific evidence is found, no one's sure.

Evidence must be looked at in a scientific way

Learn what to look out for before you put too much faith in what you read. Think about who's making a claim, how much evidence there is to support it, and whether that evidence is reliable. And always remember to look at any health claim, whether it's to do with diets or drugs, in a scientific way.

Warm-Up and Exam Questions

There's no point in whizzing through the section and glancing over the questions. Do the warm-up questions and go back over any bits you don't know. Then practise and practise the exam questions.

Warm-Up Questions

1) What is a drug?
2) What are carcinogens?
3) Name two lung diseases, other than cancer, caused by smoking.
4) Name one legal drug to which people may become addicted.
5) Give one possible argument for a link between cannabis use and hard drug use.
6) List four things that should be considered when deciding if a health claim is reliable.

Exam Questions

1 The following chemicals are all found in cigarette smoke.
Explain what effect each has on the body.

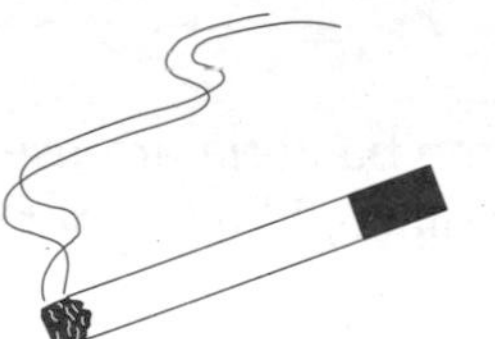

(a) Tar

(1 mark)

(b) Carbon monoxide

(1 mark)

(c) Nicotine

(1 mark

2 In the UK it is illegal to drive if your blood alcohol concentration exceeds 80 mg of alcohol per 100 ml of blood.

(a) Explain the effect alcohol has on the body, that increases the risk of having a car accident when drink driving.

(2 marks)

(b) Give two long term health effects of excessive alcohol consumption.

(2 marks)

(c) Other than drink-related driving accidents, give two ways in which excessive alcohol consumption has a negative effect on society.

(2 marks)

3 (a) Give four stages of testing that a new drug will usually go through before it can be sold to the general public.

(4 marks)

(b) Thalidomide was used to treat morning sickness in pregnant women, but it hadn't been tested for this use.

(i) Describe the effect that thalidomide had on fetuses.

(1 mark)

(ii) Name one disease that thalidomide is currently used to treat.

(1 mark)

Pathogens

When certain microorganisms (called pathogens) enter the body they cause disease.

There Are **Two Main Types of Pathogen: Bacteria** and **Viruses**

...and they can both multiply quickly inside your body — they love the warm conditions.

1) ***Bacteria*** *Are Very Small* ***Living Cells***

1) Bacteria are very small cells (about 1/100th the size of your body cells), which can reproduce rapidly inside your body.

2) They make you feel ill by doing two things:

   a) damaging your cells

   b) producing toxins (poisons)

3) But... some bacteria are useful if they're in the right place, like in your digestive system.

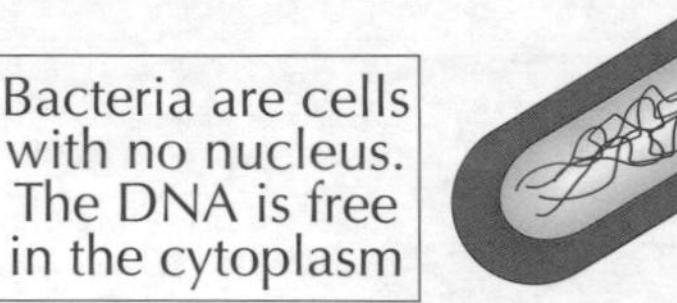

Bacteria are cells with no nucleus. The DNA is free in the cytoplasm

These are some different types of bacteria

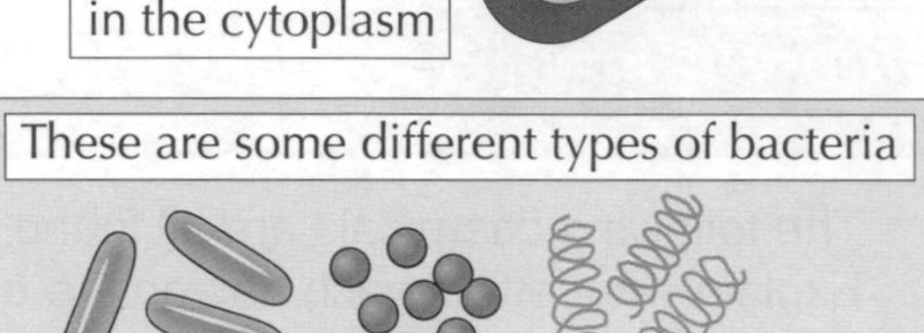

2) ***Viruses*** *Are* ***Not*** *Cells — They're Much Smaller*

1) Viruses are not cells. They're tiny, about 1/100th the size of a bacterium. They're usually no more than a coat of protein around some genetic material.

2) They replicate themselves by invading your cells and using the cells' machinery to produce many copies of themselves. The cell will usually then burst, releasing all the new viruses.

3) This cell damage is what makes you feel ill.

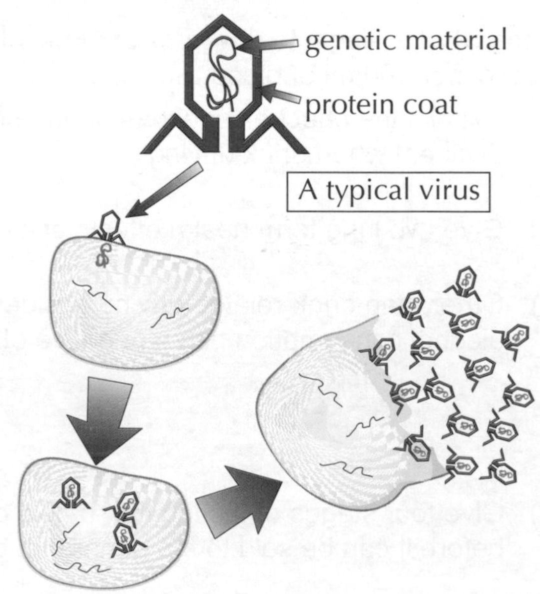

A typical virus

Trillions of bacteria call your digestive system home...

It's strange to think that such small things can have such massive effects on your body. But bacteria and viruses can multiply extremely quickly and make you feel ill by cell damage (bacteria and viruses) or by producing toxins (bacteria). It's a good job our bodies have ways of attacking them...

Fighting Disease

Your body is constantly fighting off attack from all sorts of nasties — yep, things really are out to get you. The body has lots of ways to stop pathogens causing disease.

Your Body Has a Pretty Sophisticated ***Defence System***

1) Your skin, plus hairs and mucus in your respiratory tract (breathing pipework), stop a lot of nasties getting inside your body.

2) And to try and prevent microorganisms getting into the body through cuts, small fragments of cells (called platelets) help blood clot quickly to seal wounds. If the blood contains low numbers of platelets then it will clot more slowly.

3) But if something does make it through, your immune system kicks in. The most important part of your immune system is the white blood cells. They travel around in your blood and crawl into every part of you, constantly patrolling for microbes. When they come across an invading microbe they have three lines of attack.

1) ***Consuming*** *Them*

White blood cells can engulf foreign cells and digest them.

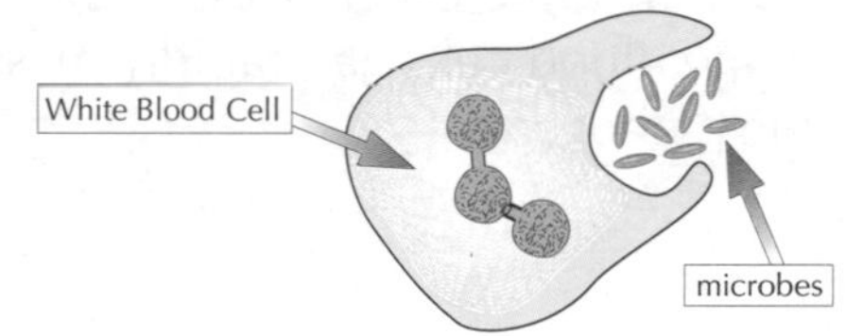

2) Producing ***Antibodies***

1) Every invading cell has unique molecules (called antigens) on its surface.

2) When your white blood cells come across a foreign antigen (i.e. one it doesn't recognise), they will start to produce proteins called antibodies to lock on to and kill the invading cells. The antibodies produced are specific to that type of antigen — they won't lock on to any others.

3) Antibodies are then produced rapidly and flow all round the body to kill all similar bacteria or viruses.

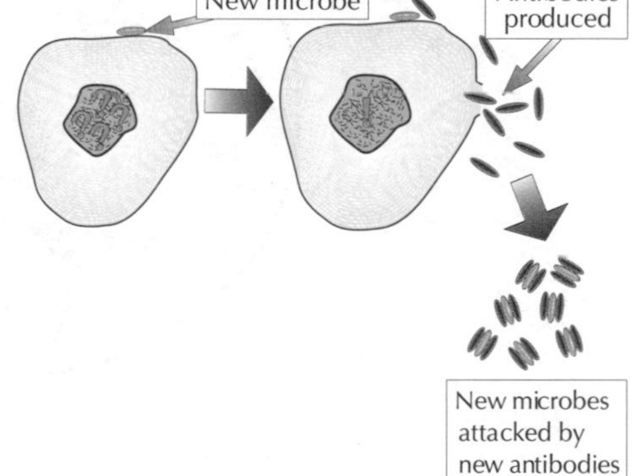

4) If the person is infected with the same pathogen again the white blood cells will rapidly produce the antibodies to kill it — the person is naturally immune to that pathogen and won't get ill.

3) Producing ***Antitoxins***

These counter toxins produced by the invading bacteria.

White blood cells protect our bodies from pathogens

So by now you might have worked out that if you have a low level of white blood cells you'll be more susceptible to infections. In fact, HIV/AIDS doesn't kill people directly, it just makes it easier for something else to by attacking white blood cells and weakening the immune system. However, other diseases (e.g. leukaemia) can increase the number of white blood cells — and that's no good either.

Fighting Disease

Immunisation changed the way we deal with disease. Not bad for a little jab.

Immunisation — Protects from Future Infections

1) When you're infected with a new microorganism, it takes your white blood cells a few days to learn how to deal with it. But by that time, you can be pretty ill.

2) Immunisation involves injecting dead or inactive microorganisms. These carry antigens, which cause your body to produce antibodies to attack them — even though the microorganism is harmless (since it's dead or inactive). For example, the MMR vaccine contains weakened versions of the viruses that cause measles, mumps and rubella (German measles) stuck together.

3) But if live microorganisms of the same type appear after that, the white blood cells can rapidly mass-produce antibodies to kill off the pathogen.

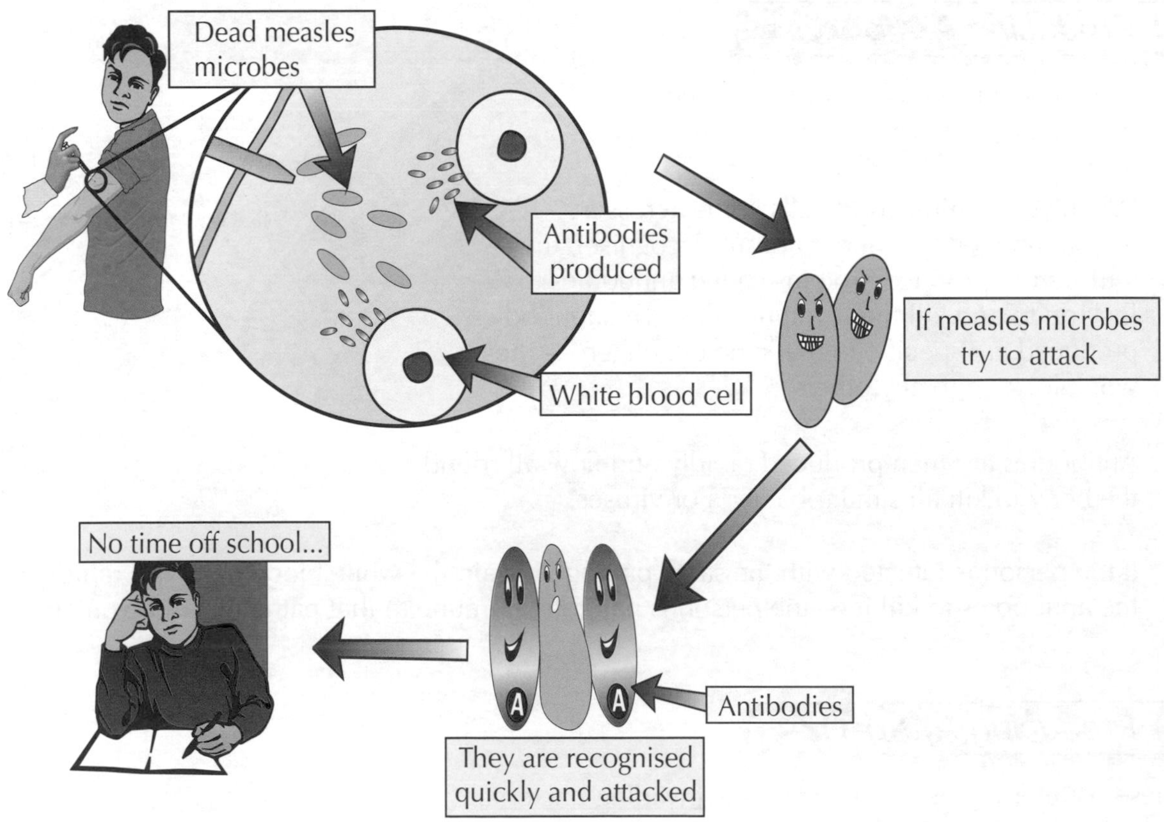

4) Vaccinations "wear off" over time. So booster injections can be given to increase levels of antibodies again.

Fighting Disease

You've probably had to take some sort of medicine if you've been ill, e.g. cough remedies, painkillers. If you've taken antibiotics you'll soon find out why it was really important to finish the course.

Some Drugs Just **Relieve Symptoms** — Others **Cure** the Problem

1) Painkillers (e.g. aspirin) are drugs that relieve pain (no, really). However, they don't actually tackle the cause of the disease, they just help to reduce the symptoms.

2) Other drugs do a similar kind of thing — reduce the symptoms without tackling the underlying cause. For example, lots of "cold remedies" don't actually cure colds.

3) Antibiotics (e.g. penicillin) work differently — they actually kill (or harm) the bacteria causing the problem without killing your own body cells.

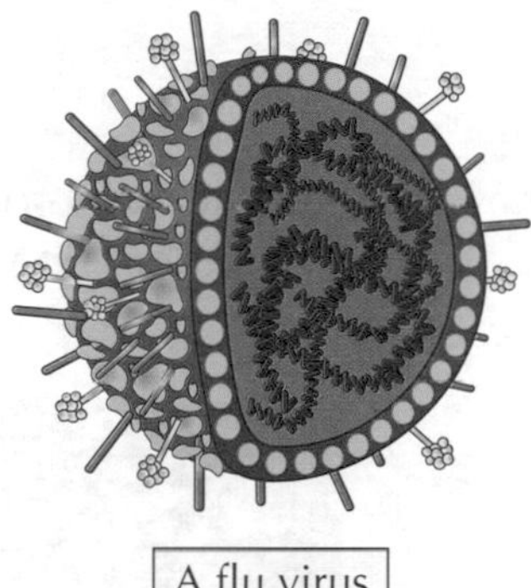

A flu virus

4) However, antibiotics don't destroy viruses. Viruses reproduce using your own body cells which makes it very difficult to develop drugs that destroy just the virus without killing the body's cells.

5) Flu and colds are caused by viruses. Usually you just have to wait for your body to deal with the virus, and relieve the symptoms if you start to feel really grotty. There are some antiviral drugs available, but they're usually reserved for very serious viral illnesses (such as AIDS and hepatitis).

Bacteria Can Become **Resistant** to **Antibiotics**

1) Antibiotics were an incredibly important (but accidental) discovery. Some killer diseases (e.g. pneumonia and tuberculosis) suddenly became much easier to treat. The 1940s are sometimes called the era of the antibiotics revolution — it was that big a deal.

2) Unfortunately, bacteria evolve (adapt to their environment). If antibiotics are taken to deal with an infection but not all the bacteria are killed, those that survive may be resistant to the antibiotic and go on to flourish. This process (an example of natural selection) leaves you with an antibiotic-resistant strain of bacteria — not ideal.

3) A good example of antibiotic-resistant bacteria is MRSA (methicillin-resistant *Staphylococcus aureus*) — it's resistant to the powerful antibiotic methicillin.

4) This is why it's important for patients to always finish a course of antibiotics, and for doctors to avoid over-prescribing them.

Antibiotic resistance is inevitable...

Antibiotic resistance is scary. Bacteria reproduce quickly, and so are pretty fast at evolving to deal with threats (e.g. antibiotics). If we were back in the situation where we had no way to treat bacterial infections, we'd have a nightmare. So do your bit, and finish your courses of antibiotics.

Treating Disease — Past and Future

The treatment of disease has changed somewhat over the last 200 years or so.

Semmelweiss *Cut Deaths by Using* ***Antiseptics***

1) While Ignaz Semmelweiss was working in Vienna General Hospital in the 1840s, he saw that women were dying in huge numbers after childbirth from a disease called puerperal fever.
2) He believed that doctors were spreading the disease on their unwashed hands. By telling doctors entering his ward to wash their hands in an antiseptic solution, he cut the death rate from 12% to 2%.
3) The antiseptic solution killed bacteria on doctors' hands, though Semmelweiss didn't know this (the existence of bacteria and their part in causing disease wasn't discovered for another 20 years). So Semmelweiss couldn't prove why his idea worked, and his methods were dropped when he left the hospital (allowing death rates to rise once again).
4) Nowadays we know that basic hygiene is essential in controlling disease (though recent reports have found that a lack of it in some modern hospitals has helped the disease MRSA spread — see below).

Vaccinations *Also Help to* ***Prevent*** *Disease*

Vaccinations have changed the way we fight disease. We don't always have to deal with the problem once it's happened — we can prevent it happening in the first place. (See page 34 for more on vaccines.)

1) Vaccines have helped control lots of infectious diseases that were once common in the UK (e.g. polio, measles, whooping cough, rubella, mumps, tetanus...).
2) And if an outbreak does occur, vaccines can slow down or stop the spread (if people don't catch the disease, they won't pass it on).
3) Vaccination is now used all over the world. Smallpox no longer occurs at all, and polio infections have fallen by 99%.
4) Vaccines don't always work — sometimes they don't give you immunity, and sometimes you can have a bad reaction (e.g. swelling, or maybe something more serious such as a fever or seizures). But bad reactions are very rare. Vaccines are very safe (see below).

We Face ***New*** *and* ***Scary Dangers*** *All the Time*

1) For the last few decades, humans have been able to deal with bacterial infections pretty easily using antibiotics.
2) But bacteria evolve — MRSA bacteria are already resistant to certain antibiotics (see page 35).
3) And there'd be a real problem if a virus evolved so that it was both deadly and could easily pass from person to person. (Flu viruses, for example, evolve quickly so this is quite possible.)
4) If this happened, precautions could be taken to stop the virus spreading in the first place (though this is hard nowadays — millions of people travel by plane every day). And vaccines and antiviral drugs could be developed (though these take time to mass produce).
5) But in the worst-case scenario, a flu pandemic (e.g. one evolved from bird flu) could kill billions of people all over the world.

A pandemic is when a disease spreads all over the world.

Prevention is better than cure...

Deciding whether to have a vaccination means balancing risks — the risk of catching the disease if you don't have a vaccine, against the risk of having a bad reaction if you do. As always, you need to look at the evidence. For example, if you get measles (the disease), there's about a 1 in 15 chance that you'll get complications (e.g. pneumonia) — and about 1 in 500 people who get measles actually die. However, the number of people who have a problem with the vaccine is more like 1 in 1 000 000.

Warm-Up and Exam Questions

It's easy to think you've learnt everything in the section until you try the warm-up questions. Don't panic if there's a bit you've forgotten, just go back over that bit until it's firmly fixed in your brain.

Warm-Up Questions

1) What is a pathogen?
2) Explain how viruses replicate within your body.
3) What are antigens?
4) What are antibiotics designed to do?
5) Name two diseases that are controlled by vaccinations.
6) Give one side effect that could result from a vaccine.
7) What is a pandemic?

Exam Questions

1 Read the following passage.

Typhoid is an infectious bacterial disease. The typhoid bacterium is often found in food and water where there is poor sanitation. The bacterium causes fever and severe diarrhoea. Typhoid can be fatal but can be treated using antibiotics. Fortunately, the spread of the disease can be reduced by vaccination.

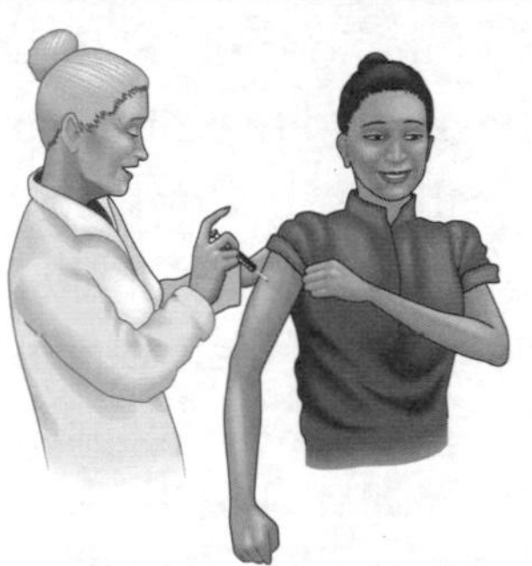

Put the following stages in order to describe how the typhoid vaccine works.

1. Antibodies attack the typhoid bacteria even though it is harmless.
2. When live typhoid bacteria infect the body, white blood cells rapidly mass produce antibodies to kill off the pathogen.
3. Antigens on the dead/inactive bacteria stimulate the production of antibodies by white blood cells.
4. Dead/inactive typhoid bacteria are injected.
5. White blood cells remain in the body to provide a memory.

(1 mark)

2 (a) Why would a course of antibiotics not be suitable for treatment of flu?

(2 marks)

(b) What might the inappropriate use of antibiotics lead to?

(1 mark)

3 Describe three ways that white blood cells fight pathogens.

(3 marks)

Revision Summary for Biology 1a

That was a long(ish) section, but kind of interesting, I reckon. These questions will show what you know and what you don't... if you get stuck, have a look back to remind yourself. But before the exam, make sure you can do all of them without any help — if you can't, you know you're definitely not ready.

1) Where would you find the following receptors in a dog: a) smell b) taste c) light d) pressure e) sound?
2) Describe the structure of the central nervous system.
3) What are the following: a) sensory neurone, b) motor neurone, c) effector?
4) How do nerve signals get from one neurone to another?
5) What is the purpose of a reflex action?
6) Name one hormone produced by each of the following glands:
   a) pituitary gland, b) ovaries, c) pancreas, d) testes.
7) *Here's a table of data about response times.
   a) Which response (A or B) is carried by nerves?
   b) Which is carried by hormones?

Response	Reaction time (s)	Response duration (s)
A	0.005	0.05
B	2	10

8) Draw a timeline of the 28-day menstrual cycle. Label the four stages of the cycle and label when the egg is released.
9) What are the two functions of FSH?
10) State two advantages and two disadvantages of using the contraceptive pill.
11) Name three other things, besides ion content, that need to be kept at the right levels in your body.
12) If you've got too much of a certain ion in your blood, what organ removes it?
13) Name the six food groups that you need in a balanced diet.
14) *Put these people in order of how much energy they are likely to need from their food (from highest to lowest): a) builder, b) professional runner, c) waitress, d) secretary.
15) Explain why it may be difficult to get accurate data on: a) malnutrition, b) obesity.
16) If you never sprinkle any salt onto your food, are you safe from having too much salt in your diet?
17) Why is it dangerous to have high levels of cholesterol?
18) Explain what is meant by 'good cholesterol' and 'bad cholesterol'.
19) Name a drug that was not tested thoroughly enough and describe the consequences of its use.
20) Describe three ways that could help someone stop smoking. Are all of these ways proven to work?
21) *Here is a graph of Mark's blood alcohol concentration against time.
   a) When did Mark have his first alcoholic drink?
   b) When did Mark have his second alcoholic drink?
   c) The legal limit for driving is 80 mg of alcohol per 100 ml of blood. Would Mark have been legally allowed to drive at 9 pm?

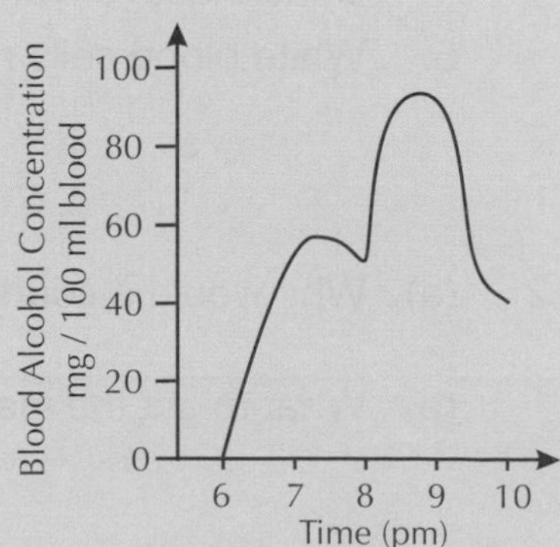

22) Explain the difference between bacteria and viruses.
23) Explain how immunisation can stop someone getting ill.
24) What problem can be made worse by the over-prescription of antibiotics?
25) What practice did Semmelweiss introduce in the 1840s? Explain why this reduced death rates on his ward.

*Answers on page 223

Adaptation

Animals and plants survive in many different environments — from hot deserts to cold polar regions, and pretty much everywhere in between — they can do this because they have adapted to their environment.

Desert Animals Have Adapted to Save Water

Animals that live in hot, dry conditions need to keep cool and use water efficiently.

Large Surface Area Compared to Volume

This lets desert animals lose more body heat — which helps to stop them overheating.

Efficient with Water

1) Desert animals lose less water by producing small amounts of concentrated urine.
2) They also make very little sweat. Camels are able to do this by tolerating big changes in body temperature, while kangaroo rats live in burrows underground where it's cool.

Good in Hot, Sandy Conditions

1) Desert animals have very thin layers of body fat to help them lose body heat. Camels keep nearly all their fat in their humps.
2) Large feet spread their weight across soft sand — making getting about easier.
3) A sandy colour gives good camouflage — so they're not as easy for their predators to spot.

Arctic Animals Have Adapted to Reduce Heat Loss

Animals that live in really cold conditions need to keep warm.

Small Surface Area compared to Volume

Animals living in cold conditions have a compact (rounded) shape to keep their surface area to a minimum — this reduces heat loss.

Well Insulated

1) They also have a thick layer of blubber for insulation — this also acts as an energy store when food is scarce.
2) Thick hairy coats keep body heat in, and greasy fur sheds water (this prevents cooling due to evaporation).

Good in Snowy Conditions

1) Arctic animals have white fur to match their surroundings — for camouflage.
2) Big feet help by spreading weight — which stops animals sinking into the snow or breaking thin ice.

Adaptation

Whether you're an animal or a plant, you have to adapt to your environment — and that includes adapting to deal with other plants and animals...

Some **Plants** Have Adapted to Living in a **Desert**

Desert-dwelling plants make best use of what little water is available.

Minimising Water **Loss**

1) Cacti have spines instead of leaves — to reduce water loss.
2) They also have a small surface area compared to their size (about 1000 times smaller than normal plants), which also reduces water loss.
3) A cactus stores water in its thick stem.

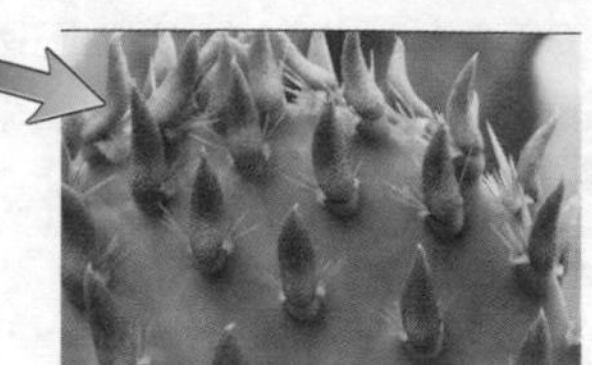

Maximising Water **Absorption**

Some cacti have shallow but extensive roots to absorb water quickly over a large area. Others have deep roots to access underground water.

Some **Plants** and **Animals** Are Adapted to **Deter Predators**

There are various special features used by animals and plants to help protect them against being eaten.

1) Some plants and animals have armour — like roses (with thorns), cacti (with sharp spines) and tortoises (with hard shells).

2) Others produce poisons — like bees, wasps and poison ivy.

3) And some have amazing warning colours to scare off predators — like wasps and caterpillars.

In a nutshell, it's horses for courses...

It's no accident that animals and plants look like they do. So by looking at an animal's characteristics, you should be able to have a pretty good guess at the kind of environment it lives in — or vice versa. Why does it have a large/small surface area... what are those spines for... why is it green... and so on.

Populations and Competition

Often different organisms have adapted to suit the same environment and use the same resources — which means that sooner or later they'll probably end up competing with each other for survival...

*The **Size** of Any **Population** Depends on **Three Main Factors***

A population is a group of organisms of one species that live in a particular environment. The size of a population will go up and down due to THREE MAIN FACTORS:

1. Competition

Organisms compete with other species (and members of their own species) for the same resources. Plants and animals compete in similar ways:

PLANTS

Plants often compete with each other for light, water and nutrients from the soil.

All the trees and plants in a forest compete for sunlight.

ANIMALS

Animals often compete with each other for space (territory), food, water and mates — e.g. red and grey squirrels live in the same habitat and eat the same food. Competition with the grey squirrels for these resources means there's not enough food for the reds — so the population of red squirrels is decreasing (see page 42).

Red and grey squirrels compete for the same food.

2. Disease

Infectious diseases caused by bacteria and viruses can kill off many members of a population — but organisms that are fit and healthy stand the best chance of survival.

3. Predation

If an organism gets eaten its population will decrease. For example, humans have eaten a lot of cod, which has reduced the cod population dramatically.

Populations and Competition

Competition for resources can affect the location, size and distribution of populations in the wild.

Organisms **Compete** for **Resources**

1) Organisms will live where they can find the resources they need to survive (food, water, etc.). For example, a puffin eats small seafish, so it lives by the sea.

2) Competition for the same resources means that a habitat will only be able to support a certain number of organisms. If the amount of resources in an area decreases, the size of a population there will also decrease — because the organisms will either die or move to where there are more resources.

3) Competition also affects how far apart members of a population are in a habitat (i.e. the distribution of members of the population). If there aren't many resources an organism will need a lot of space to find enough food, water etc. — but if there are loads of resources you can have loads of organisms in a smaller space.

e.g. **Red** and **Grey Squirrels**

1) In 1876 the grey squirrel was introduced into the UK.
2) The native red squirrels were unable to compete very well with the larger grey squirrels — causing the red squirrel population to decrease.
3) The grey squirrel is better adapted to deciduous woodland than the red squirrel and so out competes it.
4) Red squirrels can only outcompete grey squirrels in coniferous woodland because they can eat conifer seeds, so their distribution is now mostly confined to pine forests.

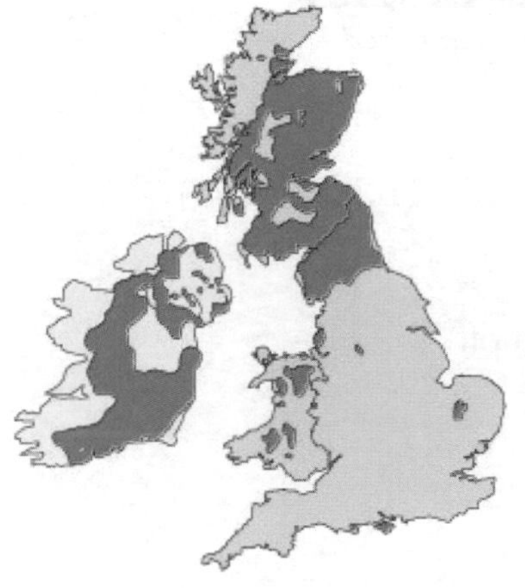

Distribution of red squirrels, 1998

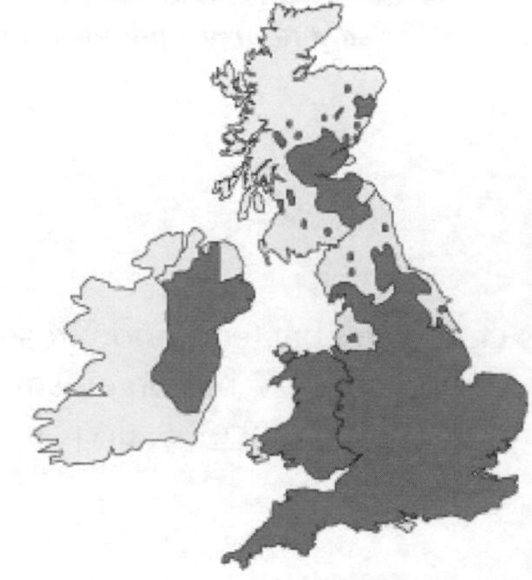

Distribution of grey squirrels, 1998

Maps © Forest Research

Organisms compete for water, food, shelter etc.

In the exam you might get asked about the distribution of any animals or plants. Just think about what the organisms would need to survive. Remember, if things are in limited supply then there's going to be competition. And the more similar the needs of the organisms, the more they'll have to compete.

Warm-Up and Exam Questions

Learning facts and practising exam questions is the only recipe for success.
That's what the questions on this page are all about. All you have to do — is do them.

Warm-Up Questions

1) Why is a small body surface area compared to its volume an advantage for an animal living in cold conditions?
2) Give two adaptations that a wasp has developed to help deter predators.
3) State three factors that limit the population size for any organism.
4) Give two ways in which competition for resources can affect populations in the wild.

Exam Questions

1 Arctic animals are adapted to their environment.
The table below is about the adaptations of a polar bear.
Match each adaptation, **A**, **B**, **C** and **D** in the list with its purpose (**1 - 4**).

A Large feet

B Thick layer of blubber

C White fur

D Greasy fur

	Purpose
1	Prevents cooling due to evaporation.
2	Stops them sinking into snow.
3	Helps them retain body heat.
4	Makes it hard for prey to spot them.

(4 marks)

2 Explain how the features of a cactus help it to survive in desert conditions.

(3 marks)

3 Species A is a type of small mammal that eats beetles found in woodland areas.

(a) Where is Species A likely to live?

(1 mark)

(b) Species B moves into the same area as Species A.
Species B feeds on the same type of beetle as Species A.

(i) What word is used to describe how Species A and Species B interact with each other?

(1 mark)

(ii) What is likely to happen to the population of Species A after Species B has moved into the area?
Explain your answer.

(3 marks)

Variation in Plants and Animals

You'll probably have noticed that not all people are identical. There are reasons for this.

Organisms of the Same Species Have Differences

1) Different species look... well... different — my dog definitely doesn't look like a daisy.
2) But even organisms of the same species will usually look at least slightly different — e.g. in a room full of people you'll see different colour hair, individually shaped noses, a variety of heights etc.
3) These differences are called the variation within a species — and there are two types of variation: genetic variation and environmental variation.

Different Genes Cause Genetic Variation

1) All plants and animals have characteristics that are in some ways similar to their parents'.
2) This is because an organism's characteristics are determined by the genes inherited from their parents. (Genes are the codes inside your cells that control how you're made — more about these on page 45.)
3) Most animals (and quite a lot of plants) get some genes from the mother and some from the father.
4) This combining of genes from two parents causes genetic variation — no two of the species are genetically identical (other than identical twins).
5) Some characteristics are determined only by genes (e.g. a plant's flower colour). In animals these include: eye colour, blood group and inherited disorders (e.g. haemophilia or cystic fibrosis).

Characteristics are also Influenced by the Environment

1) The environment that organisms live and grow in also causes differences between members of the same species — this is called environmental variation.
2) Environmental variation covers a wide range of differences — from losing your toes in an accident, to getting a suntan, to plants having yellow leaves, and so on.
3) Basically, any difference that has been caused by the conditions something lives in, is an environmental variation.

A plant grown on a nice sunny windowsill would grow luscious and green.

The same plant grown in darkness would grow tall and spindly and its leaves would turn yellow — these are environmental variations.

Most Characteristics are Due to Genes AND the Environment

1) Most characteristics (e.g. body weight, height, skin colour, condition of teeth, academic or athletic prowess, etc.) are determined by a mixture of genetic and environmental factors.
2) For example, the maximum height that an animal or plant could grow to is determined by its genes. But whether it actually grows that tall depends on its environment (e.g. how much food it gets).

Most variation is a mixture of genes and the environment

So, you are the way you are partly because of the genes you inherited off your parents. But you can't blame it all on them, as your environment then takes over and begins to mould you in many ways.

Genes, Chromosomes and DNA

This page is a bit tricky, but it's dead important you get to grips with all the stuff on it — because you're going to hear a lot more about it over the next few pages...

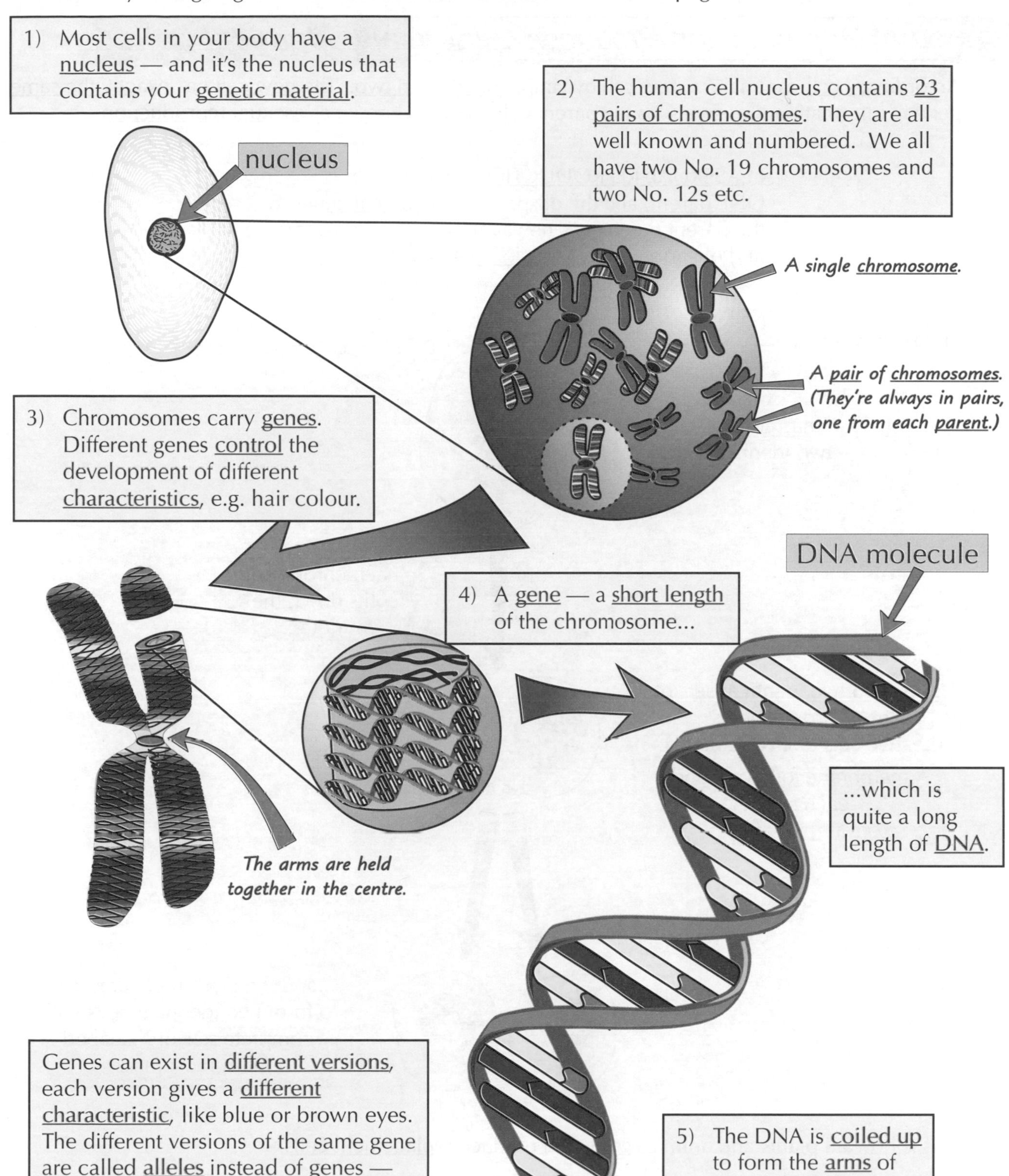

1) Most cells in your body have a <u>nucleus</u> — and it's the nucleus that contains your <u>genetic material</u>.

2) The human cell nucleus contains <u>23 pairs of chromosomes</u>. They are all well known and numbered. We all have two No. 19 chromosomes and two No. 12s etc.

3) Chromosomes carry <u>genes</u>. Different genes <u>control</u> the development of different <u>characteristics</u>, e.g. hair colour.

4) A <u>gene</u> — a <u>short length</u> of the chromosome...

...which is quite a long length of <u>DNA</u>.

5) The DNA is <u>coiled up</u> to form the <u>arms</u> of the <u>chromosome</u>.

Genes can exist in <u>different versions</u>, each version gives a <u>different characteristic</u>, like blue or brown eyes. The different versions of the same gene are called <u>alleles</u> instead of genes — it's more sensible than it sounds!

It's hard being a DNA molecule, there's so much to remember...

This is the nitty gritty of genetics, so you definitely need to understand <u>everything</u> on this page or you'll find the rest of this topic dead hard. The best way to get all of these important facts engraved in your mind is to <u>cover</u> the page, <u>scribble</u> down the main points and <u>sketch</u> out the diagrams...

Reproduction

Organisms can reproduce in two different ways.
The first way you need to know about is called asexual reproduction.

Asexual Reproduction Produces **Genetically Identical Cells**

1) An ordinary cell can make a new cell by simply dividing in two. The new cell has exactly the same genetic information (i.e. genes) as the parent cell — this is known as asexual reproduction.

> In ASEXUAL REPRODUCTION there is only ONE parent, and the offspring has identical genes to the parent (i.e. there's no variation between parent and offspring, so they're clones — see page 49).

2) Here's how it works...

X-shaped chromosomes have two identical halves.

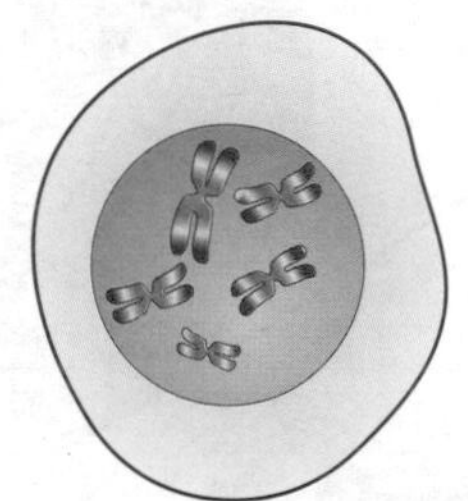

So each chromosome splits down the middle...

...to form two identical sets of 'half-chromosomes' (i.e. two sets of DNA strands).

A membrane forms around each set...

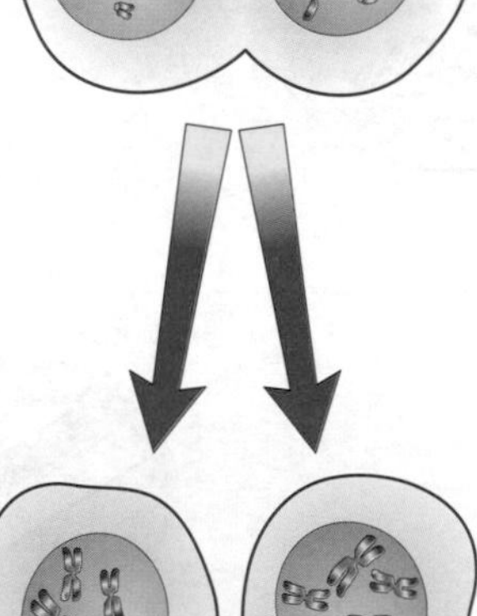

...and the DNA replicates itself to form two identical cells with complete sets of X-shaped chromosomes.

3) This is how all plants and animals grow and produce replacement cells.
4) Some organisms also produce offspring using asexual reproduction, e.g. bacteria and certain plants.

You need to reproduce these facts in the exam...

The main message on this page is that asexual reproduction needs just one parent to make genetically identical cells (clones), so there's no variation in the offspring. Make sure you know this page off by heart before moving onto sexual reproduction, so you don't get them mixed up.

Reproduction

The second way that organisms can reproduce is called sexual reproduction.

Sexual *Reproduction Produces* ***Genetically Different Cells***

1) Sexual reproduction is where genetic information from two organisms (a father and a mother) is combined to produce offspring which are genetically different to either parent.
2) In sexual reproduction the mother and father produce gametes — e.g. egg and sperm cells in animals.
3) In humans, each gamete contains 23 chromosomes — half the number of chromosomes in a normal cell. (Instead of having two of each chromosome, a gamete has just one of each.)
4) The egg (from the mother) and the sperm cell (from the father) then fuse together (fertilisation) to form a cell with the full number of chromosomes (half from the father, half from the mother).

SEXUAL REPRODUCTION involves the fusion of male and female gametes.

Because there are TWO parents, the offspring contains a mixture of their parents' genes.

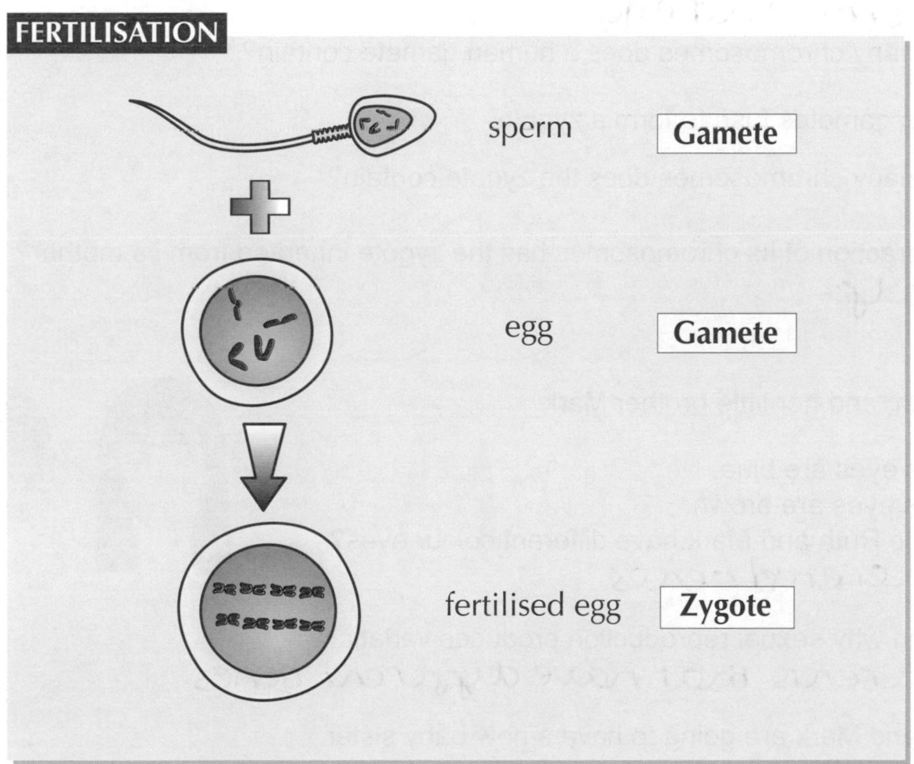

5) This is why the offspring inherits features from both parents — it's received a mixture of chromosomes from its mum and its dad (and it's the chromosomes that decide how you turn out).
6) This is why sexual reproduction produces more variation than asexual reproduction.

Sexual reproduction creates genetic variation...

Sexual reproduction needs two parents and forms cells that are genetically different to the parents, so there's lots of variation. Have a look back at the previous page and make sure you know the differences between asexual and sexual reproduction — shut the book and try writing them down.

Warm-Up and Exam Questions

Take a deep breath and go through these warm-up questions one by one.
If you don't know these basic facts there's no way you'll cope with the exam questions.

Warm-Up Questions

1) A pair of identical twins have green eyes. Twin A has a scar above her eye. Twin B weighs half a stone more than twin A. Which of these characteristics are due to:
   a) genes green eyes.
   b) the environment scar
   c) genes and the environment? weight
2) Where is DNA found in an animal or plant cell? In the nucleus → chromosomes → genes.
3) What are alleles? Different versions of the same gene.
4) In asexual reproduction, how many parents are there? one

Exam Questions

1 (a) What are the male and female human gametes?
sperm and egg
(2 marks)

(b) How many chromosomes does a human gamete contain?
23
(1 mark)

Two human gametes fuse to form a zygote.

(c) How many chromosomes does the zygote contain?
46
(1 mark)

(d) What fraction of its chromosomes has the zygote inherited from its mother?
half.
(1 mark)

2 This is Ruth, and her little brother Mark.

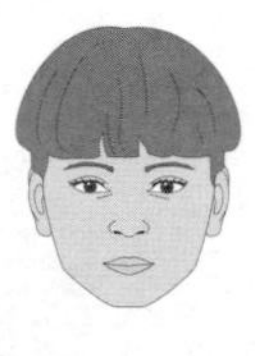

(a) Ruth's eyes are blue.
Mark's eyes are brown.
Why do Ruth and Mark have different colour eyes?
Inhereted genes.
(1 mark)

(b) Explain why sexual reproduction produces variation.
2 parents that have different genes.
(2 marks)

(c) Ruth and Mark are going to have a new baby sister.

Which **one** of the following statements about the baby's eye colour is true?

A The baby's eyes will be the same colour as Ruth's eyes.

B The baby's eye colour will depend on the genes that it inherits from both parents.

C The baby's eyes will be the same colour as its mother's eyes.

D The baby's eyes will definitely be a different colour to both parents' eyes.

(1 mark)

Cloning

We can use asexual reproduction to clone plants and animals in several different ways...

Plants Can Be Cloned from Cuttings and by Tissue Culture

Cuttings

1) Gardeners can take cuttings from good parent plants, and then plant them to produce genetically identical copies (clones) of the parent plant.
2) These plants can be produced quickly and cheaply.

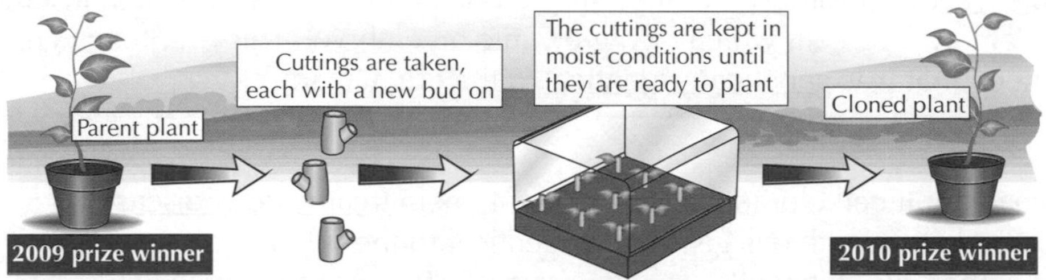

Tissue Culture

This is where a few plant cells are put in a growth medium with hormones, and they then grow into new plants — clones of the parent plant. The advantages of using tissue culture are that you can make new plants very quickly, in very little space, and you can grow all year.

The disadvantage to both these methods is a 'reduced gene pool' (see below).

You Can Make Animal Clones Using Embryo Transplants

Farmers can produce cloned offspring from their best bull and cow — using embryo transplants.

1) Sperm cells are taken from a prize bull and egg cells are taken from a prize cow. The sperm are then used to artificially fertilise an egg cell. The embryo that develops is then split many times (to form clones) before any cells become specialised.
2) These cloned embryos can then be implanted into lots of other cows where they grow into baby calves (which will all be genetically identical to each other).

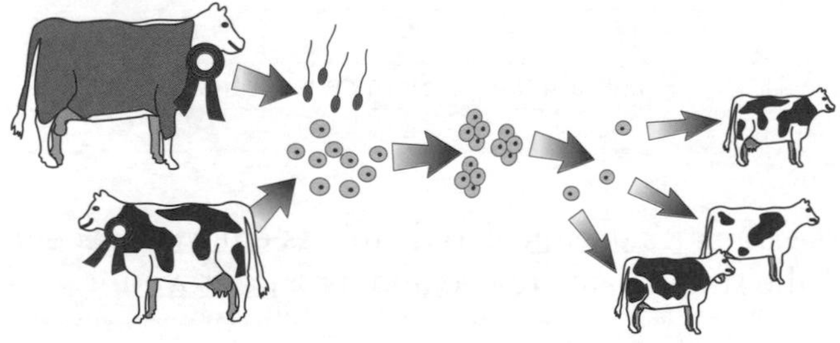

3) The advantage of this is that hundreds of "ideal" offspring can be produced every year from the best bull and cow.
4) The big disadvantage (as usual) is a reduced gene pool.

> A "reduced gene pool" means fewer alleles in a population — which will happen if you breed from the same plants or animals all the time. If a population are all closely related and a new disease appears, all the plants or animals could be wiped out — there may be no allele in the population giving resistance to the disease.

Cloning

There's a second way to clone animals, and it's a bit controversial...

Adult Cell Cloning is Another Way to Make a Clone...

1) Adult cell cloning is the technique that was used to create Dolly — the world-famous cloned sheep.

2) Dolly was made by taking a sheep egg cell and removing its genetic material. A complete set of chromosomes from the cell of an adult sheep was then inserted into the 'empty' egg cell, which then grew into an embryo. This eventually grew into a sheep that was genetically identical to the original adult.

3) Human adult cell cloning could be used to help treat various diseases. A cloned embryo that is genetically identical to the sufferer is created and embryonic stem cells extracted from it. (These can become any cell in the body and could be used to grow replacement cells or organs — without fear of them being rejected by the sufferer's immune system.)

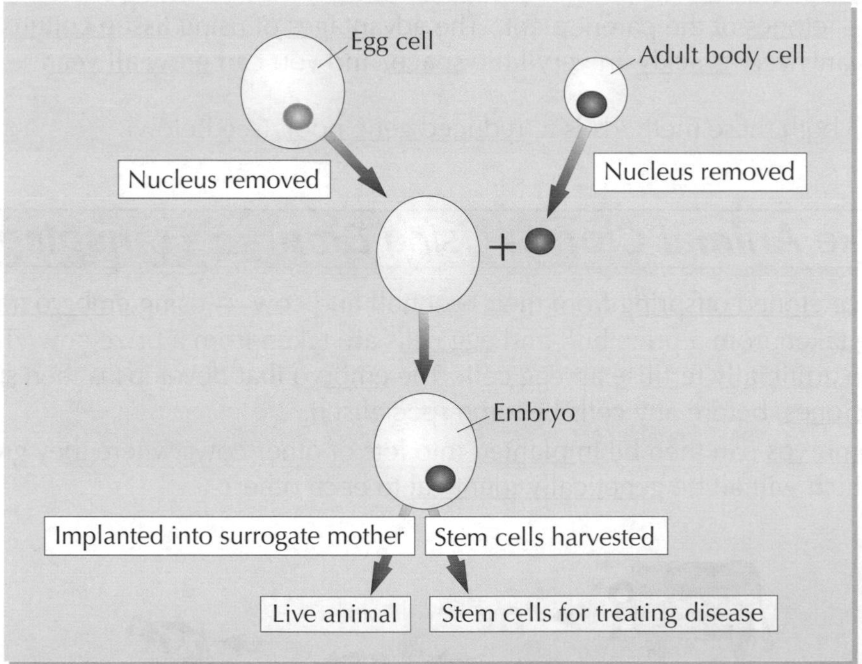

4) Some people think it's unethical to do this as embryos genetically identical to the sufferer are created and then destroyed.

5) Fusion cloning will avoid this problem. Here, an adult cell is fused (joined) to an already existing (but genetically different) embryonic stem cell. The result has the properties of a stem cell but the same genes as the adult.

Cloning produces genetically identical organisms

Cloning can be a controversial topic — especially when it's to do with cloning animals (and especially humans). Is it healthy scientific progress, or are we trying to 'play God'?

Genetic Engineering

Scientists can now add, remove or change an organism's genes to alter its characteristics.

Genetic Engineering Uses Enzymes to Cut and Paste Genes

The basic idea is to move useful genes from one organism's chromosomes into the cells of another...

1) A useful gene is "cut" from one organism's chromosome using enzymes.
2) Enzymes are then used to cut another organism's chromosome and then to insert the useful gene. This technique is called gene splicing.
3) Scientists use this method to do all sorts of things — for example, the human insulin gene can be inserted into bacteria to produce human insulin:

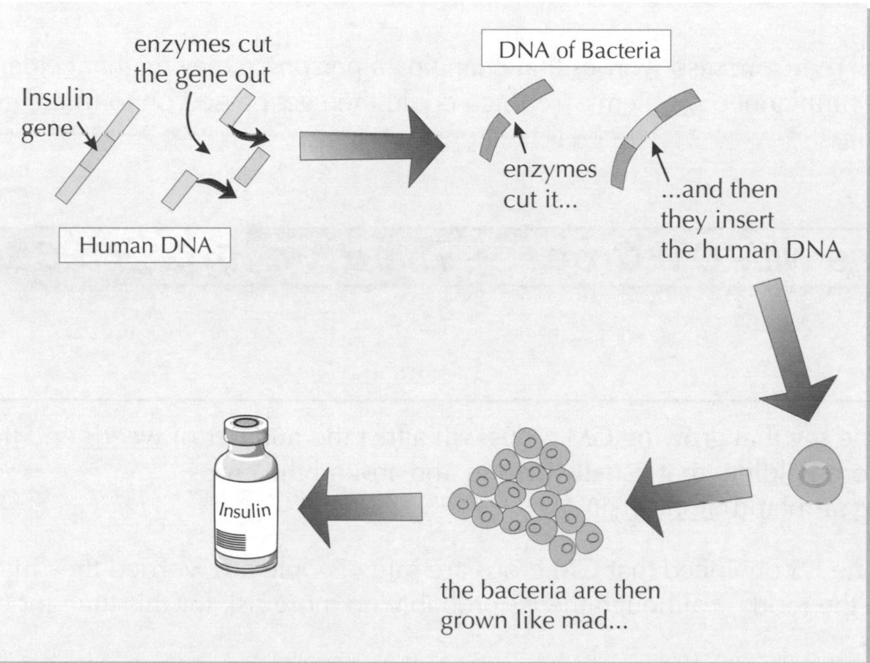

Genes can be Transferred into Animals and Plants

The same method can be used to transfer useful genes into animals and plants at the very early stages of their development (i.e. shortly after fertilisation). This has (or could have) some really useful applications.

1) Genetically modified (GM) plants have been developed that are resistant to viruses and herbicides (chemicals used to kill weeds). And long-life tomatoes can be made by changing the gene that causes the fruit to ripen.

'Bt corn' contains a gene from a bacterium that protects against some insects.

2) Genes can also be inserted into animal embryos so that the animal grows up to have more useful characteristics. For example, sheep have been genetically engineered to produce substances, like drugs, in their milk that can be used to treat human diseases.

3) Genetic disorders like cystic fibrosis are caused by faulty genes. Scientists are trying to cure these disorders by inserting working genes into sufferers. This is called gene therapy.

Genetic Engineering

On the face of it, genetic engineering is great.
But like most other things, there are benefits and risks that you need to consider.

Genetic Engineering is a **Controversial Topic...**

So, genetic engineering is an exciting new area in science which has the potential for solving many of our problems (e.g. treating diseases, more efficient food production etc.) but not everyone thinks it's a great idea.

1) Some people strongly believe that we shouldn't go tinkering about with genes because it's not natural.

2) There are also worries that changing a person's genes might accidentally create unplanned problems — which could then get passed on to future generations.

It's the Same with **GM Crops** — There Are **Pros** and **Cons...**

Cons

1) Some people say that growing GM crops will affect the number of weeds and flowers (and therefore wildlife) that usually lives in and around the crops — reducing farmland biodiversity.
2) Not everyone is convinced that GM crops are safe. People are worried they may develop allergies to the food — although there's probably no more risk for this than for eating usual foods.
3) A big concern is that transplanted genes may get out into the natural environment. For example, the herbicide resistance gene may be picked up by weeds, creating a new 'superweed' variety.

Pros

1) On the plus side, GM crops can increase the yield of a crop, making more food.
2) People living in developing nations often lack nutrients in their diets. GM crops could be engineered to contain the nutrient that's missing. For example, they're testing 'golden rice' that contains beta-carotene — lack of this substance can cause blindness.
3) GM crops are already being used elsewhere in the world (not the UK) often without any problems.

Genetic engineering has exciting and frightening possibilities

At the end of the day it's up to the Government to weigh up all the evidence for the pros and cons before making a decision on how this scientific knowledge is used. All scientists can do is make sure the Government has all the information it needs to make the decision.

Warm-Up and Exam Questions

By doing these warm-up questions, you'll soon find out if you've got the basic facts straight. If not, you'll really struggle, so take the time to go back over the bits you don't know.

Warm-Up Questions

1) Briefly describe how plant clones can be produced using tissue culture.
2) Other than tissue culture, name another way that plant clones can be produced.
3) Give one advantage of cloning using cow embryo transplantation.
4) What is a reduced gene pool?
5) What is gene splicing?

Exam Questions

1 Organisms can be genetically modified.
This means an organism's genes can be altered to alter its characteristics.

(a) Give three functions of enzymes used in genetic engineering.

(3 marks)

(b) Suggest one useful way that plants can be genetically modified.

(1 mark)

(c) Suggest one useful way that animals can be genetically modified.

(1 mark)

(d) Some people think that it is wrong to genetically modify plants.
Give two different objections that people might have.

(2 marks)

2 In 1997 scientists at the Roslin Institute issued a press release to tell the world about the birth of Dolly, a sheep that had been cloned using adult cells.

(a) Explain how Dolly was made using adult cell cloning.

(3 marks)

(b) Human adult cell cloning could be used to help treat various diseases.

(i) Suggest how this could be done.

(2 marks)

(ii) Explain why some people are opposed to human adult cell cloning.

(1 mark)

Evolution

There are many different species on Earth today, but how life first got started on the planet is still a mystery.

***No One** Knows How Life Began*

We know that living things come from other living things — that's easy enough.
But where did the first living thing come from... that's a much more difficult question.

1) There are various theories suggesting how life first came into being, but no one really knows.
2) Maybe the first life forms came into existence in a primordial swamp (or under the sea) here on Earth. Maybe simple organic molecules were brought to Earth on comets — these could have then become more complex organic molecules, and eventually very simple life forms.
3) These suggestions (and others) have been put forward. But we don't know — the evidence has long since been destroyed. All we know is that life started somehow. And from that point on, we're on slightly firmer ground...

The Fossil Record** Shows That Organisms Have **Evolved

1) A fossil is any evidence of an animal or plant that lived ages ago.
2) Fossils form in rocks as minerals replace slowly decaying tissue (or where no decay happens) and show features like shells, skeletons, soft tissue (occasionally), footprints, etc. They show what was on Earth millions of years ago. They can also give clues about an organism's habitat and the food it ate.
3) We also know that the layers of rock where fossils are found were made at different times. This means it's possible to tell how long ago a particular species lived.
4) From studying the similarities and differences between fossils in differently aged rocks, we can see how species have evolved (changed and developed) over billions of years.

   > Theory of Evolution — Life on Earth began as simple organisms from which all the more complex organisms evolved (rather than just popping into existence).

   Unfortunately, very few organisms turn into fossils when they die — most just decay away completely. This creates gaps in the fossil record, which means there are many species that no one will ever know about.
5) In theory, you could put all species on a 'family tree' — where each new branch shows the evolution of a new species. Then you could easily find the most recent common ancestor of any two species. The more recent the common ancestor, the more closely related the two species.

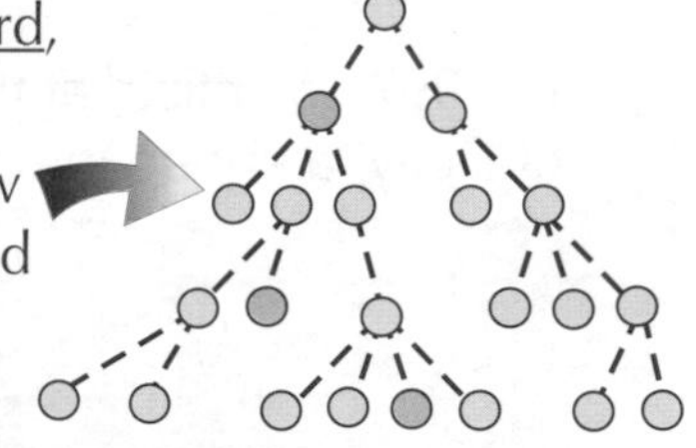

***Extinction** Happens if You Can't **Evolve** Quickly Enough*

The fossil record contains many species that don't exist any more — these species are said to be extinct. Dinosaurs and mammoths are extinct animals, with only fossils to tell us they existed at all.

Species become extinct for THREE MAIN REASONS:

1) The environment changes too quickly (e.g. destruction of habitat).
2) A new predator or disease kills them all (e.g. humans hunting them).
3) They can't compete with another (new) species for food.

Fossils give us information about the history of life on Earth

The fossil record provides good evidence for evolution, but it can't prove it. But proving a theory about something that happens over millions of years was never going to be straightforward.

Evolution

Scientists have a pretty good understanding of why species evolve, and how.

Mutations *Are When* ***DNA Changes***

(See page 45 for more on genes.)

1) An organism's DNA can change (called a mutation) through everyday wear and tear, e.g. from coming into contact with nasty chemicals. Most of the time mutations have no effect.
2) But, if the mutation happens within a gene AND it's passed on to the next generation it can cause new characteristics. Very occasionally it can give the organism a better chance of survival (e.g. warmer fur, longer legs, larger leaves etc.).
3) Over a long period of time, these 'useful' mutations can help a species adapt to an environment — and eventually may lead to the evolution of a completely new species.

Natural Selection *Explains How* ***Evolution*** *Can Occur*

1) Charles Darwin came up with the idea of natural selection.
2) He noticed that species tend to be well-adapted to the environment they live in.
3) He argued that organisms that are better adapted have a better chance of survival, and are therefore more likely to breed successfully — passing on their characteristics to the next generation.
4) So if an organism is born with a useful characteristic (either due to the normal shuffling up of mum and dad's genes, or due to mutations), that characteristic has a good chance of being passed on. Whereas if a mutation leads to a disadvantage, the organism may well die before it can breed.
5) So 'good' characteristics accumulate, 'bad' ones are lost. And this is how animals adapt. For example:

> Once upon a time maybe all rabbits had short ears and managed OK. Then one day out popped a mutant with BIG EARS who was always the first to hear predators coming and dive for cover. Pretty soon he's had a whole family with BIG EARS, all diving for cover before the other rabbits, and before you know it there's only BIG-EARED rabbits left because the short-eared rabbits just didn't hear trouble coming quick enough.

Not Everyone Agreed *with Darwin...*

Darwin's theory of natural selection was very controversial at the time — for various reasons...

1) The theory went against common religious beliefs about how life on Earth developed. But Darwin was gradually able to persuade people with his scientific evidence.
2) There were different scientific theories of evolution around at the same time. For example, Lamarck (1744-1829) argued that if a characteristic was used a lot by an organism then it would become more developed — and that these developed characteristics would be passed on to the next generation. So if a rabbit looked a lot it would develop good eyes, and this would mean its offspring would have good eyes too. (Darwin's theory was different because he argued that a rabbit might by chance be born with good eyes that would help it spot predators.)
3) Darwin couldn't give a good explanation about why these new, useful characteristics appeared (but then he didn't know anything about genes or mutations).

Natural selection — the fittest pass on their characteristics

In a nutshell, individuals in a species show variation due to different genes. Those individuals that have characteristics most suited to their environment are more likely to breed successfully and this means those genes (coding for the useful characteristics) will be passed on. Learn this off by heart.

Warm-Up and Exam Questions

The warm-up questions run quickly over the basic facts you'll need in the exam. The exam questions come later — but unless you've learnt the facts first you'll find the exams tougher than stale bread.

Warm-Up Questions

1) What can a fossil of an organism tell us?
2) Explain why there are gaps in the fossil record.
3) What is an extinct species?
4) What is a mutation?
5) Explain the difference between evolution and natural selection.

Exam Questions

1 Which of the following could **not** cause a species to become extinct?

A Competition from another species for food.

B The environment changing more quickly than the species can adapt.

C The species producing too many offspring.

D A new disease emerging.

(1 mark)

2 The picture on the right shows what scientists believe the dinosaur **Stegosaurus** looked like.

(a) What evidence is there that Stegosaurus existed?

(1 mark)

(b) It is estimated that Stegosaurus lived about 150 million years ago. How can scientists tell approximately how old a fossil is?

(1 mark)

(c) Fossils of Stegosaurus teeth have been discovered. What useful information about Stegosaurus might the fossils of its teeth provide?

(1 mark)

(d) Scientists believe that all dinosaurs have a common ancestor. Why might it be difficult to find evidence of this common ancestor?

(1 mark)

3 Charles Darwin developed the theory of evolution by natural selection.

(a) According to Darwin's theory, explain how natural selection occurs.

(4 marks)

(b) Why did Darwin have trouble getting his theory accepted?

(1 mark)

Human Impact on the Environment

We have an impact on the world around us — and the more humans there are, the bigger the impact.

There are **Six Billion People** in the World...

1) The population of the world is currently rising very quickly, and it's not slowing down — look at the graph...

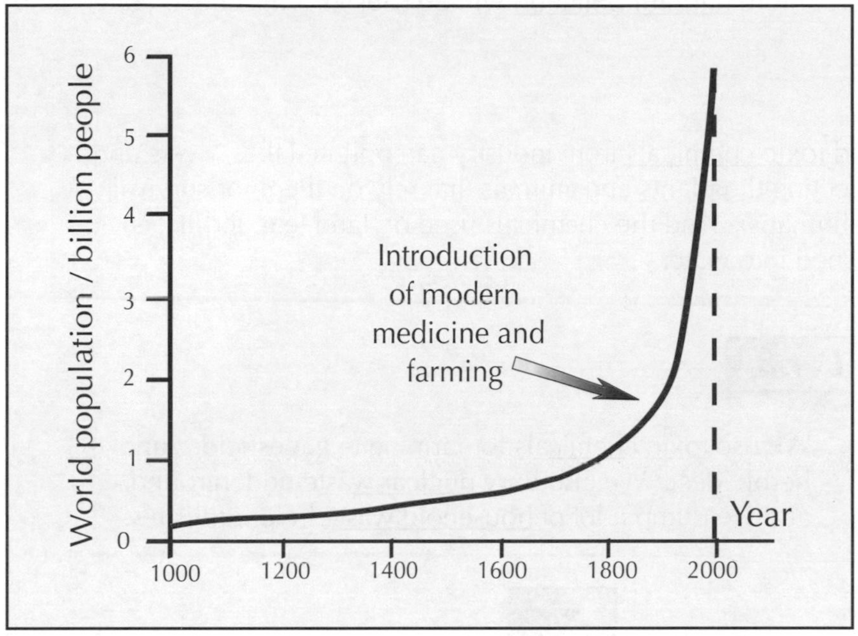

2) This rise is mostly due to modern medicine and farming methods, which have reduced the number of people dying from disease and hunger.
3) This is great for all of us humans, but it means we're having a bigger effect on the environment we live in...

...With **Increasing Demands** on the **Environment**

When the Earth's population was much smaller, the effects of human activity were usually small and local. Nowadays though, our actions can have a far more widespread effect.

1) Our rapidly increasing population puts pressure on the environment, as we take the resources we need to survive.

2) But people around the world are also demanding a higher standard of living (and so demand luxuries to make life more comfortable — cars, computers, etc.). So we use more raw materials (e.g. oil to make plastics), but we also use more energy for the manufacturing processes. This all means we're taking more and more resources from the environment more and more quickly.

3) Unfortunately, many raw materials are being used up quicker than they're being replaced. So if we carry on like we are, one day we're going to run out.

Human Impact on the Environment

It's not just that we're using more resources, more and more quickly — we're also making an awful lot of rubbish in the process.

We're Also Producing More Waste

As we make more and more things we produce more and more waste. And unless this waste is properly handled, more harmful pollution will be caused. This affects water, land and air.

Water

Sewage and toxic chemicals from industry can pollute lakes, rivers and oceans, affecting the plants and animals that rely on them for survival (including humans). And the chemicals used on land (e.g. fertilisers) can be washed into water.

Land

We use toxic chemicals for farming (e.g. pesticides and herbicides). We also bury nuclear waste underground, and we dump a lot of household waste in landfill sites.

Air

Smoke and gases released into the atmosphere can pollute the air (see page 60 for more info). For example, sulfur dioxide can cause acid rain.

More People Means Less Land for Plants and Other Animals

Humans also reduce the amount of land and resources available to other animals and plants. The four main human activities that do this are:

1) Building

2) Farming

3) Dumping Waste

4) Quarrying

More people, more mess, less space, less resources...

Well, I feel guilty, I don't know about you. First we kill off loads of animals by hunting them, then we try to manipulate their DNA, and now we're destroying the land they live on. In the exam you might be given some data about environmental impact, so make sure you understand what's going on...

The Greenhouse Effect

The greenhouse effect is always in the news. We need it, since it makes Earth a suitable temperature for living on. But it's starting to trap more heat than is necessary.

Carbon Dioxide and *Methane Trap Heat* from the *Sun*

1) The temperature of the Earth is a balance between the heat it gets from the Sun and the heat it radiates back out into space.

2) Gases in the atmosphere naturally act like an insulating layer. They absorb most of the heat that would normally be radiated out into space, and re-radiate it in all directions (including back towards the Earth).

This is what happens in a greenhouse. The sun shines in, and the glass helps keeps some of the heat in.

3) If this didn't happen, then at night there'd be nothing to keep any heat in, and we'd quickly get very cold indeed. But recently we've started to worry that this effect is getting a bit out of hand...

4) There are several different gases in the atmosphere which help keep the heat in. They're called "greenhouse gases" (oddly enough) and the main ones whose levels we worry about are carbon dioxide and methane — because the levels of these two gases are rising quite sharply.

5) The Earth is gradually heating up because of the increasing levels of greenhouse gases — this is global warming. Global warming is a type of climate change and causes other types of climate change, e.g. changing rainfall patterns.

We need greenhouse gases in the atmosphere, but not too much

Some people find the idea of the greenhouse effect quite confusing — it's more physics than biology really, with heat being absorbed and radiated all over the place. Don't waste time worrying about why the Earth radiates heat and why the gases absorb it — just remember the facts for your exam.

The Greenhouse Effect

On the last page you read that levels of carbon dioxide and methane are rising sharply — now read on to find out why.

Human Activity Produces Lots of *Carbon Dioxide*

1) Humans release carbon dioxide into the atmosphere all the time as part of our everyday lives — in car exhausts, industrial processes, as we burn fossil fuels etc.
2) People around the world are also cutting down large areas of forest (deforestation) for timber and to clear land for farming — and this activity affects the level of carbon dioxide in the atmosphere in various ways:

- Carbon dioxide is released when trees are burnt to clear land. (Carbon in wood is 'locked up' and doesn't contribute to atmospheric pollution — until it's released by burning.)

- Microorganisms feeding on bits of dead wood release CO_2 as a waste product of respiration.

- Cutting down loads of trees means that the amount of carbon dioxide removed from the atmosphere during photosynthesis is reduced.

So we're putting more CO_2 into the atmosphere and taking less out.

Methane is Also a Problem...

1) Methane gas is also contributing to the greenhouse effect.
2) It's produced naturally from various sources, e.g. rotting plants in marshland.
3) However, two 'man-made' sources of methane are on the increase:

   a) Rice growing

   b) Cattle rearing — it's the cows' "pumping" that's the problem, believe it or not.

Levels of methane and carbon dioxide are both on the increase

Global warming is rarely out of the news. Scientists accept that it's happening and that human activity has caused most of the recent warming (because we produce lots of carbon dioxide, see above). However, they don't know exactly what the effects will be...

Climate Change

The Earth is getting warmer. Climate scientists are now trying to work out what the effects of global warming might be — sadly, it's not as simple as everyone having nicer summers.

*The **Consequences** of **Global Warming** Could be Pretty **Serious***

There are several reasons to be worried about global warming.
Here are a few:

1) As the sea gets warmer, it expands, causing sea level to rise. Sea level has risen a little bit over the last 100 years. If it keeps rising it'll be bad news for people living in low-lying places like the Netherlands, East Anglia and the Maldives — they'd be flooded.

2) Higher temperatures make ice melt. Water that's currently 'trapped' on land (as ice) runs into the sea, causing sea level to rise even more.

3) Global warming has changed weather patterns in many parts of the world. It's thought that many regions will suffer more extreme weather because of this, e.g. longer, hotter droughts. Hurricanes form over water that's warmer than 27 °C — so with more warm water, you'd expect more hurricanes.

4) Changing weather patterns also affect food production — some regions are now too dry to grow food, some too wet. This will get worse as temperature increases and weather patterns change more.

5) The climate is a very complicated system. For instance, if the ice melts, there's less white stuff around to reflect the sun's rays out to space, so maybe we'll absorb more heat and get even warmer. But... when the sea's warmer, more water evaporates, making more clouds — and they reflect the Sun's rays, so maybe we'd cool down again. So it's hard to predict exactly what will happen, but lots of people are working on it, and it's not looking too good.

Global warming = rising sea level and changing climate

Global warming could cause some very big problems for us all. Make sure you learn what they are. You can test yourself by turning over the page and seeing if you can write them all down.

Climate Change

At GCSE level, it's not as simple as just learning all the facts any more (if that was ever simple). Sometimes you've got to be able to look at the scientific evidence and judge how useful it really is.

Scientists Collect **Evidence** to Show How the **Climate** is **Changing**

To find out how our climate is changing, scientists are busy collecting data about the environment.

1) Satellites are used to monitor snow and ice cover.
2) Satellites can also be used to measure the temperature of the sea surface.
3) The temperature and speed of ocean currents are monitored for any changes.
4) Automatic weather stations are constantly recording atmospheric temperatures.

You Need to **Weigh** the **Evidence** Before **Making Judgements**

All this data is only useful if it covers a wide enough area and a long enough time scale.

AREA

Generally, observations of a very small area aren't much use. Noticing that your local glacier seems to be melting does not mean that ice everywhere is melting, and it's certainly not a valid way to show that global temperature is changing. (That would be like going to Wales, seeing a stripy cow and concluding that all the cows in Wales are turning into zebras.) Looking at the area of ice cover over a whole continent, like Antarctica, would be better.

TIME

The same thing goes for time. It's no good going to the Arctic, seeing four polar bears one week but only two the next week and concluding that polar bears are dying out because the ice is disappearing. You need to do your observations again and again, year after year.

Scientists can make mistakes — so don't take one person's word for something, even if they've got a PhD. But if lots of scientists get the same result using different methods, it's probably right. That's why most governments around the world are starting to take climate change seriously.

To find out how the climate is changing, look at the evidence

Many people, and some governments, think we ought to start cleaning up the environmental problems we have caused. Scientists can help, mainly in understanding the problems and suggesting solutions, but it's society as a whole that has to do something.

Sustainable Development

There is a growing feeling among scientists and politicians that if we carry on behaving as we are, we may end up causing huge problems for future generations...

Sustainable Development Needs Careful Planning

1) Human activities can damage the environment (e.g. pollution). And some of the damage we do can't easily be repaired (e.g. the destruction of the rainforests).

2) We're also placing greater pressure on our planet's limited resources (e.g. oil is a non-renewable resource so it will eventually run out).

3) This means that we need to plan carefully to make sure that our activities today don't mess things up for future generations — this is the idea behind sustainable development...

> SUSTAINABLE DEVELOPMENT meets the needs of today's population without harming the ability of future generations to meet their own needs.

Learn this definition carefully so you can repeat it in the exam.

4) This isn't easy — it needs detailed thought at every level to make it happen. For example, governments around the world will need to make careful plans. But so will the people in charge at a regional level.

Reduction in Biodiversity Could Be a Big Problem

1) Biodiversity is the variety of different species present in an area — the more species, the higher the biodiversity.

2) Ecosystems (especially tropical rainforests) can contain a huge number of different species, so when a habitat is destroyed there is a danger of many species becoming extinct — biodiversity is reduced.

3) This causes a number of lost opportunities for humans and problems for those species that are left — some examples of this are described on the next page.

If we can't manage sustainable development, the future looks bleak

So we're using up resources, destroying habitats, dumping waste... all unavoidable as the human population grows, but also pretty harsh on future generations. They're going to be left with a great big mess and no resources if we're not careful. That's why we need to do sustainable development stuff like recycling, conserving energy, planting forests, protecting vulnerable habitats, etc.

Sustainable Development

For those of you who aren't bothered about your future grandchildren (yes, trouble really could be that close — or closer), there are other reasons not to let biodiversity disappear without a fight.

Learn These **Examples** of Why **Biodiversity** is so Important

Amazing **New Products**

There are probably loads of useful products that we will never know about because the organisms that produced them have become extinct. Newly discovered plants and animals are a great source of new foods, new fibres for clothing and new medicines, e.g. the rosy periwinkle flower from Madagascar has helped treat Hodgkin's disease (a type of cancer), and a chemical in the saliva of a leech has been used to help prevent blood clots during surgery.

Organisms **Need Each Other** to **Survive**

Loss of one or more species from an ecosystem unbalances it, e.g. the extinct animal's predators may die out or be reduced. Loss of biodiversity can have a 'snowball effect' which prevents the ecosystem providing things we need, such as rich soil, clean water, and the oxygen we breathe.

Human Impact can be **Measured** Using **Indicator Species**

Getting an accurate picture of the human impact on the environment is hard. But one technique that's used involves indicator species.

1) Some organisms are very sensitive to changes in their environment and so can be studied to see the effect of human activities — these organisms are known as indicator species.

2) For example, air pollution can be monitored by looking at particular types of lichen, which are very sensitive to levels of sulfur dioxide in the atmosphere (and so can give a good idea about the level of pollution from car exhausts, power stations, etc.). The number and type of lichen at a particular location will indicate how clean the air is (e.g. the air is clean if there are lots of lichen).

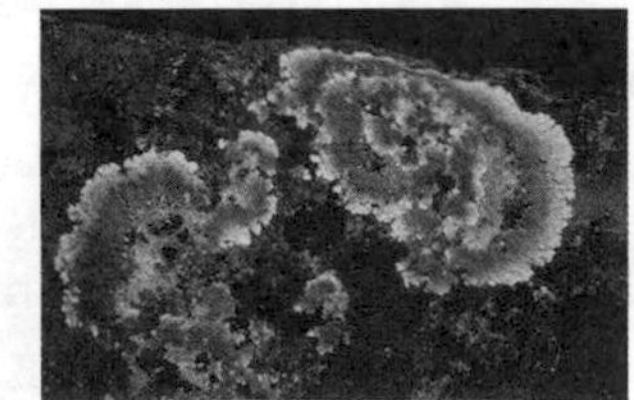

3) And if raw sewage is released into a river, the bacterial population in the water increases and uses up the oxygen. Animals like mayfly larvae are good indicators for water pollution, because they are very sensitive to the level of oxygen in the water. If you find mayfly larvae in a river, it indicates that the water is clean.

Lichen and mayfly larvae are examples of indicator species

For the exam, make sure you know a couple of different indicator species and how they work as indicators of pollution. To test yourself, you know the drill — shut the book and write it all down.

Warm-Up and Exam Questions

Now's your chance to practise some incredibly life-like exam questions — but do the warm-up first — you don't want to end up straining something.

Warm-Up Questions

1) Give two reasons why the human population of the world has increased so much over the last 200 years.
2) Why, apart from the increased population, is pollution by humans increasing?
3) Name one way in which humans pollute: (a) air (b) land (c) water
4) What is meant by the 'greenhouse effect'?
5) What are the two main gases that are causing an increase in the greenhouse effect?
6) List four possible harmful effects of global warming.
7) What is meant by sustainable development?
8) Name an indicator species used to monitor air pollution.

Exam Questions

1 The graph shows the carbon dioxide concentration in the Earth's atmosphere between AD 1000 and AD 2000.

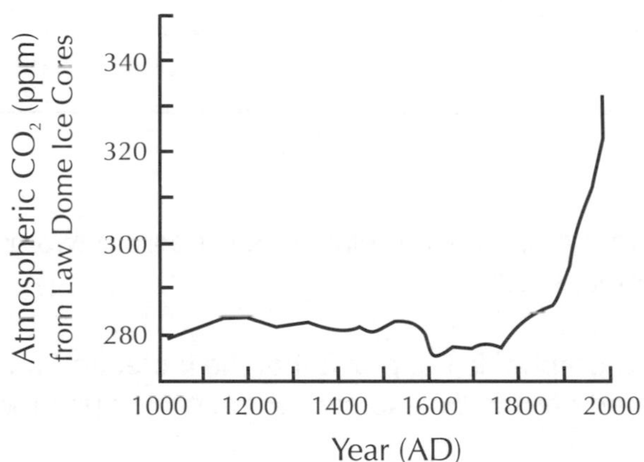

(a) Use the graph to describe the trend in carbon dioxide concentration:

(i) between AD 1000 and AD 1500.

(1 mark)

(ii) between AD 1850 and AD 2000.

(1 mark)

(b) Name two human activities that may have caused the changes in concentration between AD 1850 and AD 2000.

(2 marks)

2 (a) Explain how global warming could lead to a rise in sea levels.

(1 mark)

(b) Explain how global warming might cause more hurricanes.

(1 mark)

Exam Questions

3 The tropical island of Hannaria has an area of approximately 2000 km^2. Most of the island is covered with tropical rainforest. However, the inhabitants of Hannaria want to clear large areas of the rainforest to make room for more housing. Opponents say that this development will contribute to global warming.

(a) Explain how clearing the forest could contribute to global warming.

(2 marks)

(b) If the trees are cut down, they could be used as fuel or they could be used to make wooden buildings and furniture. Which of these uses is likely to contribute more to global warming? Explain your answer.

(2 marks)

4 A scientist was examining some data to see if there is a link between the global human population and the carbon dioxide concentration in the atmosphere.
Here are the two graphs that the scientist examined.

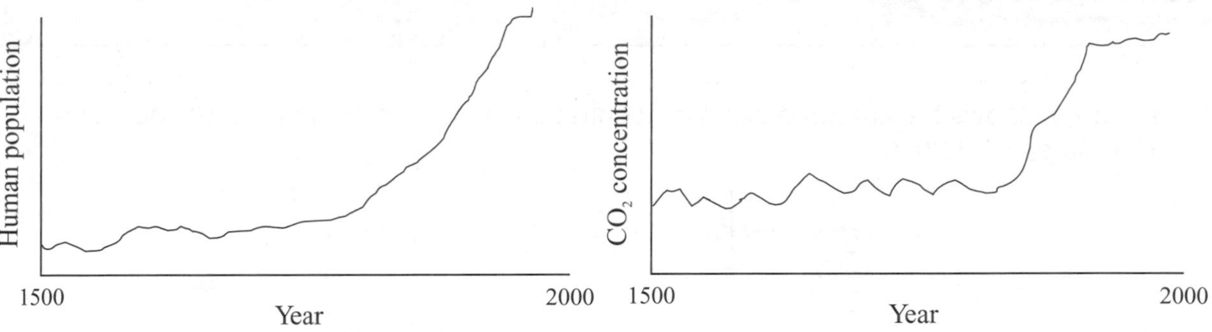

(a) The scientist said that there is a correlation between the two graphs. Explain what this means.

(1 mark)

(b) On their own, these graphs do not prove that the increased human population caused the increased carbon dioxide concentration. Explain why not.

(1 mark)

5 (a) Explain the meaning of the term biodiversity.

(1 mark)

(b) Give two reasons why it is important to maintain biodiversity in ecosystems.

(2 marks)

(c) (i) Explain why sewage pollution can reduce biodiversity.

(1 mark)

(ii) Explain how indicator species can be used to monitor sewage pollution in water.

(1 mark)

Revision Summary for Biology 1b

There's a lot to remember in this section and quite a few of the topics are controversial, e.g. cloning, genetic engineering, and so on. You need to know all sides of the story, as well as all the facts. So, here are some questions to help you. If you get any wrong, go back and learn that bit again.

1) Give four ways in which a desert animal may be adapted to its environment.
2) Name three things that: a) plants compete for, b) animals compete for.
3) What are the two types, or causes, of variation?
4) List three features of animals which aren't affected at all by their environment, and three which are.
5) Draw a set of diagrams showing the relationship between: cell, nucleus, chromosomes, DNA.
6) How many pairs of chromosomes does a normal human cell nucleus contain? Which cells, found in every adult human, have a different number of chromosomes in their nucleus?
7) Give a definition of asexual reproduction.
8) Describe how to make plant clones from cuttings.
9) Give an advantage and a disadvantage of producing cloned plants.
10) Describe two different ways to clone an animal.
11) Give an account of the important stages of genetic engineering.
12) Give an example of an application of genetic engineering, and explain why it is useful.
13) What's the basic idea behind gene therapy?
14) Write down the theory of evolution.
15) Give three reasons why some species become extinct.
16) What is happening to the size of the world's population?
17) Suggest three ways in which an increasing population is affecting the environment.
18) What are the main four human activities that use up land?
19) Draw and label a diagram to explain the greenhouse effect.
20) Give two human activities (apart from deforestation) that release carbon dioxide.
21) Name two human activities that are increasing the release of methane.
22) *Read the statement below and consider how valid it is.

> The Malaspina Glacier in Alaska is losing over 2.7 km³ of water each year. This proves global warming is happening.

23) *The graph on the right shows human population growth and an estimate of the number of species that have become extinct between 1800 and 2000.
    a) How are the size of the human population and the number of extinct species related?
    b) Suggest a reason for this relationship.

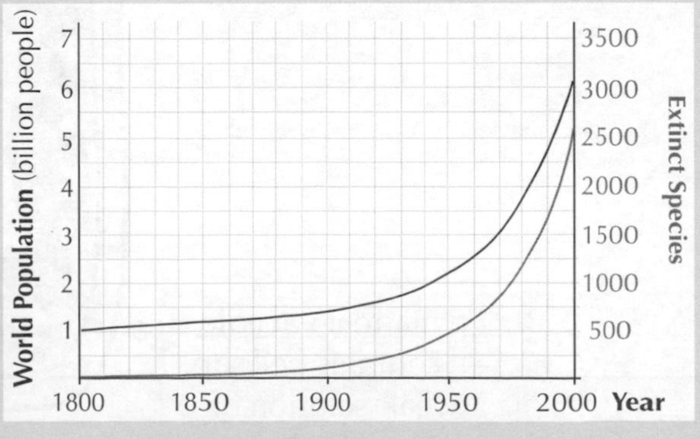

24) Explain how lichen can be used as an indicator of air pollution.
25) What does it suggest about the cleanliness of the water if you find mayfly larvae in a river?

* Answers on page 224.

Cells

Ah cells. After all that information on cloning and fretting over the state of the environment, it must come as quite a relief to get back to some, old-fashioned science.

Most Animal Cells have Certain Features in Common

Most human cells, like most animal cells, have the following parts — make sure you know them all:

1) Cytoplasm — gel-like substance where most of the chemical reactions happen. It contains enzymes (see page 93) that control these chemical reactions.

2) Nucleus — contains genetic material that controls the activities of the cell.

3) Cell membrane — holds the cell together and controls what goes in and out.

4) Mitochondria — these are where most of the reactions for respiration take place (see page 95). Respiration releases energy that the cell needs to work.

5) Ribosomes — these are where proteins are made in the cell.

Plant Cells have Some Extra Features

Plant cells usually have all the bits that animal cells have, plus a few extra things that animal cells don't have:

1) Rigid cell wall — made of cellulose. It supports the cell and strengthens it.

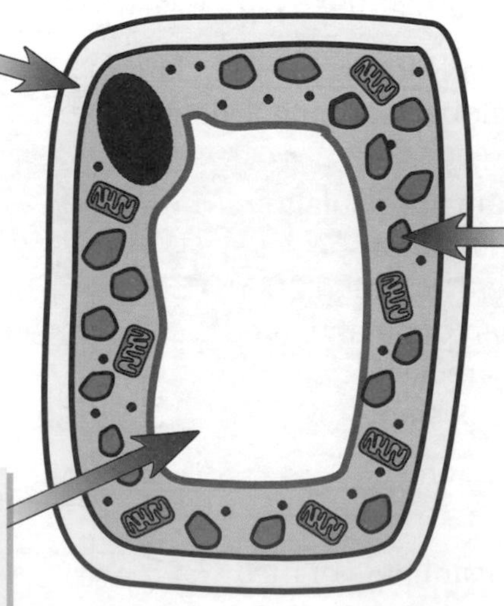

2) Chloroplasts — these are where photosynthesis occurs, which makes food for the plant (see page 76). They contain a green substance called chlorophyll.

3) Permanent vacuole — contains cell sap, a weak solution of sugar and salts.

water, sugar and salt.

Cells, Tissues, Organs and Systems

Cells Make Up Tissues, Organs and Systems

1) Cells have structures that are specialised so they can carry out their function (see next page).
2) Similar cells are grouped together to make a tissue, and different tissues work together as an organ.
3) Organs have a particular job to do in the body — e.g. the heart circulates the blood.
4) Groups of organs working together make up an organ system, like the digestive system.
5) And finally, groups of organs and organ systems working together make up a full organism like you or me.

Here's a plant example, but there are loads of animal examples as well of course.

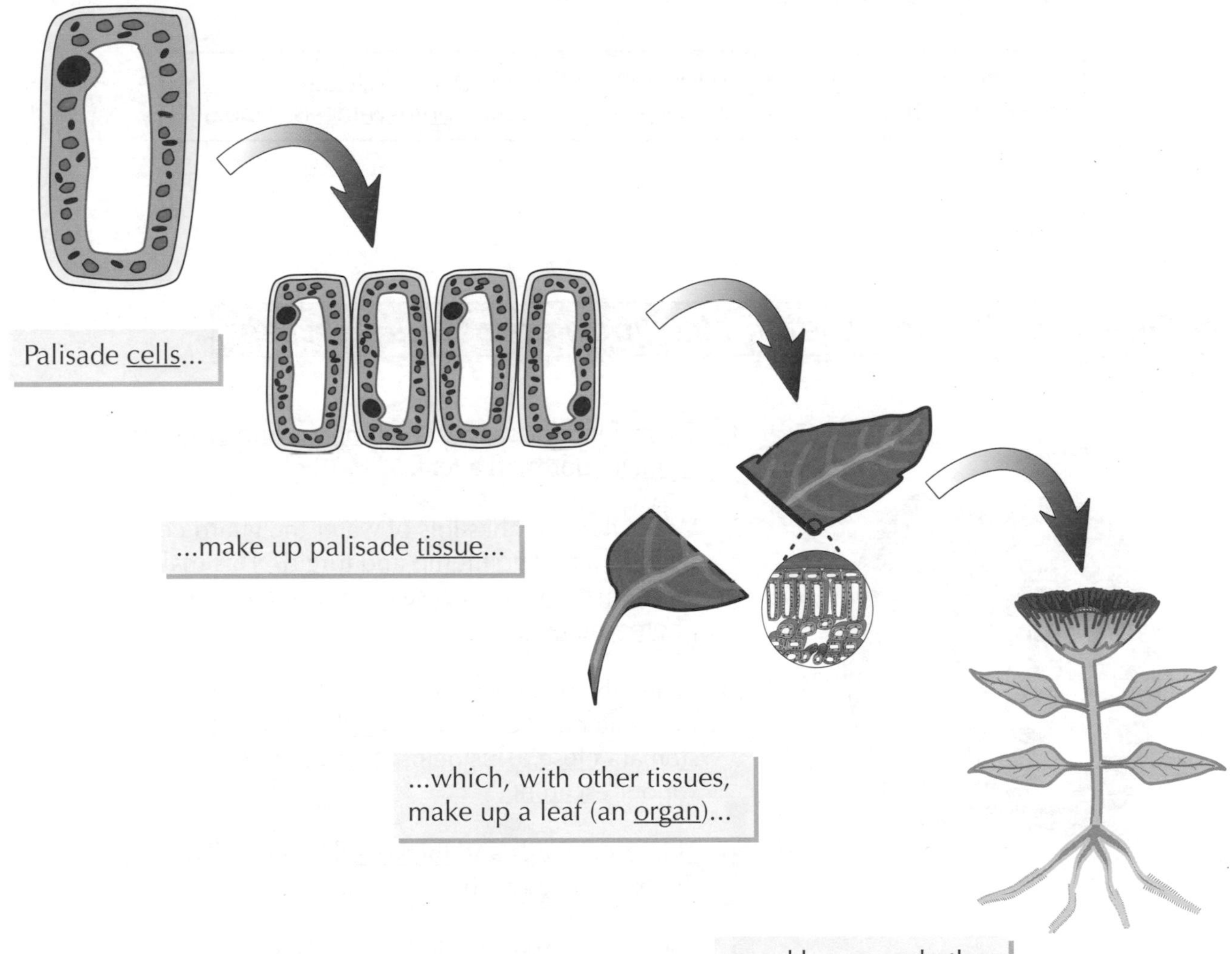

There's quite a bit to learn in biology...

Cells aren't all the same — they have different structures and produce different substances depending on the job they do. There are a few examples of specialised cells over on the next two pages.

Specialised Cells

Most cells are specialised for their specific function within a tissue or organ. In the exam you might have to explain how a particular cell is adapted for its function. Here are a few examples that might come up:

1) Palisade Leaf Cells Are Adapted for Photosynthesis

1) Packed with chloroplasts for photosynthesis. More of them are crammed at the top of the cell — so they're nearer the light.
2) Tall shape means a lot of surface area exposed down the side for absorbing CO_2 from the air in the leaf.
3) Thin shape means that you can pack loads of them in at the top of a leaf.

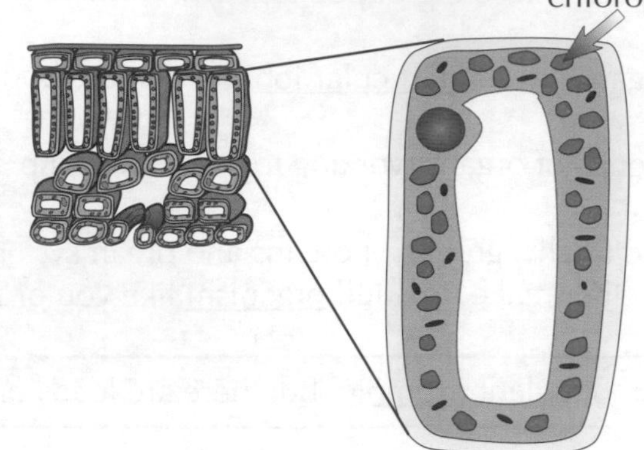

Palisade leaf cells are grouped together to give the palisade layer of a leaf — this is the leaf tissue where most of the photosynthesis happens.

2) Guard Cells Are Adapted to Open and Close Pores

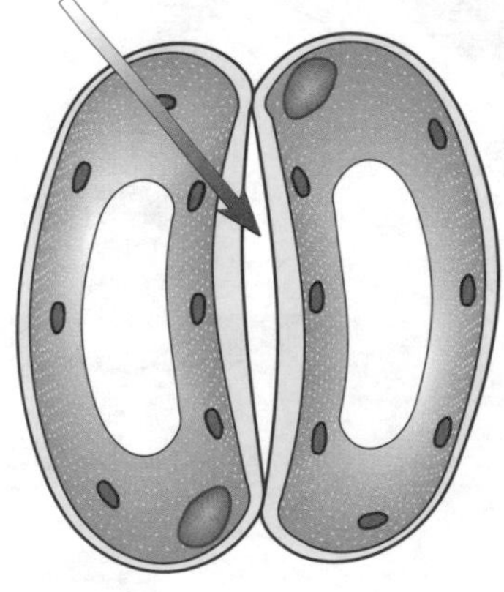

1) Special kidney shape which opens and closes the stomata (pores) in a leaf.
2) When the plant has lots of water the guard cells fill with it and go plump and turgid. This makes the stomata open so gases can be exchanged for photosynthesis.
3) When the plant is short of water, the guard cells lose water and become flaccid, making the stomata close. This helps stop too much water vapour escaping.
4) Thin outer walls and thickened inner walls make the opening and closing work.
5) They're also sensitive to light and close at night to save water without losing out on photosynthesis.

Guard cells are therefore adapted to their function of allowing gas exchange and controlling water loss within the leaf organ.

Specialised Cells

3) Red Blood Cells Are Adapted to Carry Oxygen

1) Concave shape gives a big surface area for absorbing oxygen. It also helps them pass smoothly through capillaries to reach body cells.
2) They're packed with haemoglobin — the pigment that absorbs the oxygen.
3) They have no nucleus, to leave even more room for haemoglobin.

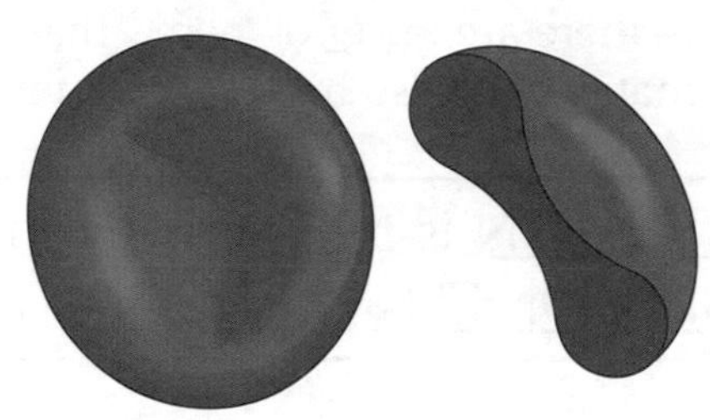

Red blood cells are an important part of the blood (blood's actually counted as a tissue — weird).

4) Sperm and Egg Cells Are Specialised for Reproduction

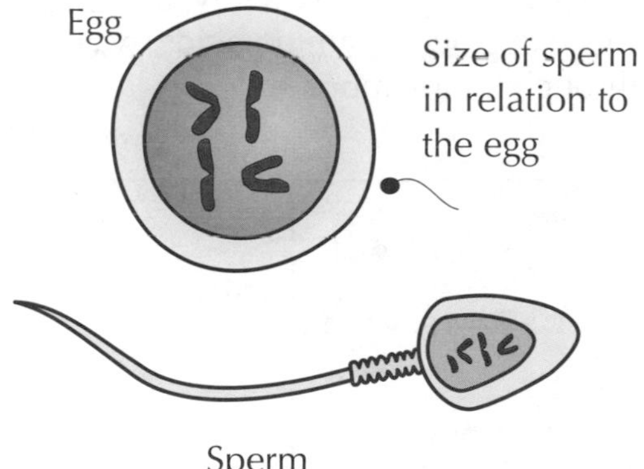

1) The main functions of an egg cell are to carry the female DNA and to nourish the developing embryo in the early stages. The egg cell contains huge food reserves to feed the embryo.
2) When a sperm fuses with the egg, the egg's membrane instantly changes its structure to stop any more sperm getting in. This makes sure the offspring end up with the right amount of DNA.
3) The function of a sperm is basically to get the male DNA to the female DNA. It has a long tail and a streamlined head to help it swim to the egg. There are a lot of mitochondria in the cell to provide the energy needed.
4) Sperm also carry enzymes in their heads to digest through the egg cell membrane.

Sperm and eggs are very important cells in the reproductive system.

Cells have the same basic bits but are specialised for their functions

Okay so the red blood cell doesn't have a nucleus, but apart from that all these cells have all the bits you learnt about on page 68, even though they look completely different and do totally different jobs.

Diffusion

Particles move about randomly, and after a bit they end up evenly spaced.

Don't Be Put Off by the Fancy Word

"Diffusion" is simple. It's just the gradual movement of particles from places where there are lots of them to places where there are fewer of them. That's all it is — just the natural tendency for stuff to spread out. Unfortunately you also have to learn the fancy way of saying the same thing, which is this:

> DIFFUSION is the passive movement of particles from an area of HIGH CONCENTRATION to an area of LOW CONCENTRATION

Diffusion happens in both liquids and gases — that's because the particles in these substances are free to move about randomly. The simplest type is when different gases diffuse through each other. This is what's happening when the smell of perfume diffuses through a room (see diagram).

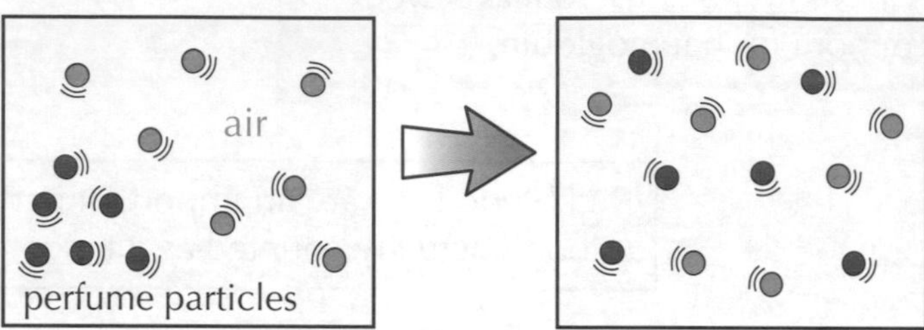

The bigger the difference in concentration, the faster the diffusion rate.

Small Molecules Diffuse Across Membranes

Membranes are clever because they hold the cell together BUT they let stuff in and out as well. Substances can move in and out of cells by diffusion and osmosis (see next page). Only very small molecules can diffuse through cell membranes though — things like glucose, amino acids, water and oxygen. Big molecules like starch and proteins can't fit through the membrane.

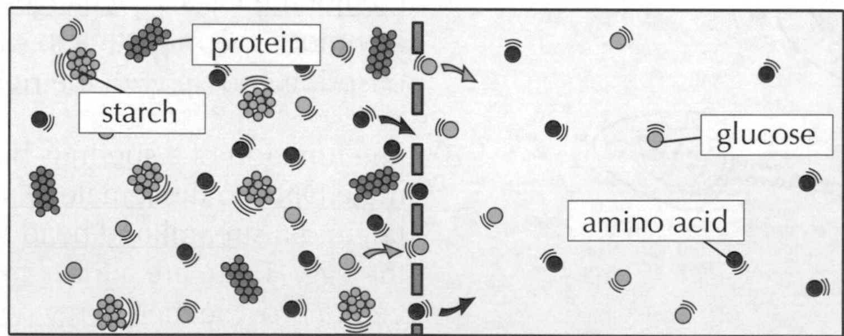

1) Just like with diffusion in air, particles flow through the cell membrane from where there's a high concentration (a lot of them) to where there's a low concentration (not such a lot of them).
2) They're only moving about randomly of course, so they go both ways — but if there are a lot more particles on one side of the membrane, there's a net (overall) movement from that side.
3) The rate of diffusion depends on three main things:
   a) Distance — substances diffuse more quickly when they haven't as far to move.
   b) Concentration difference (gradient) — substances diffuse faster if there's a big difference in concentration. If there are lots more particles on one side, there are more there to move across.
   c) Surface area — the more surface there is available for molecules to move across, the faster they can get from one side to the other.

Osmosis

If you've got your head round diffusion, osmosis will be a breeze.
And if you haven't, what are you doing looking at this page? Go back and learn it.

Osmosis is a Special Case of Diffusion, That's All

Learn this definition of osmosis:

> OSMOSIS is the movement of water molecules across a partially permeable membrane from a region of high water concentration to a region of low water concentration.

1) A partially permeable membrane is just one with very small holes in it. So small, in fact, only tiny molecules (like water) can pass through them, and bigger molecules (e.g. sucrose) can't.

2) The water molecules actually pass both ways through the membrane during osmosis. This happens because water molecules move about randomly all the time.

3) But because there are more water molecules on one side than on the other, there's a steady net flow of water into the region with fewer water molecules, i.e. into the stronger sugar solution.

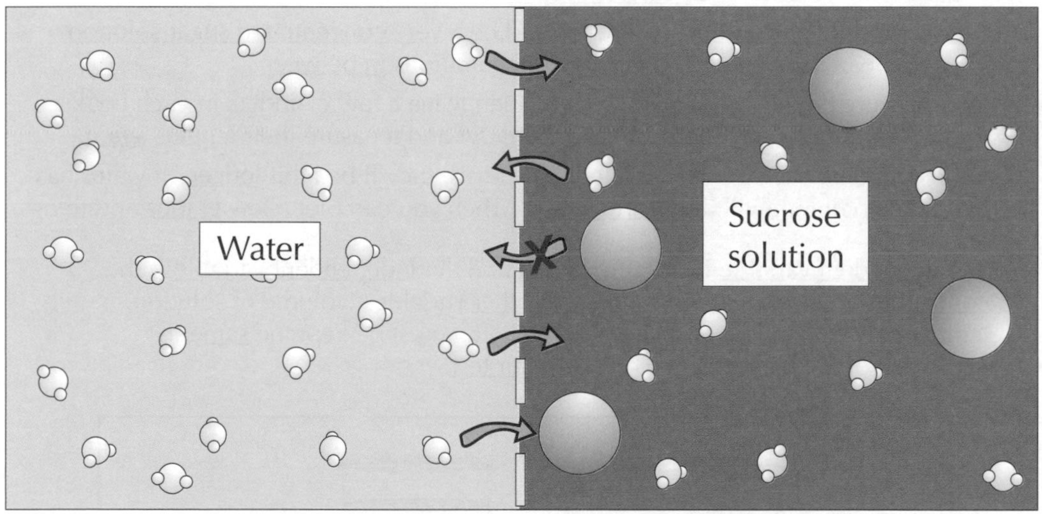

4) This means the strong sugar solution gets more dilute. The water acts like it's trying to "even up" the concentration either side of the membrane.

5) Osmosis is a type of diffusion — passive movement of water particles from an area of high water concentration to an area of low water concentration.

Osmosis

You're not learning about osmosis just for fun — it's how water moves into and out of cells, so it's pretty important in biology.

Water Moves Into and Out of **Cells** by **Osmosis**

1) Tissue fluid surrounds the cells in the body — it's basically just water with oxygen, glucose and stuff dissolved in it. It's squeezed out of the blood capillaries to supply the cells with everything they need.

2) The tissue fluid will usually have a different concentration to the fluid inside a cell. This means that water will either move into the cell from the tissue fluid, or out of the cell, by osmosis.

3) If a cell is short of water, the solution inside it will become quite concentrated. This usually means the solution outside is more dilute, and so water will move into the cell by osmosis.

4) If a cell has lots of water, the solution inside it will be more dilute, and water will be drawn out of the cell and into the fluid outside by osmosis.

Osmosis Experiment

There's an experiment you can do to show osmosis at work.

1) You cut up a potato into identical cylinders, and get some beakers with different sugar solutions in them.
2) One should be pure water, another should be a very concentrated sugar solution. Then you can have a few others with concentrations in between.
3) You measure the length of the cylinders, then leave a few cylinders in each beaker for half an hour or so. Then you take them out and measure their lengths again.
4) If the cylinders have drawn in water by osmosis, they'll be a bit longer. If water has been drawn out, they'll have shrunk a bit. Then you can plot a few graphs and things.

The dependent variable is the chip length and the independent variable is the concentration of the sugar solution. All other variables (volume of solution, temperature, time, type of sugar used, etc. etc.) must be kept the same in each case or the experiment won't be a fair test.

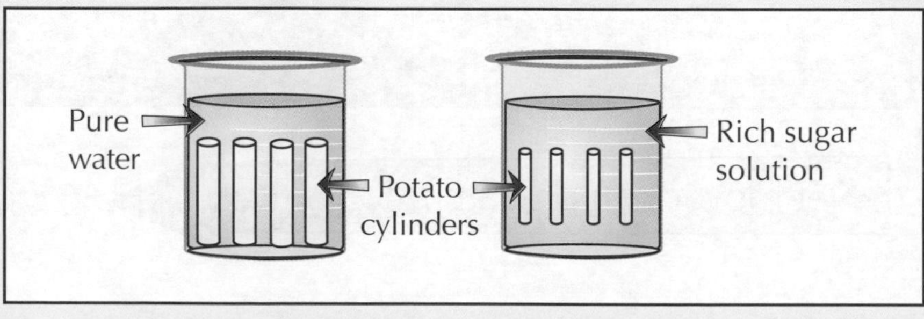

Water always moves into the more concentrated solution

That's why it's bad to drink sea-water. The high salt content means you end up with a lower water concentration in your blood and tissue fluid than in your cells. Lots of water is sucked out of your cells by osmosis and they shrivel and die. So next time you're stranded at sea, remember this page...

Warm-Up and Exam Questions

So, hopefully you've read the last seven pages. But could you cope if a question on cells, diffusion or osmosis came up in the exam? With amazing new technology we can simulate that very situation....

Warm-Up Questions

1) Give three ways in which animal cells are different from plant cells.
2) a) What is the function of a red blood cell?
   b) Describe two ways in which a red blood cell is adapted to its function.
3) Define diffusion.
4) In terms of osmosis, explain what will happen if an animal cell is placed in a concentrated sugar solution.
5) Explain what is meant by a partially permeable membrane.

Exam Questions

1 The diagram shows a palisade cell from a leaf.

(a) Which label points to a chloroplast?

(1 mark)

(b) Name the green substance present in chloroplasts.

(1 mark)

(c) Apart from having chloroplasts, state two other ways in which a palisade cell is adapted for photosynthesis.

(2 marks)

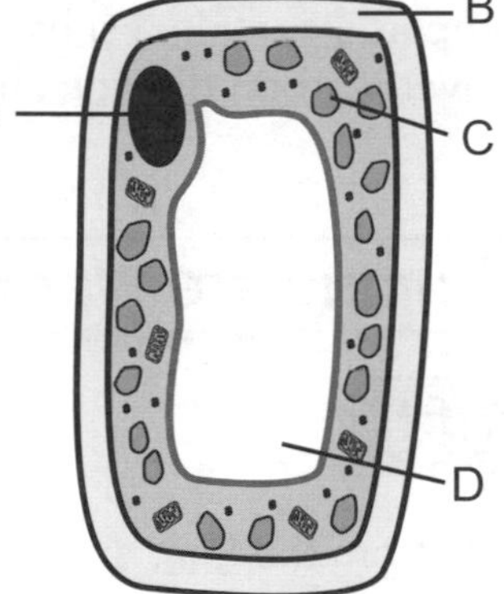

2 In an experiment, four 5 cm long cylinders were cut from a fresh potato.
The cylinders were then placed in different sugar solutions, as shown in the diagram.
After four hours the potato cylinders were removed and measured.

Tube A

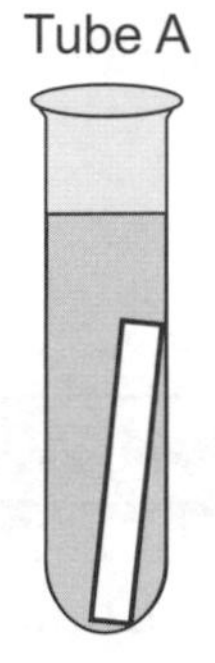

distilled water

Tube B

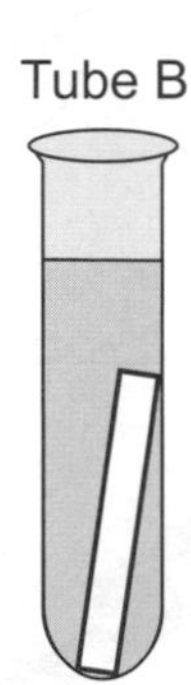

1.0 mol dm^3 sugar solution

Tube C

2.0 mol dm^3 sugar solution

Tube D

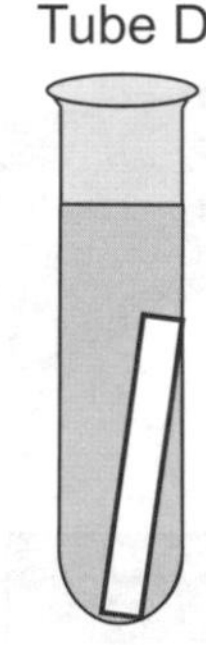

3.0 mol dm^3 sugar solution

(a) Which potato cylinder would you expect to be shortest after four hours?
Explain your answer.

(2 marks)

(b) The potato cylinder in tube A increased in length during the four hours.
Explain why this happened.

(2 marks)

Photosynthesis

You must learn the photosynthesis equation. Learn it so well you'll still remember it when you're 109.

Learn the Equation for Photosynthesis:

$$\text{carbon dioxide} + \text{water} \xrightarrow[\text{chlorophyll}]{\text{SUNLIGHT}} \text{glucose} + \text{oxygen}$$

Photosynthesis Produces Glucose Using Sunlight

1) Photosynthesis is the process that produces 'food' in plants. The 'food' it produces is glucose.
2) Photosynthesis happens in the leaves of all green plants — this is largely what the leaves are for.
3) Photosynthesis happens inside the chloroplasts, which are found in leaf cells and in other green parts of a plant.
4) Chloroplasts contain a substance called chlorophyll, which absorbs sunlight and uses its energy to convert carbon dioxide and water into glucose. Oxygen is also produced.

Four Things are Needed for Photosynthesis to Happen:

1) Light

Usually from the Sun.

2) Chlorophyll

This is the green substance which is found in chloroplasts and which makes leaves look green. Chlorophyll absorbs the energy in sunlight and uses it to combine CO_2 and water to make glucose. Oxygen is just a by-product of this reaction.

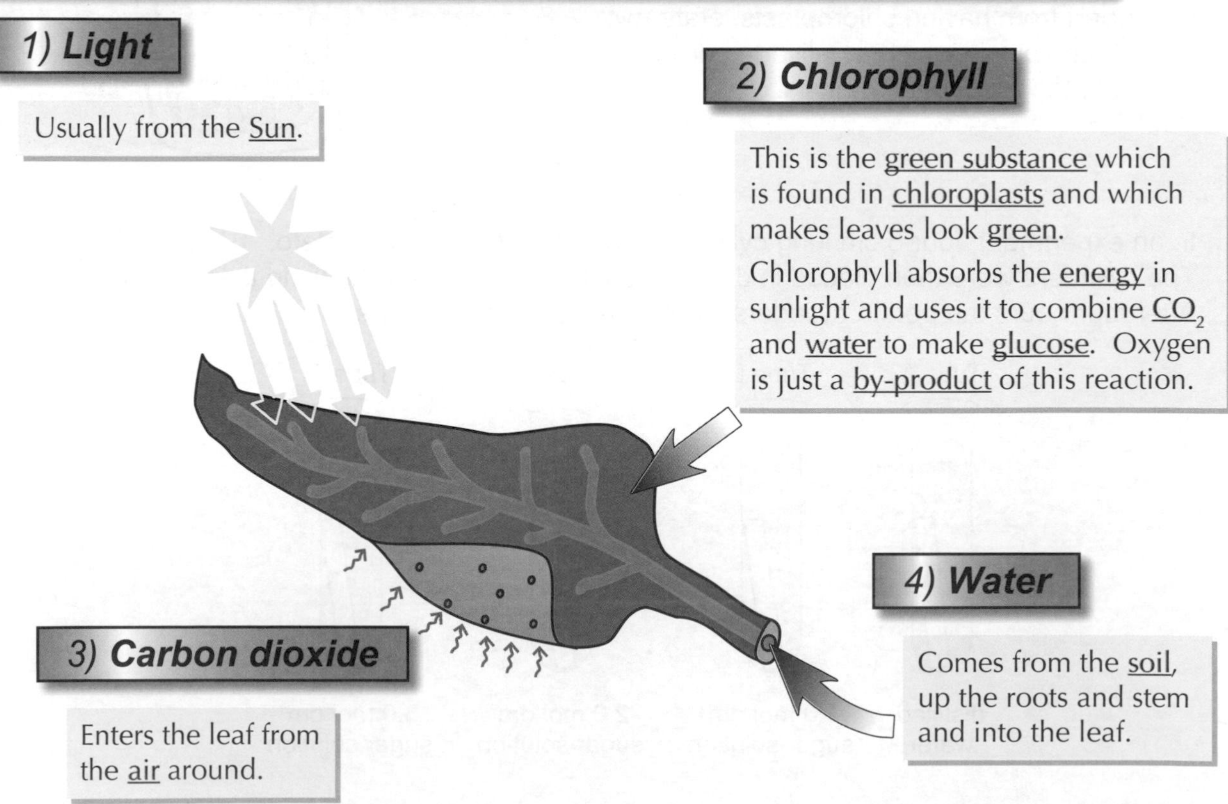

3) Carbon dioxide

Enters the leaf from the air around.

4) Water

Comes from the soil, up the roots and stem and into the leaf.

'Photo' means light and 'synthesis' means putting together...

...so photosynthesis is 'putting together glucose'. Despite it sounding quite scary, the basics of photosynthesis are actually pretty straightforward. Just make sure the equation on this page is etched onto your memory and don't forget about sunlight and chlorophyll — they're vital to the process.

The Rate of Photosynthesis

The rate of photosynthesis is affected by the amount of light, the amount of CO_2, and the temperature. Plants also need water for photosynthesis, but when a plant is so short of water that it becomes the limiting factor in photosynthesis, it's already in such trouble that this is the least of its worries.

The *Limiting Factor* Depends on the Conditions

1) Any of the above three factors can become the limiting factor. This just means that it's stopping photosynthesis from happening any faster.
2) Which factor is limiting at a particular time depends on the environmental conditions:
   - at night it's pretty obvious that light is the limiting factor,
   - in winter it's often the temperature,
   - if it's warm enough and bright enough, the amount of CO_2 is usually limiting.

You can do experiments to work out the ideal conditions for photosynthesis in a particular plant. The easiest type to use is a water plant like Canadian pondweed — you can easily measure the amount of oxygen produced in a given time to show how fast photosynthesis is happening (remember, oxygen is made during photosynthesis).

You could either count the bubbles given off, or if you want to be a bit more accurate you could collect the oxygen in a gas syringe.

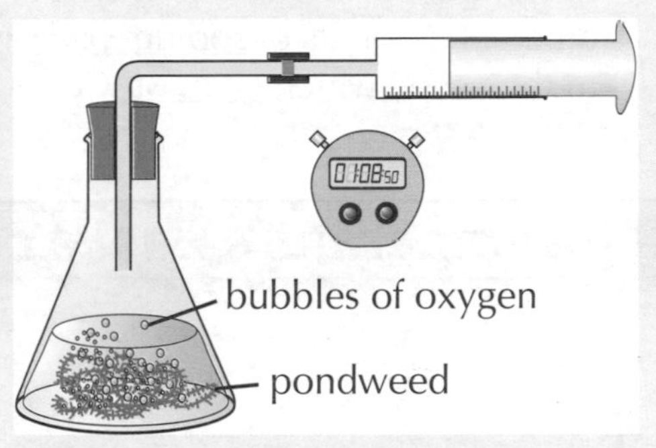

Not Enough *Light* Slows Down the Rate of Photosynthesis

1) Light provides the energy needed for photosynthesis.
2) As the light level is raised, the rate of photosynthesis increases steadily — but only up to a certain point.
3) Beyond that, it won't make any difference because then it'll be either the temperature or the CO_2 level which is the limiting factor.
4) In the lab you can change the light intensity by moving a lamp closer to or further away from your plant.

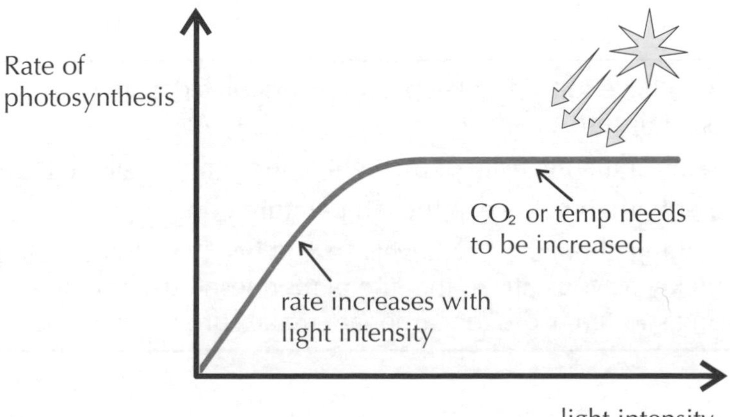

5) But if you just plot the rate of photosynthesis against "distance of lamp from the beaker", you get a weird-shaped graph. To get a graph like the one above you either need to measure the light intensity at the beaker using a light meter or do a bit of nifty maths with your results.

The Rate of Photosynthesis

Too Little Carbon Dioxide Also Slows it Down

1) CO_2 is one of the raw materials needed for photosynthesis.
2) As with light intensity the amount of CO_2 will only increase the rate of photosynthesis up to a point. After this the graph flattens out showing that CO_2 is no longer the limiting factor.
3) As long as light and CO_2 are in plentiful supply then the factor limiting photosynthesis must be temperature.
4) There are loads of different ways to control the amount of CO_2. One way is to dissolve different amounts of sodium hydrogencarbonate in the water, which gives off CO_2.

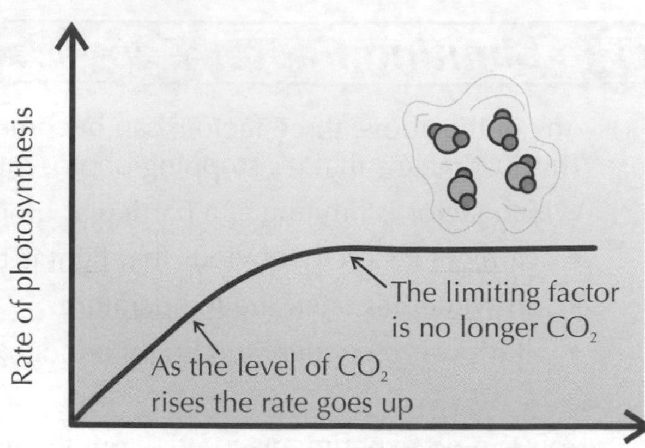

The Temperature has to be Just Right

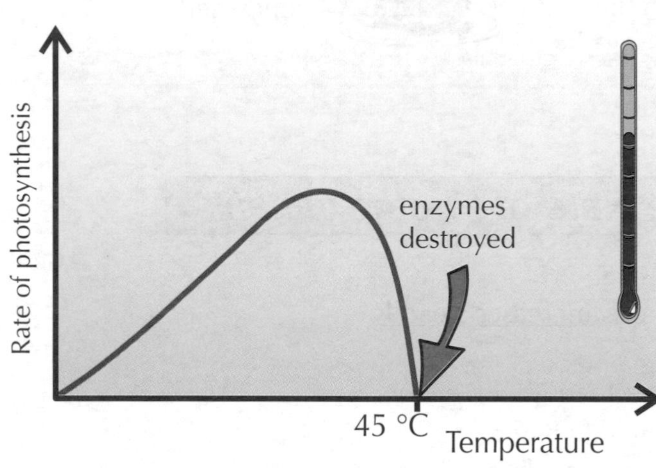

1) Usually, if the temperature is the limiting factor it's because it's too low — the enzymes needed for photosynthesis work more slowly at low temperatures.
2) But if the plant gets too hot, the enzymes it needs for photosynthesis and its other reactions will be damaged (see p.94).
3) This happens at about 45 °C (which is pretty hot for outdoors, although greenhouses can get that hot if you're not careful).
4) Experimentally, the best way to control the temperature of the flask is to put it in a water bath.

In all these experiments, you have to try and keep all the variables constant apart from the one you're investigating, so it's a fair test:

- use a bench lamp to control the intensity of the light (careful not to block the light with anything)
- keep the flask in a water bath to help keep the temperature constant
- you can't really do anything about the CO_2 levels — you just have to use a large flask, and do the experiments as quickly as you can, so that the plant doesn't use up too much of the CO_2 in the flask. If you're using sodium hydrogencarbonate make sure it's changed each time.

Plants are fussy things, everything has to be just right...

First request is plenty of light, then plenty of carbon dioxide, then the temperature has to be high, but not too high or enzymes denature and everything goes wrong. Add to all that their need for water and minerals from the soil (see page 82) and it's a wonder that plants can actually survive at all...

The Rate of Photosynthesis

Growing plants outdoors can be very difficult, especially on a large scale — it's almost impossible to control the weather and other conditions. But there's a way around that...

You can *Artificially Create* the *Ideal Conditions* for *Farming*

1) The most common way to artificially create the ideal environment for plants is to grow them in a greenhouse.

2) Greenhouses help to trap the sun's heat, and make sure that the temperature doesn't become limiting. In winter a farmer or gardener might use a heater as well to keep the temperature at the ideal level. In summer it could get too hot, so they might use shades and ventilation to cool things down.

3) Light's always needed for photosynthesis, so commercial farmers often supply artificial light after the Sun goes down to give their plants more quality photosynthesis time.

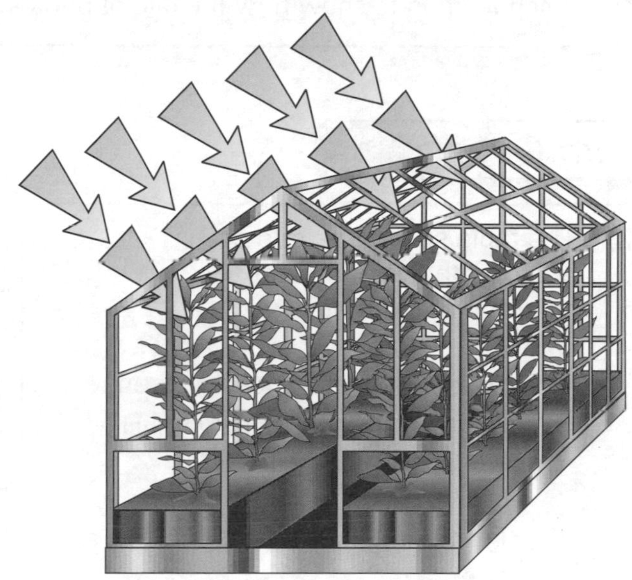

Greenhouses are used to grow plants, including food crops, flowers and tobacco plants.

4) Farmers and gardeners can also increase the level of carbon dioxide in the greenhouse. A fairly common way is to use a paraffin heater to heat the greenhouse. As the paraffin burns, it makes carbon dioxide as a by-product.

5) Keeping plants enclosed in a greenhouse also makes it easier to keep them free from pests and diseases. The farmer can add fertilisers to the soil as well, to provide all the minerals needed for healthy growth (see page 82).

6) If the farmer can keep the conditions just right for photosynthesis, the plants will grow much faster and a decent crop can be harvested much more often.

Greenhouses control the growing environment

Farmers use greenhouses to make sure crops get the right amount of carbon dioxide, light and heat. They can alter the conditions using paraffin heaters, artificial light and ventilation. This ensures nothing becomes a limiting factor for photosynthesis, which means a good crop is produced.

Warm-Up and Exam Questions

So, here we go again — another set of questions to test your knowledge. But don't roll your eyes, I promise they'll be really, really enjoyable. OK, don't hold me to that, but make sure you do them...

Warm-Up Questions

1) Name four factors that are needed for photosynthesis.
2) What is meant by a limiting factor for the rate of photosynthesis?
3) Sketch a graph to show how the rate of photosynthesis varies with increasing CO_2.

Exam Questions

1 The table shows the rate of photosynthesis of a plant at different temperatures.

Temperature (°C)	Rate of photosynthesis (arbitrary units)
0	0
10	17
20	35
30	67
40	82
50	0

(a) Explain the difference between:

(i) the rates of photosynthesis at 10 °C and at 20 °C.

(1 mark)

(ii) the rates of photosynthesis at 40 °C and at 50 °C.

(1 mark)

(b) A student said that the optimum temperature for photosynthesis in this plant was 40 °C. Comment on this statement.

(2 marks)

2 Jane did an experiment to see how the rate of photosynthesis depends on light intensity. The diagram shows her apparatus.

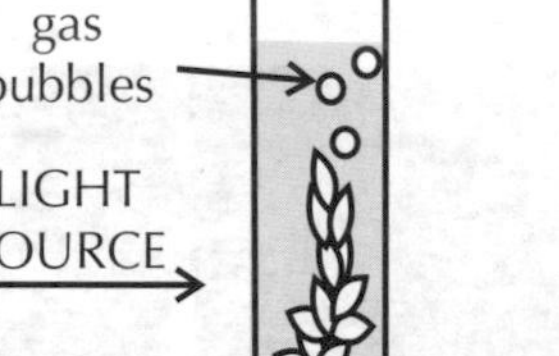

(a) How can Jane measure the rate of photosynthesis?

(1 mark)

(b) In this experiment:

(i) what is the dependent variable?

(1 mark)

(ii) what is the independent variable?

(1 mark)

(c) State one factor that should be kept constant during this experiment.

(1 mark)

3 The graph shows how a plant's rate of photosynthesis varies with the light intensity.

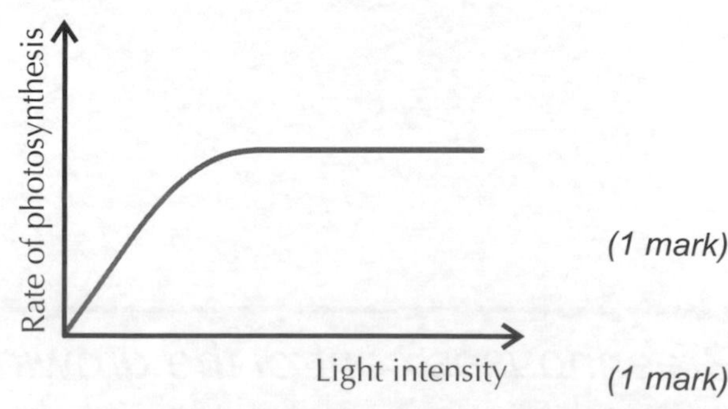

(a) Label a point at which light intensity is the limiting factor for photosynthesis.

(1 mark)

(b) What else can limit a plant's rate of photosynthesis?

(1 mark)

How Plants Use the Glucose

Once plants have made the glucose, there are various ways they can use it.

1) For Respiration

1) Plants manufacture glucose in their leaves.
2) They then use some of the glucose for respiration.
3) This releases energy which enables them to convert the rest of the glucose into various other useful substances which they can use to build new cells and grow.
4) To produce some of these substances they also need to gather a few minerals from the soil.

2) Making Fruits

Glucose, along with another sugar called fructose, is turned into sucrose for storing in fruits. Fruits deliberately taste nice so that animals will eat them and spread the seeds all over the place in their poo.

3) Making Cell Walls

Glucose is converted into cellulose for making cell walls, especially in a rapidly growing plant.

4) Making Proteins

Glucose is combined with nitrates (collected from the soil) to make amino acids, which are then made into proteins.

There's more on nitrates on page 82.

5) Stored in Seeds

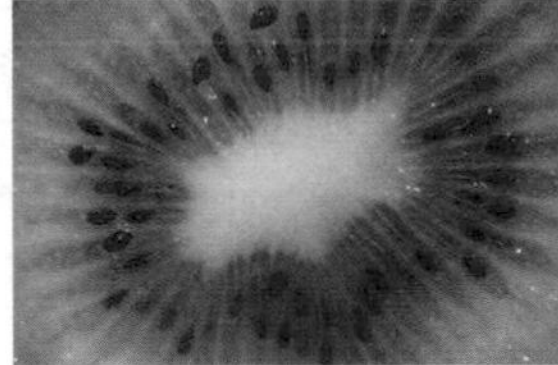

Glucose is turned into lipids (fats and oils) for storing in seeds. Sunflower seeds, for example, contain a lot of oil — we get cooking oil and margarine from them. Seeds also store starch (see below).

6) Stored as Starch

1) Glucose is turned into starch and stored in roots, stems and leaves, ready for use when photosynthesis isn't happening, like in the winter.
2) Starch is insoluble which makes it much better for storing, because it doesn't bloat the storage cells by osmosis like glucose would.
3) Potato and carrot plants store a lot of starch underground over the winter so a new plant can grow from it the following spring. We eat the swollen storage organs.

All life depends on photosynthesis

Plants are pretty crucial in ensuring the flow of energy through nature. They are able to use the Sun's energy to make glucose, the energy source which humans and animals need for respiration (see p.95). Make sure you know the photosynthesis equation inside out — look back at p.76 if you don't.

Minerals for Healthy Growth

Plants need various mineral salts, as well as the carbohydrates they make by photosynthesis, in order to grow properly. They get these mineral ions from the soil by absorbing them through their roots:

You Need to Know About **Two Minerals** in Particular

1) **Nitrates**

Nitrates are needed for making amino acids, which are then used to make proteins.

2) **Magnesium**

Magnesium is needed to make chlorophyll, which in turn is needed for photosynthesis.

Other minerals needed by plants include potassium and phosphates, which are used for things like making DNA and cell membranes, and helping the enzymes involved in photosynthesis and respiration to work properly.

Lack of These Nutrients Causes **Deficiency Symptoms**

Sometimes plants can't get all of the mineral ions they need to be healthy. It depends what's there in the soil — if the supply of nitrates in the soil gets low, the plant can't just wander off and find some more. It has to put up with it, and eventually it will start to show symptoms of the deficiency.

1) Lack of **Nitrates**

If the soil is deficient in nitrates, the plant starts to show stunted growth and won't reach its usual size. This is because proteins are needed for new growth, and they can't be made without nitrates.

2) Lack of **Magnesium**

If the soil is deficient in magnesium, the leaves of the plant start to turn yellow. This is because magnesium is needed to make chlorophyll, and this gives leaves their green colour.

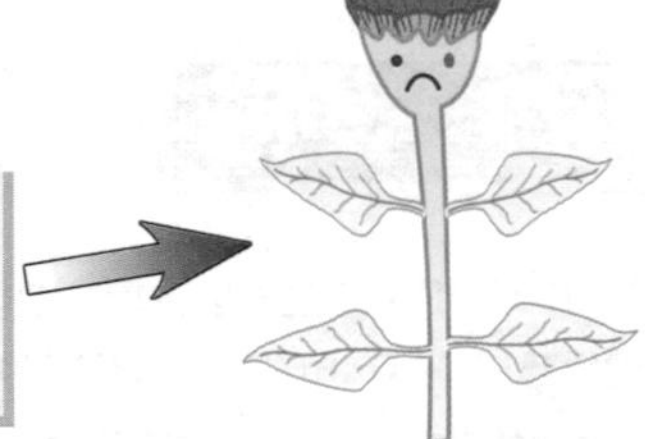

If the plant is left short of the minerals it needs for a long time, it might die.

Deficiencies Can be Caused by **Monoculture**

1) Monoculture is where just one type of crop is grown in the same field year after year.
2) All the plants are the same crop, so they need the same minerals. This means the soil becomes deficient in the minerals which that crop uses lots of.
3) Deficiency of just one mineral is enough to cause poor growth and give a reduced yield.
4) This soon results in poor crops unless fertiliser is added to replenish the depleted minerals.

Plants get minerals from the soil for healthy growth

When a farmer or a gardener buys fertiliser, that's pretty much what they're buying — a nice big bag of mineral salts to provide all the extra elements plants need to grow. The one they usually need most of is nitrate, which is why manure works quite well — it's full of nitrogenous waste excreted by animals.

Warm-Up and Exam Questions

More questions already? You'll be getting spoilt if I'm not careful. It's the same as always... if you get stuck, don't skip the question — go back, learn the bit that's troubling you and try it again.

Warm-Up Questions

1) Name the process that converts glucose into energy in plants.
2) Name the two sugars that sucrose is made from.
3) Why is glucose turned into starch before being stored in plants?
4) Which part of the plant absorbs mineral salts from the soil?
5) Explain how a monoculture can lead to mineral deficiencies in crops.

Exam Questions

1 Photosynthesis makes glucose. The glucose may then be converted to other substances. Some of these substances are listed below:

cellulose amino acids sucrose starch

Match each of these substances to its correct function from the list below.

- Making cell walls.
- Storing energy.
- Making enzymes.
- Making fruit sweet.

(4 marks)

2 Complete the table to show the main functions of two minerals in a plant.

Mineral	Function
	needed for making chlorophyll
nitrate	

(2 marks)

3 Mrs Foyle often wins prizes for her plants, but this year some of them aren't growing very well. She thinks this is because of a mineral deficiency.

Which mineral could her plants be lacking if:

(a) they have yellow leaves?

(1 mark)

(b) they have stunted growth?

(1 mark)

Pyramids of Number and Biomass

A trophic level is a feeding level. It comes from the Greek word trophe meaning 'nourishment'.

You Need to Be Able to Construct Pyramids of Biomass

There's less energy and less biomass every time you move up a stage (trophic level) in a food chain. There are usually fewer organisms every time you move up a level too.

This isn't always true though — for example, if 500 fleas are feeding on the fox, the number of organisms has increased as you move up that stage in the food chain. So a better way to look at the food chain is often to think about biomass instead of number of organisms. You can use information about biomass to construct a pyramid of biomass to represent the food chain:

1) Each bar on a pyramid of biomass shows the mass of living material at that stage of the food chain — basically how much all the organisms at each level would "weigh" if you put them all together.
2) So the one fox above would have a big biomass and the hundreds of fleas would have a very small biomass. Biomass pyramids are practically always the right shape (unlike number pyramids).

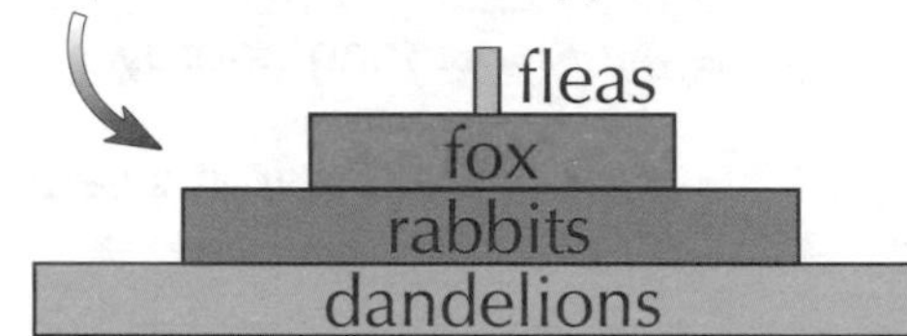

You need to be able to construct pyramids of biomass. Luckily it's pretty simple — they'll give you all the information you need to do it in the exam.

The big bar along the bottom of the pyramid always represents the producer (i.e. a plant). The next bar will be the primary consumer (the animal that eats the plant), then the secondary consumer (the animal that eats the primary consumer) and so on up the food chain. Easy.

You Need to be Able to Interpret Pyramids of Biomass

You also need to be able to look at pyramids of biomass and explain what they show about the food chain. Also very easy. For example:

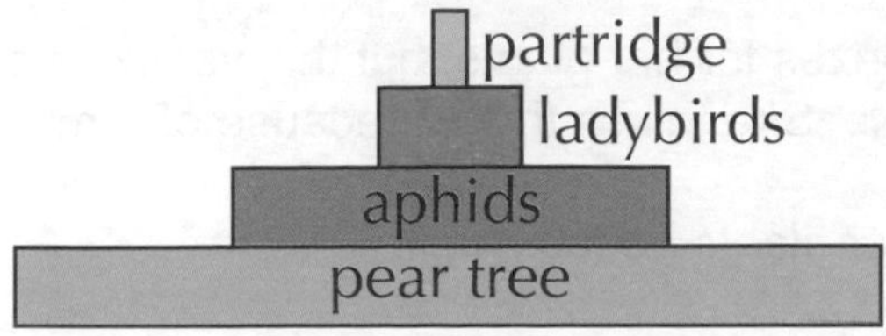

Even if you know nothing about the natural world, you're probably aware that a tree is quite a bit bigger than an aphid. So what's going on here is that lots (probably thousands) of aphids are feeding on a few great big trees. Quite a lot of ladybirds are then eating the aphids, and a few partridges are eating the ladybirds. Biomass and energy are still decreasing as you go up the levels — it's just that one tree can have a very big biomass, and can fix a lot of the Sun's energy using all those leaves.

Energy Transfer

So now you need to learn why there's less energy and biomass every time you move up a level.

*All That **Energy** Just **Disappears** Somehow...*

1) Energy from the Sun is the source of energy for nearly all life on Earth.

2) Plants use a small percentage of the light energy from the Sun to make food during photosynthesis. This energy's stored in the substances which make up the cells of plants, and then works its way through the food web as animals eat the plants and each other.

3) Respiration (see page 95), supplies the power for all life processes, including movement. Most of the energy is eventually lost to the surroundings as heat. This is especially true for mammals and birds, whose bodies must be kept at a constant temperature which is normally higher than their surroundings.

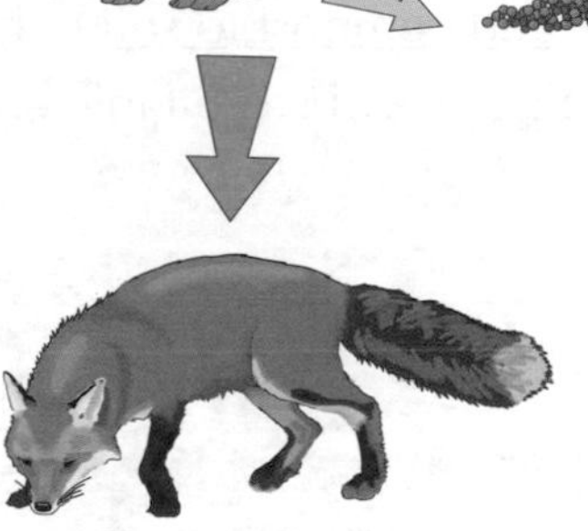

4) Some of the material which makes up plants and animals is inedible (e.g. bone), so it doesn't pass to the next stage of the food chain. Material and energy are also lost from the food chain in the droppings — excretion.

*This **Explains a lot** About **Pyramids of Biomass** and **Food Chains***

1) Material and energy are both lost at every stage of a food chain.
2) This explains why you get biomass pyramids. Most of the biomass is lost and so does not become biomass in the next level up.
3) It also explains why you hardly ever get food chains with more than about five trophic levels. So much energy is lost at each stage that there's not enough left to support more organisms after four or five stages.

There's more about the energy stored in biomass on page 84.

Decay

Decay is the reason why we're not knee-deep in waste material and dead organisms...

Elements are Cycled Back to the Start of the Food Chain by Decay

1) Living things are made of materials they take from the world around them.

2) Plants take elements like carbon, oxygen, hydrogen and nitrogen from the soil or the air. They turn these elements into the complex compounds (carbohydrates, proteins and fats) that make up living organisms, and these then pass through the food chain.

3) These elements are returned to the environment in waste products produced by the organisms, or when the organisms die. These materials decay because they're broken down (digested) by microorganisms — that's how the elements get put back into the soil.

4) Microorganisms work best in warm, moist conditions. Many microorganisms also break down material faster when there's plenty of oxygen available.

COMPOST

- Compost bins or heaps are piles of decaying material.
- Gardeners add compost to soil to help plants grow.
- Compost bins provide a suitable environment for decay in the following ways:

5) All the important elements are thus recycled — they return to the soil, ready to be used by new plants and put back into the food chain again.

6) In a stable community the materials taken out of the soil and used are balanced by those that are put back in. There's a constant cycle happening.

What goes around, comes around

The constant recycling of material by microorganisms is vital to food chains. If this didn't happen, the nutrients that plants need would be locked up in the bodies of organisms and their excrement — plant growth would be next to none and without a producer the rest of the food chain would collapse.

Managing Food Production

People have been able to use what they know about energy loss from food chains to find the most efficient ways of producing food. But most efficient isn't necessarily best. Although it is often cheapest.

The "Efficiency" of Food Production Can Be Improved...

There are two ways to improve the efficiency of food production:

1) Reduce the Number of Stages in the Food Chain

1) For a given area of land, you can produce a lot more food (for humans) by growing crops rather than by having grazing animals. This is because you are reducing the number of stages in the food chain. Only 10% of what beef cattle eat becomes useful meat for people to eat.

2) However, people do need to eat a varied diet to stay healthy, and there's still a lot of demand for meat products. Also remember that some land is unsuitable for growing crops, e.g. moorland or fellsides. In these places, animals like sheep and deer might be the best way to get food from the land.

2) Restrict the Energy Lost by Farm Animals

1) In 'civilised' countries like the UK, animals such as pigs and chickens are often intensively farmed. They're kept close together indoors in small pens, so that they're warm and can't move about.

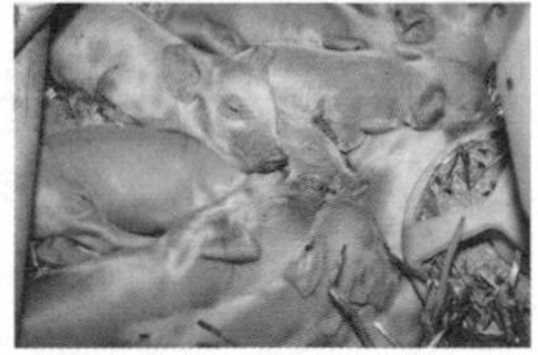

2) This saves them wasting energy on movement, and stops them giving out so much energy as heat. This makes the transfer of energy from the animal feed to the animal more efficient — so basically, the animals will grow faster on less food.

3) This makes things cheaper for the farmer, and for us when the animals finally turn up on supermarket shelves.

Many developed countries now actually produce too much food

The world produces enough food to feed the Earth's population, but there are still millions of undernourished people worldwide. The food is not equally distributed. Many people think that countries with food surpluses should give food to countries with food shortages (or sell it cheaply).

Managing Food Production

Making food production more efficient has both disadvantages and advantages. You need to be aware of both sides of the argument.

Food Production Involves **Compromises** and **Conflict**

Improving the efficiency of food production is useful — it means cheaper food for us, and better standards of living for farmers. But it all comes at a cost.

Here are some examples of arguments against the intensive farming methods used to increase the efficiency of food production:

1) Some people think that forcing animals to live in unnatural and uncomfortable conditions is cruel. There's a growing demand for organic meat, which means the animals will not have been intensively farmed.

2) The crowded conditions on factory farms create a favourable environment for the spread of diseases, like avian flu and foot-and-mouth disease.

3) To try to prevent disease, animals are given antibiotics. When the animals are eaten these can enter humans. This allows microbes that infect humans to develop immunity to those antibiotics — so the antibiotics become less effective as human medicines.

4) The environment where the animals are kept needs to be carefully controlled. The animals need to be kept warm to reduce the energy they lose as heat. This often means using power from fossil fuels — which we wouldn't be using if the animals were grazing in their natural environment.

5) Our fish stocks are getting low. Yet a lot of fish goes on feeding animals that are intensively farmed — these animals wouldn't usually eat this source of food.

In an exam, you may be asked to give an account of the positive and negative aspects of food management. You will need to put both sides, whatever your personal opinion is. If you get given some information on a particular case, make sure you use it — they want to see that you've read it carefully.

People can be very passionate about where their food comes from

You may well have a strong opinion on some of the issues above — you might think cheap meat is great because it's cheap and more people can afford it, or you might be against it because of animal welfare concerns. Either way, in exams keep it to yourself and give a nice, balanced argument instead.

The Carbon Cycle

As you've seen, all the nutrients in our environment are constantly being recycled — there's a nice balance between what goes in and what goes out again. This page is all about the recycling of carbon.

*The **Carbon Cycle** Shows How Carbon is **Recycled***

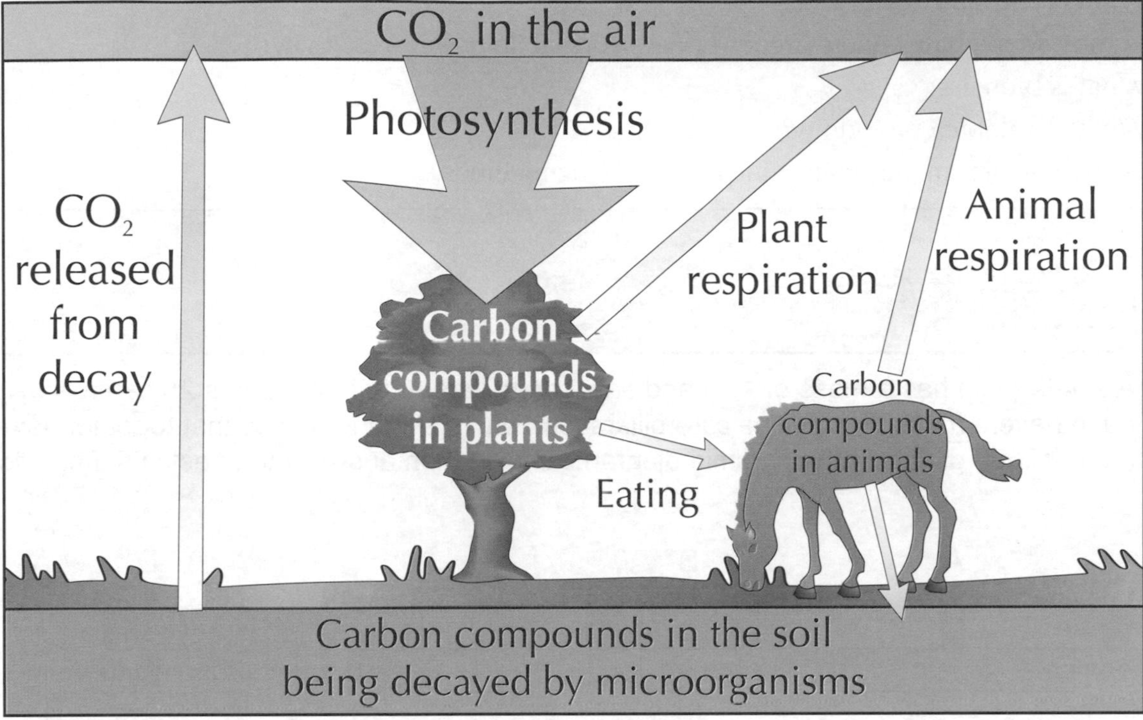

That can look a bit complicated at first, but it's actually pretty simple.
Learn these important points:

1) There's only one arrow going down from the atmosphere. The whole thing is "powered" by photosynthesis. CO_2 is removed from the atmosphere by green plants and used to make carbohydrates, fats and proteins in the plants.
2) Some of the CO_2 is returned to the atmosphere when the plants respire.
3) Some of the carbon becomes part of the compounds in animals when the plants are eaten. The carbon then moves through the food chain.
4) Some of the CO_2 is returned to the atmosphere when the animals respire.
5) When plants and animals die, other animals (called detritus feeders) and microorganisms feed on their remains. When these organisms respire, CO_2 is returned to the atmosphere.
6) Animals also produce waste, and this too is broken down by detritus feeders and microorganisms.
7) So the carbon is constantly being cycled — from the air, through food chains and eventually back out into the air again.

Carbon is also released into the atmosphere as CO_2 when plant and animal products are burnt.

Some carbon cycles look a bit different, but the basics are the same

Carbon is a very important element for living things — it's the basis for all the organic molecules.

Warm-Up and Exam Questions

There's no point in whizzing through the section and glancing over the questions. Do the warm-up questions and go back over any bits you don't know. Then practise and practise the exam questions.

Warm-Up Questions

1) What is a trophic level?
2) In most food chains, there are fewer carnivores than herbivores. Why?
3) What is biomass?
4) What is a stable community?
5) Give three arguments against intensive farming methods.

Exam Questions

1 A single robin has a mass of 15 g and eats caterpillars. Each robin eats 25 caterpillars that each have a mass of 2 g. The caterpillars feed on 10 stinging nettles that together have a mass of 500 g. Study the pyramid diagrams shown then answer the questions that follow.

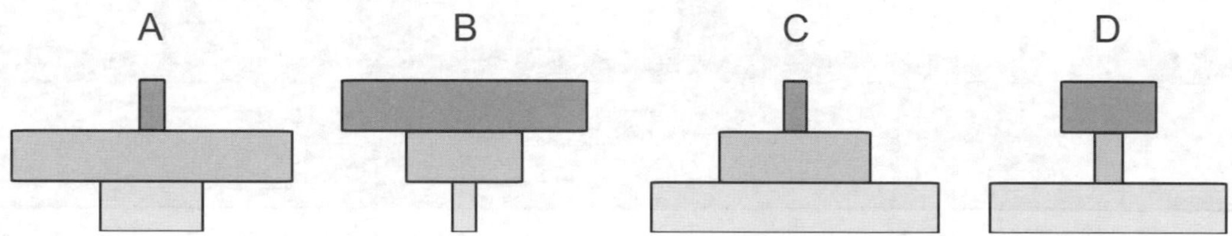

(a) Which diagram is most likely to represent a pyramid of numbers for these organisms?

(1 mark)

(b) Which is most likely to represent a pyramid of biomass for these organisms?

(1 mark)

(c) Explain how you decided on your answer to part (b) above.

(1 mark)

(d) The stinging nettles are the first trophic level.
Where does their energy initially come from?

(1 mark)

2 Put the following stages in order to describe how elements are recycled in a food chain.

1. Energy released in respiration is lost by decay, heat and movement and the production of waste.
2. Materials are recycled and returned to the soil by decay.
3. Plants take up minerals from the soil.
4. Plants use minerals and the products of photosynthesis to make complex nutrients.
5. Nutrients in plants are passed to animals through feeding and used in respiration to provide energy.
6. Waste and dead tissues are decayed by microorganisms.

(1 mark)

Exam Questions

3 All living organisms contain material taken from their surrounding environment. These materials are eventually recycled back into the environment. Some gardeners try to speed up this recycling process by producing compost in a compost bin.

(a) Describe, in as much detail as you can, how materials in living organisms are recycled back to the environment.

(3 marks)

(b) Suggest two ways in which a compost bin could provide a suitable environment for the decay of materials.

(2 marks)

4 Three different food chains are shown below.

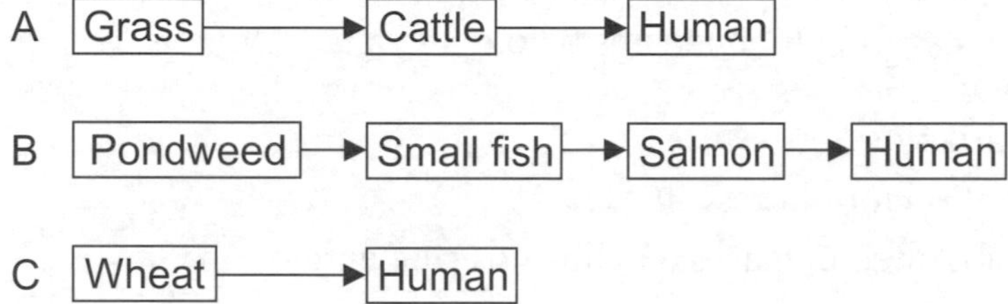

Explain which food chain shows the most efficient production of food for humans.

(2 marks)

5 Mr Bowman runs a farm in East Anglia. He raises cattle for milk and meat. He keeps the cattle in heated sheds and gives them regular injections of antibiotics, even if they're not ill.

(a) Suggest why Mr Bowman gives antibiotics to his cattle.

(1 mark)

(b) Explain the disadvantage of this practice.

(1 mark)

(c) Explain how keeping the cattle in heated sheds can improve the productivity of the farm.

(2 marks)

6 The diagram shows the carbon cycle.

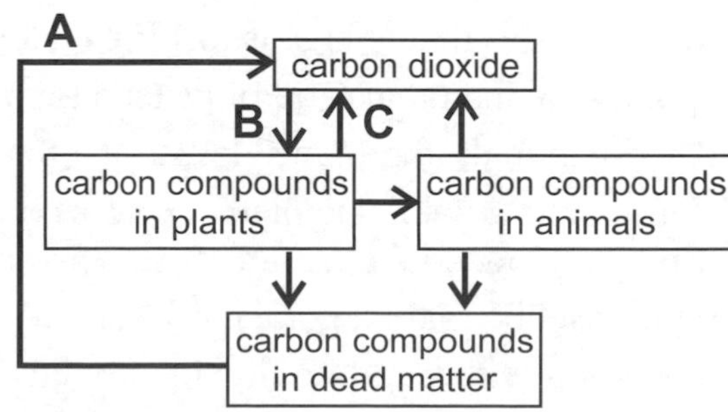

(a) What processes are occurring at stages A, B and C?

(3 marks)

(b) Describe the likely effects on the carbon cycle if large areas of forest are cut down.

(1 mark)

(c) Name the only process in the cycle that removes carbon dioxide from the air.

(1 mark)

Revision Summary for Biology 2(i)

And where do you think you're going? It's no use just reading through and thinking you've got it all — this stuff will only stick in your head if you've learnt it properly. And that's what these questions are for. I won't pretend they'll be easy — they're not meant to be, but all the information's in the section somewhere. Have a go at all the questions, then if there are any you can't answer, go back, look stuff up and try again.

1) Name five parts of a cell that both plant and animal cells have.
2) Name one organ system found in the human body.
3) Give three ways that a sperm cell is adapted for swimming to an egg cell.
4) Name three substances that can diffuse through cell membranes, and two that can't.
5) What three main things does the rate of diffusion depend on?
6) A solution of pure water is separated from a concentrated sugar solution by a partially permeable membrane. In which direction will molecules flow, and what substance will these molecules be?
7) An osmosis experiment involves placing pieces of potato into sugar solutions of various concentrations and measuring their lengths before and after. What is:
   a) the independent variable,
   b) the dependent variable?
8) Write down the equation for photosynthesis.
9) What is the green substance in leaves that absorbs sunlight?
10) *The graph on the right shows how the rate of plant growth is affected by increasing the level of carbon dioxide. Look at the graph and answer the two questions below.
    a) At what level of carbon dioxide is the plant's growth limited by another factor?
    b) Suggest two possible limiting factors on the plant's growth above this level.

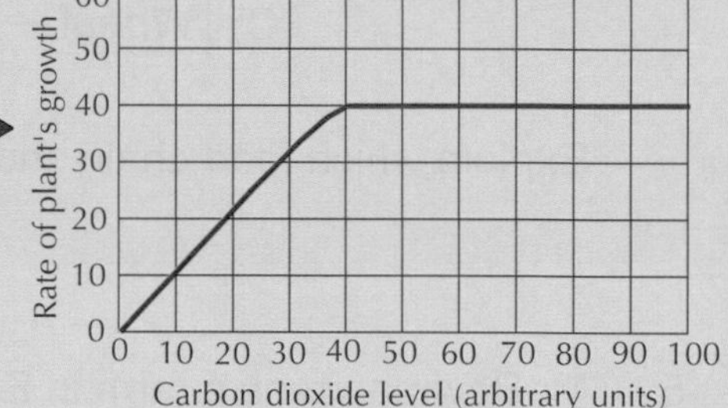

11) Explain why it's important that a plant doesn't get too hot.
12) Describe three things that a gardener could do to make sure she gets a good crop of tomatoes.
13) Write down five ways that plants can use the glucose produced by photosynthesis.
14) What is the mineral magnesium needed for in a plant?
15) Why are farmers more likely to need extra fertiliser if they grow their crops as a monoculture?
16) One oak tree produces acorns that are eaten by ten squirrels. At which stage in this section of the food chain is there the greatest:
    a) biomass,
    b) energy?
17) Give two ways that energy is lost from a food chain.
18) Explain why mammals and birds tend to lose more energy as heat than reptiles or insects.
19) Why do animals and plants decay after they die?
20) A farmer has a field. He plans to grow corn in it and then feed the corn to his cows, which he raises for meat. How could the farmer use the field more efficiently to produce food for humans?
21) Summarise the main arguments for and against the intensive farming of animals.
22) Give one way that carbon dioxide from the air enters a food chain.
23) Give three ways that carbon compounds in a food chain become carbon dioxide in the air again.

* Answers on page 226.

Biological Catalysts — Enzymes

Chemical reactions are what make you work. And enzymes are what make them work.

*Enzymes Are **Catalysts** Produced by **Living Things***

1) Living things have thousands of different chemical reactions going on inside them all the time.
2) These reactions need to be carefully controlled — to get the right amounts of substances.
3) You can usually make a reaction happen more quickly by raising the temperature. This would speed up the useful reactions but also the unwanted ones too... not good. There's also a limit to how far you can raise the temperature inside a living creature before its cells start getting damaged.
4) So... living things produce enzymes which act as biological catalysts. Enzymes reduce the need for high temperatures and we only have enzymes to speed up the useful chemical reactions in the body.

A CATALYST is a substance which INCREASES the speed of a reaction, without being CHANGED or USED UP in the reaction.

5) Enzymes are all proteins, which is one reason why proteins are so important to living things.
6) All proteins are made up of chains of amino acids. These chains are folded into unique shapes, which enzymes need to do their jobs (see below).

*Enzymes Have **Special Shapes** So They Can **Catalyse Reactions***

1) Chemical reactions usually involve things either being split apart or joined together.
2) Every enzyme has a unique shape that fits onto the substance involved in a reaction.
3) Enzymes are really picky — they usually only catalyse one reaction.
4) This is because, for the enzyme to work, the substance has to fit its special shape.
5) If the substance doesn't match the enzyme's shape, then the reaction won't be catalysed.

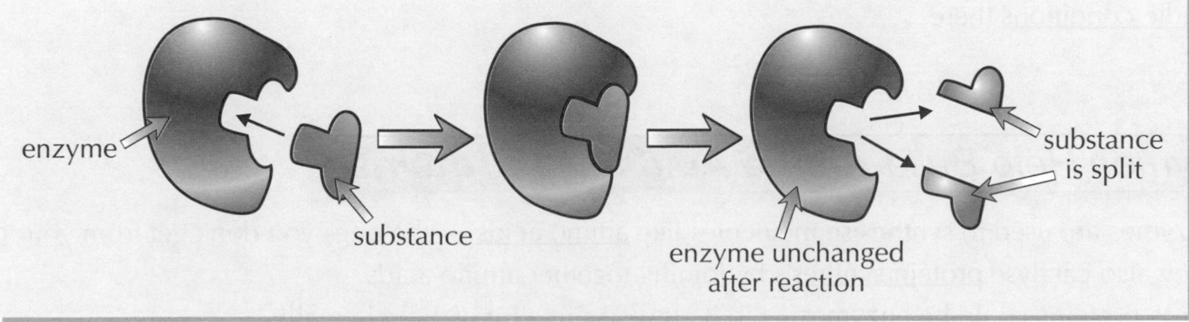

Enzymes speed up chemical reactions

Just like you've got to have the correct key for a lock, you've got to have the right substance for an enzyme. If the substance doesn't fit, the enzyme won't catalyse the reaction...

Biological Catalysts — Enzymes

Enzymes are clearly very clever, but they're not very versatile. They need just the right conditions if they're going to work properly.

Enzymes Need the Right Temperature...

1) Changing the temperature changes the rate of an enzyme-catalysed reaction.
2) Like with any reaction, a higher temperature increases the rate at first.
3) But if it gets too hot, some of the bonds holding the enzyme together break. This destroys the enzyme's special shape and so it won't work any more. It's said to be denatured.
4) Enzymes in the human body normally work best at around 37 °C — body temperature.

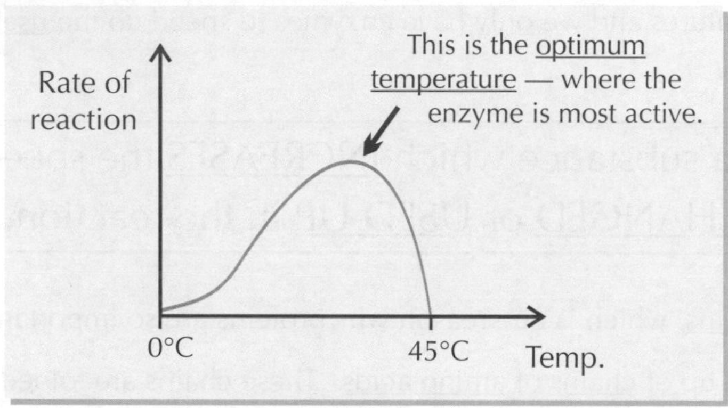

...and the Right pH

1) The pH also affects enzymes. If it's too high or too low, the pH interferes with the bonds holding the enzyme together.
2) This changes the shape and denatures the enzyme.
3) All enzymes have an optimum pH that they work best at. It's often neutral pH 7, but not always — e.g. pepsin is an enzyme used to break down proteins in the stomach. It works best at pH 2, which means it's well-suited to the acidic conditions there.

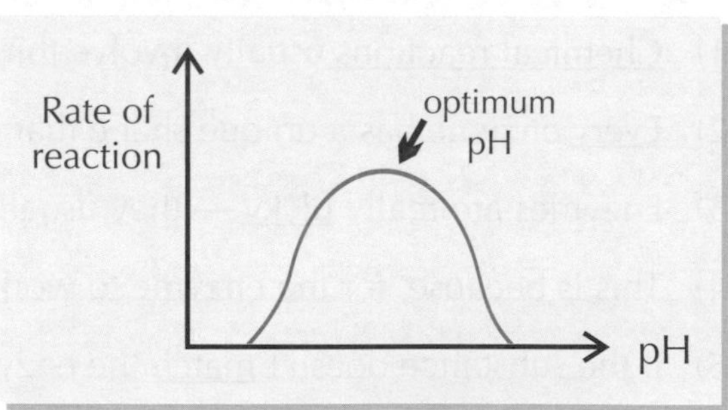

Enzymes Help Build Amino Acids and Proteins

1) Enzymes are used to synthesise molecules like amino acids — the ones you don't get from your diet.
2) They also catalyse protein synthesis by joining together amino acids.
3) These proteins could be enzymes — so it all works in a bit of a circle really.

Most enzymes catalyse just one reaction

Scientists have caught on to the idea that enzymes are really useful. They're used in biological detergents (to break down nasty stains) and in some baby foods (to predigest the food).

Enzymes and Respiration

Many chemical reactions inside cells are controlled by enzymes — including the ones in respiration, protein synthesis and photosynthesis (see page 76).

Respiration is NOT "Breathing In and Out"

Respiration involves many reactions, all of which are catalysed by enzymes. These are really important reactions, as respiration releases the energy that the cell needs to do just about everything.

1) Respiration is not breathing in and breathing out, as you might think.
2) Respiration is the process of releasing energy from the breakdown of glucose — and goes on in every cell in your body.
3) It happens in plants too. All living things respire. It's how they release energy from their food.

RESPIRATION is the process of RELEASING ENERGY FROM GLUCOSE, which goes on IN EVERY CELL.

Aerobic Respiration Needs Plenty of Oxygen

1) Aerobic respiration is respiration using oxygen. It's the most efficient way to release energy from glucose. (You can also have anaerobic respiration, which happens without oxygen, but that doesn't release nearly as much energy.)
2) Most of the reactions in aerobic respiration happen inside mitochondria (see page 68).

You need to learn the overall word equation for aerobic respiration:

Glucose + oxygen → carbon dioxide + water + ENERGY

Respiration Releases Energy for All Kinds of Things

You need to learn these four examples of what the energy released by aerobic respiration is used for:

1) To build up larger molecules from smaller ones (like proteins from amino acids).
2) In animals, to allow the muscles to contract (which in turn allows them to move about).
3) In mammals and birds the energy is used to keep their body temperature steady (unlike other animals, mammals and birds are warm-blooded).
4) In plants, to build sugars, nitrates and other nutrients into amino acids, which are then built up into proteins.

Respiration releases energy from glucose

So, respiration — that's an important thing. Cyanide is a nasty toxin that stops respiration by affecting enzymes involved in the process — so it's poisonous (it can kill you). Your brain, heart and liver are affected first because they have the highest energy demands, which makes cyanide very effective.

Warm-Up and Exam Questions

Doing well in exams isn't just about remembering all the facts, although that's important. You have to get used to the way the exams are phrased and make sure you always read the question carefully.

Warm-Up Questions

1) Enzymes are sometimes referred to as 'biological catalysts'. What is a catalyst?
2) Sketch graphs to show how the rates of enzyme-controlled reactions are affected by temperature and pH.
3) What is meant by the optimum temperature or pH of an enzyme?
4) Define respiration.
5) Write down the word equation for aerobic respiration.

Exam Questions

1 The graph shows the effect of temperature on the action of two different enzymes.

(a) What is the optimum temperature for enzyme A? *(1 mark)*

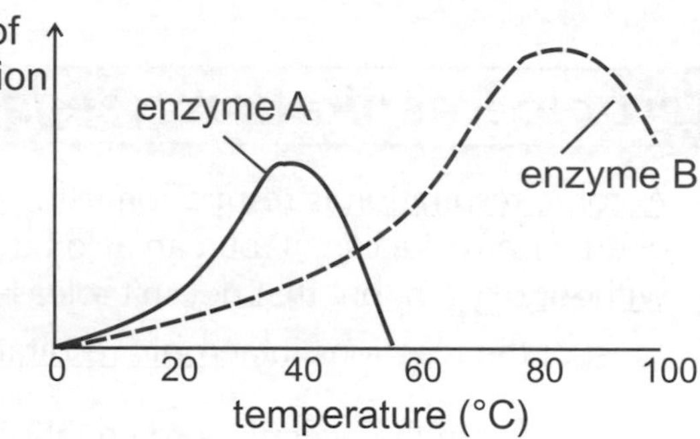

(b) One of these enzymes was extracted from human liver cells. The other was extracted from bacteria living in hot underwater vents.

Suggest which enzyme came from the bacteria, and explain your answer.

(2 marks)

(c) Enzyme B is a protein-digesting enzyme.
Suggest why it might be useful in biological washing powders.

(2 marks)

2 The diagram represents the action of an enzyme in catalysing a biological reaction.

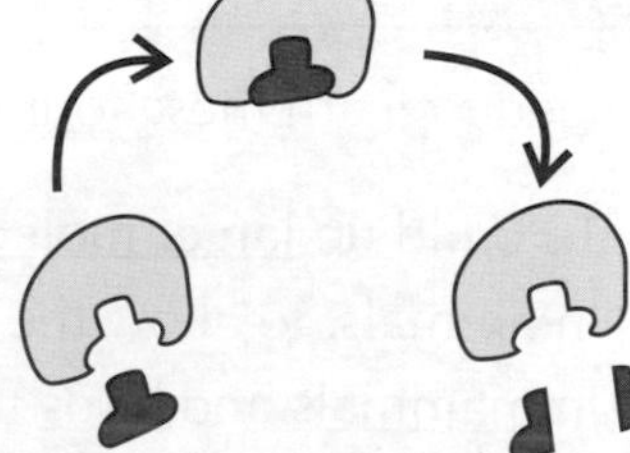

In terms of the enzyme's shape, explain the following:

(a) why an enzyme only catalyses one reaction. *(1 mark)*

(b) what happens when the enzyme is denatured. *(1 mark)*

3 Which of the following statements about aerobic respiration is **not** true?

A Aerobic respiration is respiration not using oxygen.
B Aerobic respiration releases energy.
C Aerobic respiration takes place in mitochondria.
D Carbon dioxide is a product of aerobic respiration.

(1 mark)

Enzymes and Digestion

The enzymes used in respiration work inside cells. Various different enzymes are used in digestion too, but these enzymes are produced by specialised cells and then released into the gut to mix with the food.

Digestive Enzymes *Break Down* **Big Molecules** *into* **Smaller Ones**

1) Starch, proteins and fats are BIG molecules. They're too big to pass through the walls of the digestive system.
2) Sugars, amino acids, glycerol and fatty acids are much smaller molecules. They can pass easily through the walls of the digestive system.
3) The digestive enzymes break down the BIG molecules into the smaller ones.

Amylase *Converts* **Starch** *into* **Simple Sugars**

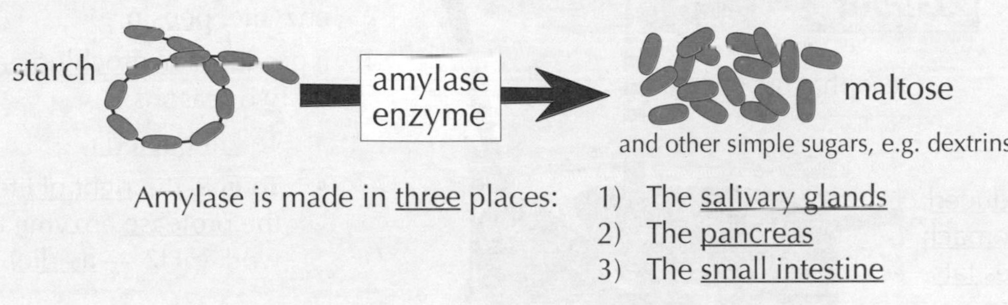

Amylase is made in three places:
1) The salivary glands
2) The pancreas
3) The small intestine

Protease *Converts* **Proteins** *into* **Amino Acids**

Protease is made in three places:
1) The stomach (it's called pepsin there)
2) The pancreas
3) The small intestine

Lipase *Converts* **Fats** *into* **Glycerol** *and* **Fatty Acids**

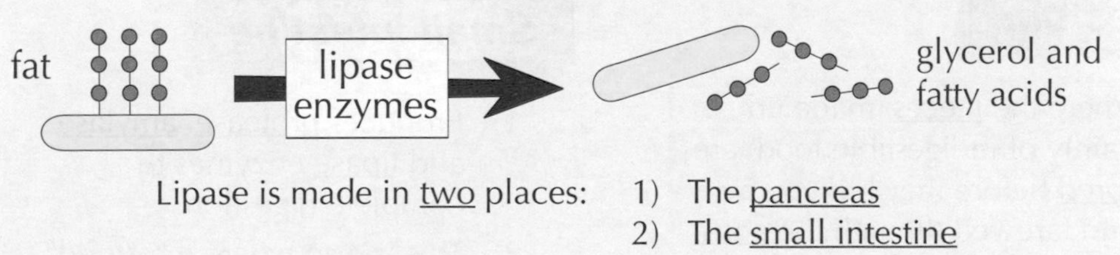

Lipase is made in two places:
1) The pancreas
2) The small intestine

Bile Neutralises *the Stomach Acid and* **Emulsifies** *Fats*

1) Bile is produced in the liver. It's stored in the gall bladder before it's released into the small intestine.
2) The hydrochloric acid in the stomach makes the pH too acidic for enzymes in the small intestine to work properly. Bile is alkaline — it neutralises the acid and makes conditions alkaline. The enzymes in the small intestine work best in these alkaline conditions.
3) It emulsifies fats. In other words it breaks the fat into tiny droplets. This gives a much bigger surface area of fat for the enzyme lipase to work on — which makes its digestion faster.

The Digestive System

So now you know what the enzymes do, here's a nice big picture of the whole of the digestive system.

The Breakdown of Food is Catalysed by Enzymes

1) Enzymes used in the digestive system are produced by specialised cells in glands and in the gut lining.
2) Different enzymes catalyse the breakdown of different food molecules.

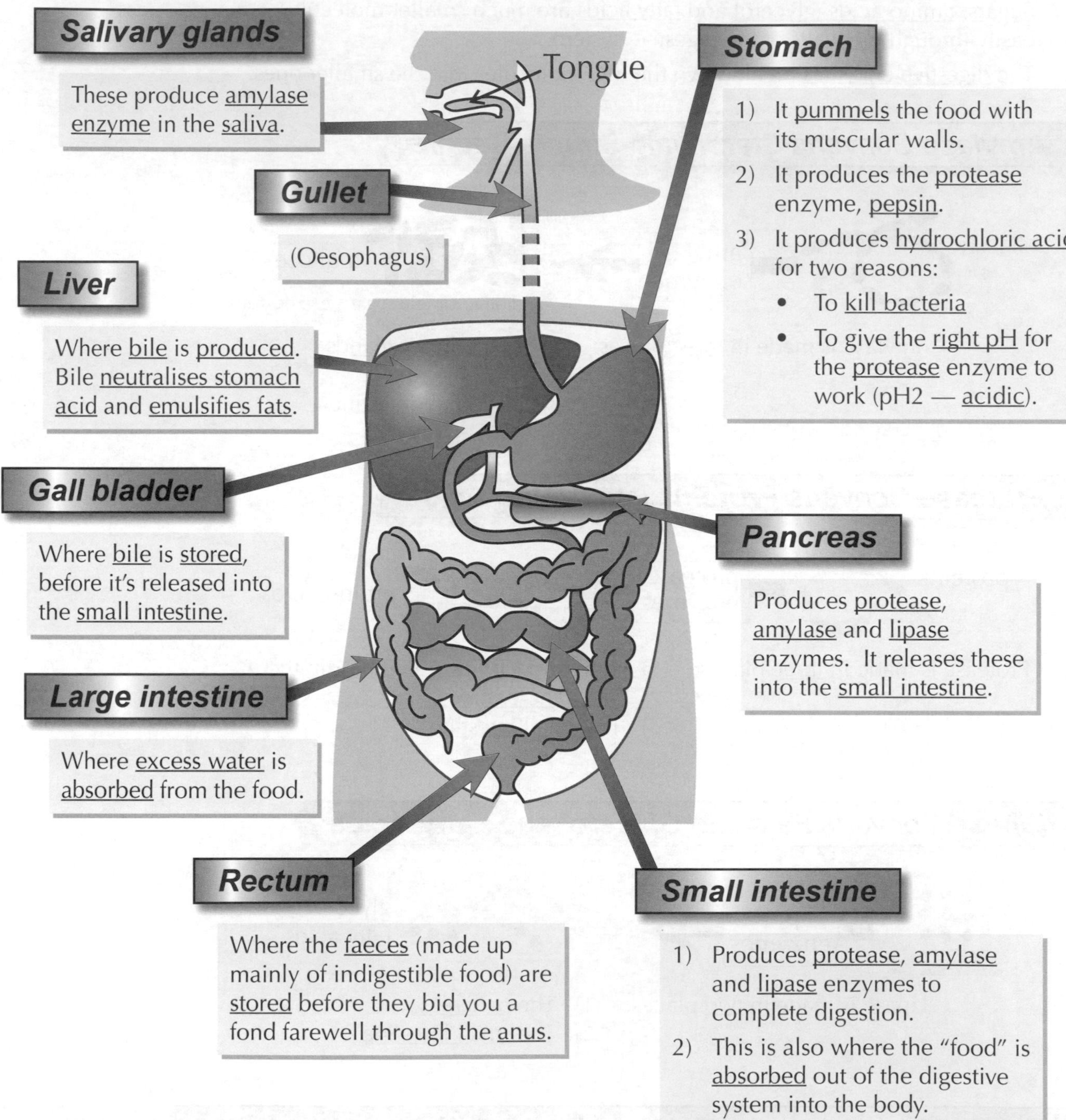

That's nine different bits of the digestive system you need to know

Did you know that pretty much the whole of your digestive system is actually a hole that goes right through your body? Think about it. It just gets loads of food, digestive juices and enzymes piled into it.

Uses of Enzymes

Some microorganisms produce enzymes which pass out of their cells and catalyse reactions outside them (e.g. to digest the microorganism's food). These enzymes have many uses in the home and in industry.

Enzymes Are Used in **Biological Detergents**

1) Enzymes are the 'biological' ingredients in biological detergents and washing powders.
2) They're mainly protein-digesting enzymes (proteases) and fat-digesting enzymes (lipases).
3) Because the enzymes attack animal and plant matter, they're ideal for removing stains like food or blood.

Enzymes Are Used to **Change Foods**

1) The proteins in some baby foods are 'pre-digested' using protein-digesting enzymes (proteases), so they're easier for the baby to digest.
2) Carbohydrate-digesting enzymes (carbohydrases) can be used to turn starch syrup into sugar syrup.
3) Glucose syrup can be turned into fructose syrup using an isomerase enzyme. Fructose is sweeter, so you can use less of it — good for slimming foods and drinks.

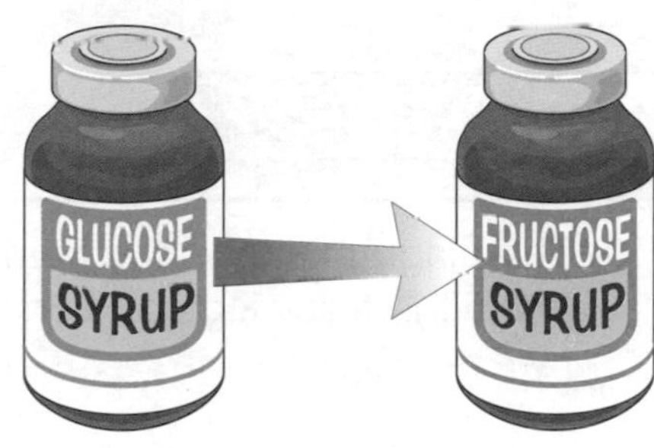

Using Enzymes in **Industry** Takes a Lot of **Control**

Enzymes are really useful in industry. They speed up reactions without the need for high temperatures and pressures. In a big industrial plant the substances are often continually run over the enzymes, so they have to be kept from washing away. They can be trapped in an alginate bead (a bead of jelly-like stuff) or in a latticework of silica gel.

You need to know the advantages and disadvantages of using them, so here are a few to get you started:

ADVANTAGES

1) They're specific, so they only catalyse the reaction you want them to.
2) Using lower temperatures and pressures means a lower cost and it saves energy.
3) Enzymes work for a long time, so after the initial cost of buying them, you can continually use them.
4) They are biodegradable and therefore cause less environmental pollution.

DISADVANTAGES

1) Some people can develop allergies to the enzymes (e.g. in biological washing powders).
2) Enzymes can be denatured by even a small increase in temperature. They're also susceptible to poisons and changes in pH. This means the conditions in which they work must be tightly controlled.
3) Contamination of the enzyme with other substances can affect the reaction.

From baby food to washing powder — enzymes make life easier

There's no denying that enzymes are useful, but they're also quite picky — e.g. tiny changes in pH can stop them working. Make sure you know both the advantages and disadvantages of using enzymes.

Warm-Up and Exam Questions

By the time the big day comes you need to know all the facts in these warm-up questions and exam questions like the back of your hand. It's not a barrel of laughs, but it's the only way to get good marks.

Warm-Up Questions

1) What is the function of digestive enzymes?
2) Which enzymes digest: (a) starch (b) protein (c) fat?
3) What are the products of the digestion of: (a) starch (b) protein (c) fat?
4) What does bile do?
5) Explain why proteases and lipases are used in biological detergents.
6) Explain why proteases are used in some baby food.
7) Give two advantages and two disadvantages of using enzymes in industry.

Exam Questions

1 The diagram shows the human digestive system.
Label the following parts on the diagram:

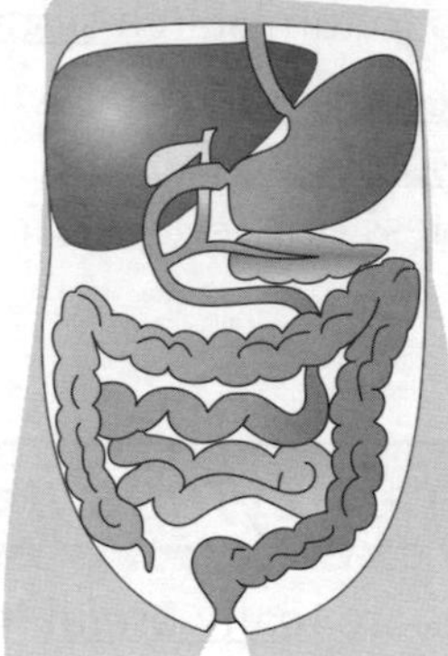

(a) the liver

(1 mark)

(b) a part which is very acidic

(1 mark)

(c) the main place where water is absorbed

(1 mark)

2 Describe the functions of each of these parts of the gut:

(a) gall bladder

(1 mark)

(b) pancreas

(1 mark)

(c) liver

(1 mark)

3 Naz did an experiment to investigate the effect of pH on enzyme action. She took four test tubes and placed some starch solution in each one. Each solution was given a different pH value as shown below. Then a digestive enzyme was added to each tube.

Test tube	A	B	C	D
pH	2	5	8	11

(a) What type of digestive enzyme do you think should be added to the tubes?

(1 mark)

(b) Name three factors that should be kept constant during this experiment.

(3 marks)

(c) At which pH do you think the enzyme will work best? Explain your answer.

(2 marks)

Homeostasis

Homeostasis is a fancy word. It covers lots of things, so I guess it has to be. Homeostasis covers all the functions of your body which try to maintain a "constant internal environment". Learn that definition:

HOMEOSTASIS is the maintenance of a constant internal environment.

There Are *Six* Main Things That Need to Be *Controlled*

The first four are all things you need, but at just the right level — not too much and not too little.

1) The body temperature can't get too hot or too cold (see below).

2) Water content mustn't get too high or low, or too much water could move into or out of cells and damage them. There's more on controlling water content on page 104.

3) If the ion content of the body is wrong, the same thing could happen. See page 104.

4) The blood sugar level needs to stay within certain limits (see page 106).

The last two are waste products — they're constantly produced in the body and you need to get rid of them.

5) Carbon dioxide is a product of respiration. It's toxic in high quantities so it's got to be removed. It leaves the body by the lungs when you breathe out.

The word equation for respiration is back on page 95.

6) Urea is a waste product made from excess amino acids. There's more about it on page 103.

Body Temperature Must Be Carefully Controlled

All enzymes work best at a certain temperature (see page 94). The enzymes within the human body work best at about 37 °C. If the body gets too hot or too cold, the enzymes won't work properly and some really important reactions could be disrupted. In extreme cases, this can even lead to death.

The next page is all about how the human body controls temperature.

Homeostasis

Body Temperature is kept at About 37 °C

1) There is a thermoregulatory centre in the brain which acts as your own personal thermostat.
2) It contains receptors that are sensitive to the temperature of the blood flowing through the brain.
3) The thermoregulatory centre also receives impulses from the skin, giving info about skin temperature.
4) If you're getting too hot or too cold, your body can respond to try and cool you down or warm you up:

When You're Too Hot:

The thermoregulatory centre is in a part of the brain called the hypothalamus.

1) Hairs lie flat.

2) Sweat is produced by sweat glands and evaporates from the skin, which removes heat.

3) The blood vessels supplying the skin dilate so more blood flows close to the surface of the skin. This makes it easier for heat to be transferred from the blood to the environment.

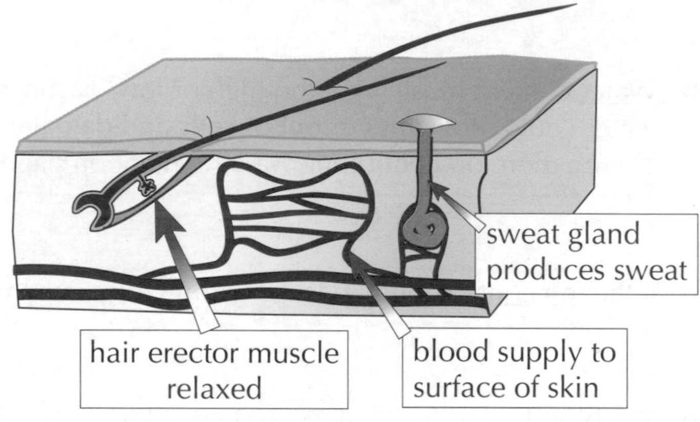

When You're Too Cold:

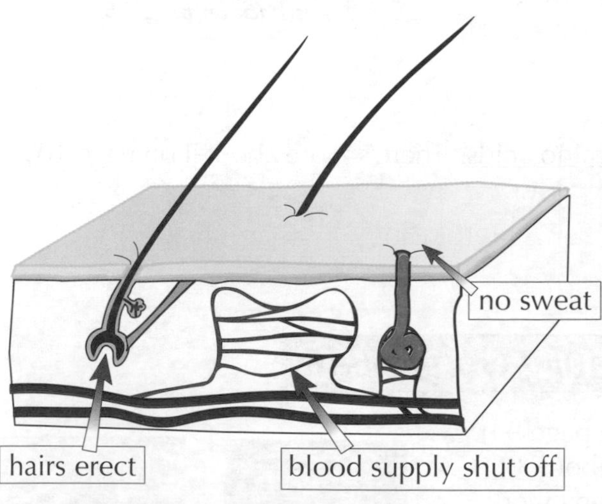

1) Hairs stand up to trap an insulating layer of air.

2) No sweat is produced.

3) Blood vessels supplying skin capillaries constrict to close off the skin's blood supply.

When you're cold you shiver too (your muscles contract automatically). This needs respiration, which releases some energy as heat.

Goose bumps — the result of hairs standing up when you're cold

People who are exposed to extreme cold for long periods of time without protection can get frostbite — the blood supply to the fingers and toes is cut off to conserve heat (but this kills the cells, and they go black).

The Kidneys and Homeostasis

The kidneys are really important in homeostasis — they control the content of the blood.

Kidneys Basically Act as Filters to 'Clean the Blood'

The kidneys perform three main roles:

1) Removal of urea from the blood.

2) Adjustment of ions in the blood.

3) Adjustment of water content of the blood.

1) Removal of Urea

1) Proteins can't be stored by the body — so any excess amino acids are converted into fats and carbohydrates, which can be stored.
2) This process occurs in the liver. Urea is produced as a waste product from the reactions.
3) Urea is poisonous. It's released into the bloodstream by the liver. The kidneys then filter it out of the blood and it's excreted from the body in urine.

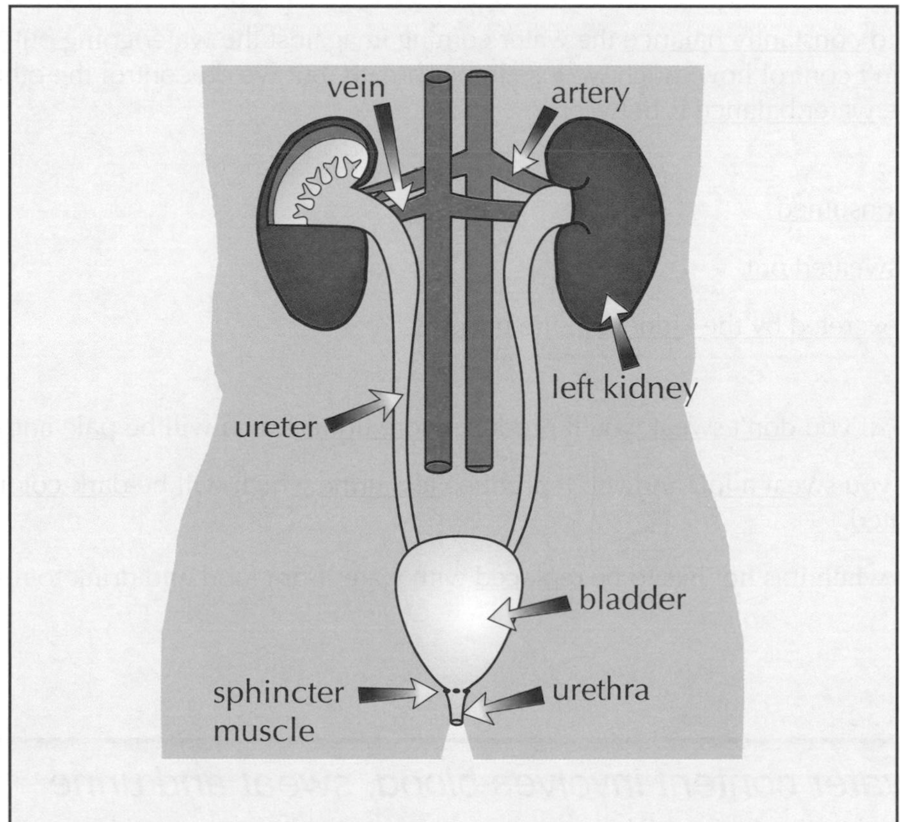

The Kidneys and Homeostasis

Urine contains some water and ions as well as urea, to help keep the balance right in the body.

2) Adjustment of Ion Content

1) Ions such as sodium are taken into the body in food, and then absorbed into the blood.
2) If the ion content of the body is wrong, this could mean too much or too little water is drawn into cells by osmosis (see page 73). Having the wrong amount of water can damage cells.
3) Excess ions are removed by the kidneys. For example, a salty meal will contain far too much sodium and so the kidneys will remove the excess sodium ions from the blood.
4) Some ions are also lost in sweat (which tastes salty, you may have noticed).
5) But the important thing to remember is that the balance is always maintained by the kidneys.

3) Adjustment of Water Content

Water is taken into the body as food and drink and is lost from the body in three main ways:

1) In urine
2) In sweat
3) In the air we breathe out.

The body has to constantly balance the water coming in against the water going out. Our bodies can't control how much we lose in our breath, but we do control the other factors. This means the water balance is between:

1) Liquids consumed
2) Amount sweated out
3) Amount excreted by the kidneys in the urine.

On a cold day, if you don't sweat, you'll produce more urine which will be pale and dilute.

On a hot day, you sweat a lot, and you'll produce less urine which will be dark-coloured and concentrated.

The water lost when it is hot has to be replaced with water from food and drink to restore the balance.

Adjusting water content involves blood, sweat and urine

Scientists have made a machine which does the same job as the kidneys — a kidney dialysis machine. People with kidney failure have to use it for 3–4 hours, three times a week. Unfortunately it's not something you can carry around with you, which makes life difficult for people with kidney failure.

Warm-Up and Exam Questions

Without a good warm-up you're likely to strain a brain cell or two. So take the time to run through these simple questions and get the basic facts straight before plunging into the exam questions.

Warm-Up Questions

1) Name two waste products produced in the body that need to be removed.
2) Name the part of the brain that controls body temperature.
3) Describe two ways that the brain monitors body temperature.
4) Describe three ways in which the body responds to a rise in temperature.
5) State the three main functions of the kidneys.

Exam Questions

1 Describe three ways in which the body responds to a drop in temperature.

(3 marks)

2 The diagram shows the human urinary system.

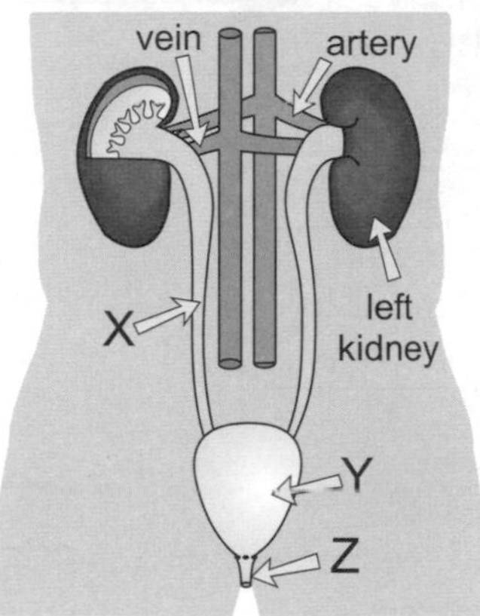

Name the structures labelled X, Y and Z.

(3 marks)

3 If someone's kidneys fail they may be given a kidney transplant, or they can use a dialysis machine. A dialysis machine does the job of the kidneys and filters the blood.

(a) What three substances would you expect a dialysis machine to remove from the blood?

(1 mark)

(b) Suggest a reason why people with kidney failure are often advised to eat low-salt diets.

(2 marks)

4 Which of the following statements about controlling water content is **not** true?

A Water needs to be taken as drink or in food to balance any water that is lost.

B Water is only lost from the body by sweating and urinating.

C If you play football on a very hot day, your urine will be dark and concentrated.

D Water is taken into the body as food and drink.

(1 mark)

Controlling Blood Sugar

Blood sugar is also controlled as part of homeostasis. Insulin is a hormone that controls how much sugar there is in your blood. Learn how it does it:

Insulin Controls *Blood Sugar* Levels

1) Eating foods containing carbohydrate puts glucose into the blood from the gut.
2) Normal metabolism (reactions) of cells removes glucose from the blood.
3) Vigorous exercise also removes a lot of glucose from the blood.
4) Levels of glucose in the blood must be kept steady. Changes in blood glucose are monitored and controlled by the pancreas, using the hormone insulin, as shown:

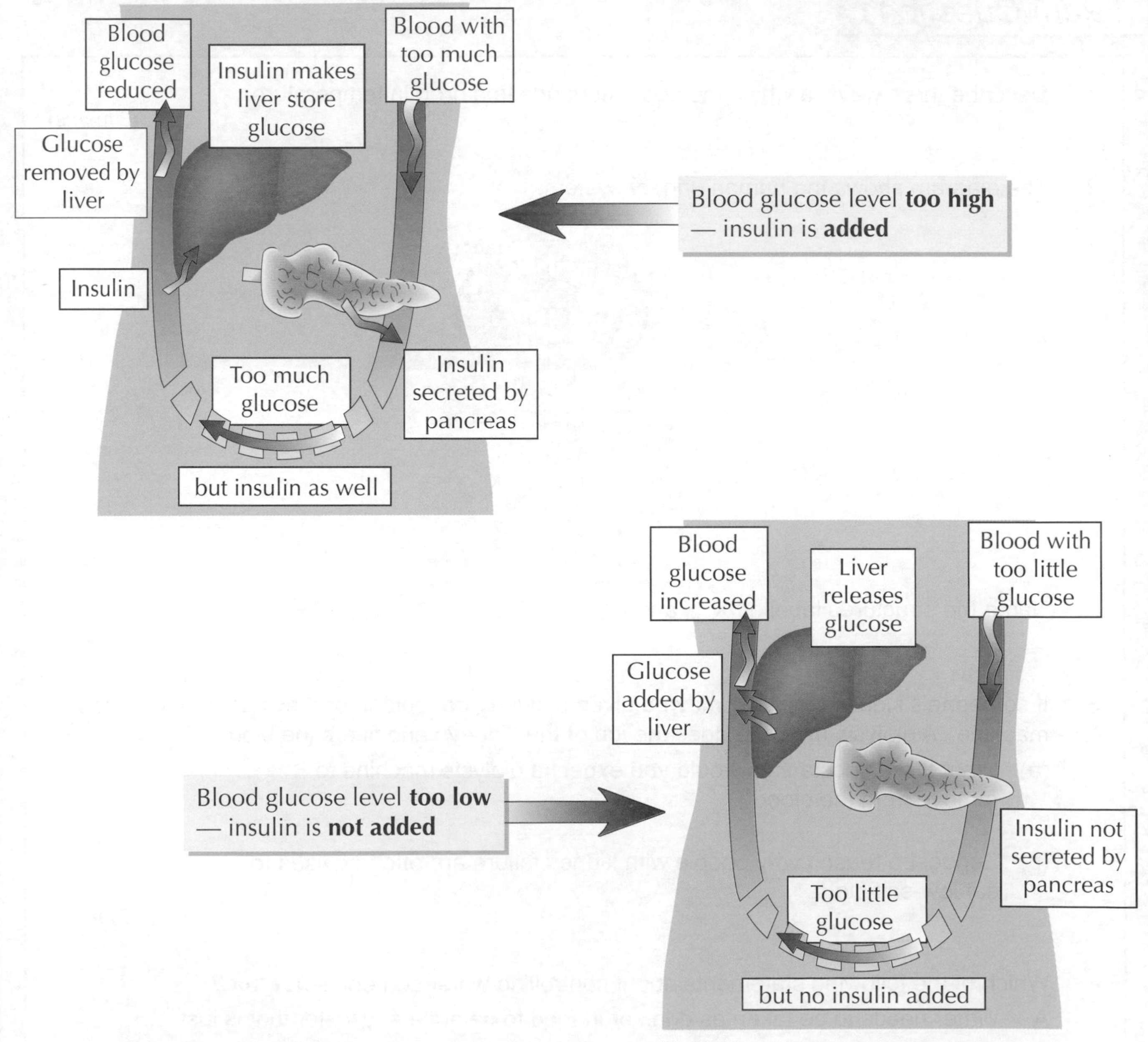

So now you know what your pancreas is for...

Learn these two diagrams and you shouldn't have any problems answering questions about how blood sugar is controlled. Don't forget that only carbohydrate foods put the blood sugar levels up.

Controlling Blood Sugar

The system described on the last page shows how insulin controls blood glucose levels. In people who suffer from diabetes this system does not function properly.

*Diabetes (type 1) — the **Pancreas** Stops Making **Enough Insulin***

1) Diabetes (type 1) is a disorder where the pancreas doesn't produce enough insulin.
2) The result is that a person's blood sugar can rise to a level that can kill them.
3) The problem can be controlled in two ways:

Method 1: Avoiding foods rich in simple carbohydrates

i.e. sugars

The digestion of simple carbohydrates causes glucose levels to rise rapidly.

It can also be helpful to take exercise after eating to try and use up the extra glucose produced during digestion — but this isn't usually very practical.

Method 2: Injecting insulin into the blood at mealtimes

(especially if the meal is high in simple carbohydrates).

This will make the liver remove the glucose as soon as it enters the blood from the gut, when the food is being digested.

This stops the level of glucose in the blood from getting too high and is a very effective treatment. However, the person must make sure they eat sensibly after injecting insulin, or their blood sugar could drop dangerously.

4) The amount of insulin that needs to be injected depends on the person's diet and how active they are.
5) Diabetics can check their blood sugar using a glucose-monitoring device. This is a little hand-held machine. They prick their finger to get a drop of blood for the machine to check.

It's important to learn how to control diabetes

Hormones control a lot of your body's functions. So if one of these functions isn't being done quite right, it might be possible to fix it by injecting suitable hormones — just like with diabetes.

Insulin and Diabetes

Scientific discoveries often take a long time, and a lot of trial and error — here's a rather famous example that led to a big advance in the control of diabetes.

Insulin Was Discovered by Banting and Best

It has been known for some time that people who suffer from diabetes have a lot of sugar in their urine.

In the 19th century, scientists removed pancreases from dogs, and the same sugary urine was observed — the dogs became diabetic. That suggested that the pancreas had to have something to do with the illness.

In the 1920s Frederick Banting and his assistant Charles Best managed to successfully isolate insulin — the hormone that controls blood sugar levels.

1) Banting and Best tied string around a dog's pancreas so that a lot of the organ wasted away — but the bits which made the hormones were left intact.

2) They removed the pancreas from the dog, and obtained an extract from it.

3) They then injected this extract into diabetic dogs and observed the effects on their blood sugar levels.

4) After the pancreatic extract was injected, the dog's blood sugar level fell dramatically. This showed that the pancreatic extract caused a temporary decrease in blood sugar level.

5) They went on to isolate the substance in the pancreatic extract — insulin.

After a lot more experiments, Banting and Best tried injecting insulin into a diabetic human. And it worked.

This is still the basis of treatment today, although there have been certain advances (see next page).

Banting won a Nobel prize for this work in 1923

And, rather sweetly, he insisted on sharing the prize money with his young assistant and made sure his contribution was recognised. They also chose to make the patent for the treatment available without charge, rather than trying to make any money out of their discovery. How refreshing.

Insulin and Diabetes

Diabetes Can Be **Controlled** by **Regular Injections** of **Insulin**

Since Banting and Best's discovery of insulin, it has been mass produced to meet the needs of diabetics.

Diabetics have to inject themselves with insulin often — 2-4 times a day. They also need to carefully control their diet and the amount of exercise they do (see page 106).

1) At first, the insulin was extracted from the pancreases of pigs or cows. Diabetics used glass syringes that had to be boiled before use.
2) In the 1980s human insulin made by genetic engineering became available. This didn't cause any adverse reactions in patients, which animal insulin sometimes did.
3) Slow, intermediate and fast acting insulins have been developed to make it easier for diabetics to control their blood sugar levels.
4) Ready sterilised, disposable syringes are now available, as well as needle-free devices.

Improving methods of treatment allow diabetics to control their blood sugar more easily.

This helps them avoid some of the damaging side effects of poor control, such as blindness and gangrene.

Diabetics May Have a **Pancreas Transplant**

Injecting yourself with insulin every day controls the effects of diabetes, but it doesn't help to cure it.

1) Diabetics can have a pancreas transplant. A successful operation means they won't have to inject themselves with insulin again. But as with any organ transplant, your body can reject the tissue. This means you have to take costly immunosuppressive drugs, which often have serious side-effects.
2) Another method, still in its experimental stage, is to transplant just the cells which produce insulin. There's been varying success with this technique, and there are still problems with rejection.
3) Modern research into artificial pancreases and stem cell research may mean the elimination of organ rejection, but there's a way to go yet (see pages 117-118).

Controlling diabetes is not the same as curing it

Insulin can't be taken in a pill or tablet — the enzymes in the stomach completely destroy it before it reaches the bloodstream. That's why diabetics have to inject it. Diabetes is becoming more and more common, partly due to our society becoming increasingly overweight. It's very serious.

Warm-Up and Exam Questions

Right then, another section down. Now there's just the small matter of answering some questions...

Warm-Up Questions

1) Where does the sugar in your blood come from?
2) Name the organ that monitors and controls blood sugar levels.
3) Explain what type 1 diabetes is.
4) How can diabetics check their blood sugar levels?

Exam Questions

1 The diagram below shows how blood sugar levels are regulated in humans.

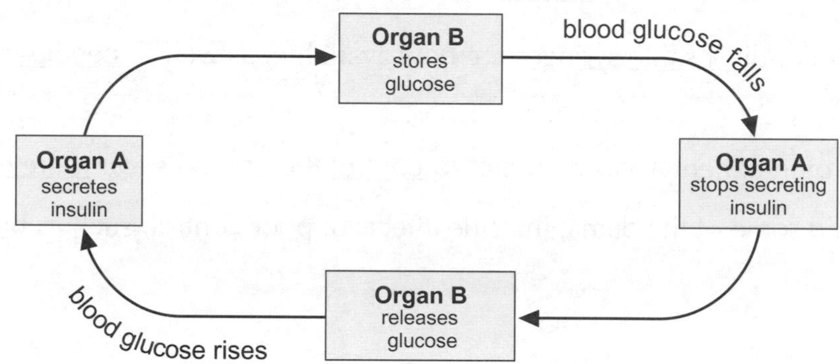

(a) From the diagram, identify:

(i) organ A

(1 mark)

(ii) organ B

(1 mark)

(b) (i) Suggest a reason why blood glucose might rise.

(1 mark)

(ii) What process constantly removes glucose from the blood?

(1 mark)

(iii) What would cause blood glucose levels to fall rapidly?

(1 mark)

2 Diabetes can be treated using insulin injections or by a pancreas transplant.

(a) Insulin used to be extracted from the pancreases of animals, but today most insulin is produced by genetically engineered bacteria.
Suggest two advantages of using the bacterial insulin.

(2 marks)

(b) Suggest one advantage and one disadvantage of treating diabetes with a pancreas transplant rather than insulin injections.

(2 marks)

Revision Summary for Biology 2(ii)

There are two quite separate bits to this section. First you've got enzymes, how they're used inside cells, in digestion, and in industry. Then the second bit is all about keeping things constant in your body. Have a bash at the questions, go back and check anything you're not sure about, then try again. Practise until you can answer all these questions really easily without having to look back at the section.

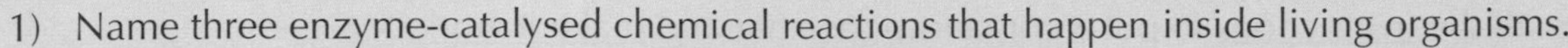

1) Name three enzyme-catalysed chemical reactions that happen inside living organisms.

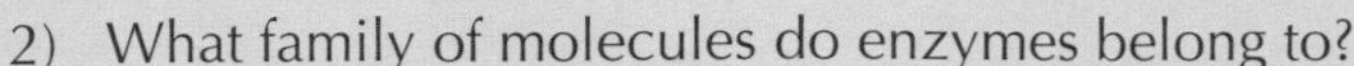

2) What family of molecules do enzymes belong to?
3) Explain why an enzyme-catalysed reaction stops when the reaction mixture is heated above a certain temperature.

4) * The graph on the right shows how the rate of an enzyme-catalysed reaction depends on pH:

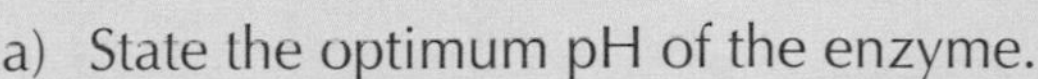

   a) State the optimum pH of the enzyme.
   b) In which part of the human digestive system would you expect to find the enzyme?

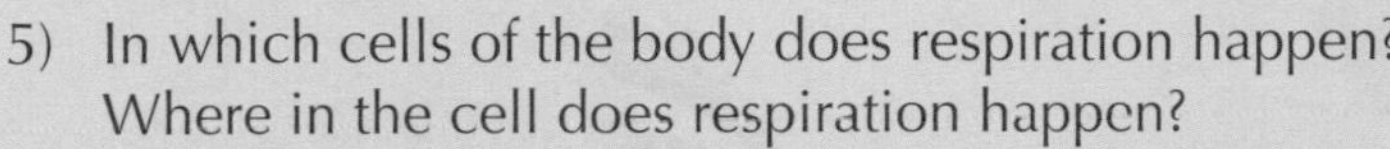

5) In which cells of the body does respiration happen? Where in the cell does respiration happen?

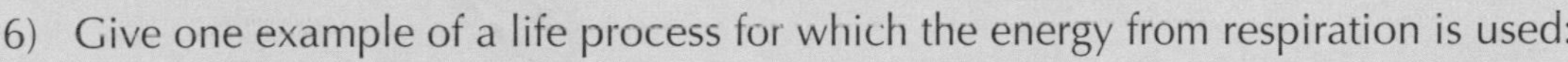

6) Give one example of a life process for which the energy from respiration is used:
   a) in a bird,
   b) in a plant.
7) In which three places in the body is amylase produced?
8) In which two places in the body is lipase made?
9) Where in the body is bile:
   a) produced?
   b) stored?
   c) used?
10) Explain why the stomach produces hydrochloric acid.
11) What is the main function of the small intestine?
12) Give an industrial use of a carbohydrase enzyme.
13) Define homeostasis.
14) Write down four conditions that the body needs to keep fairly constant.
15) At what temperature do most of the enzymes in the human body work best?
16) Where in the body is urea produced?
17) What damage could be done in the body if the ion content is wrong?
18) Give three ways in which water is lost from the body.
19) Explain why your urine is likely to be more concentrated on a hot day.
20) How does insulin lower the blood glucose level if it is too high?
21) How does the body respond if the blood glucose level is too low?
22) The amount of insulin that needs to be injected by a diabetic depend on two factors — what are they?
23) Describe the experiments by Banting and Best that led to the isolation of insulin.

* Answers on page 227

DNA

The first step in understanding genetics is getting to grips with DNA.

Chromosomes Are Really Long Molecules of *DNA*

1) DNA stands for deoxyribose nucleic acid.
2) It contains all the instructions to put an organism together and make it work.
3) It's found in the nucleus of animal and plant cells, in really long molecules called chromosomes.

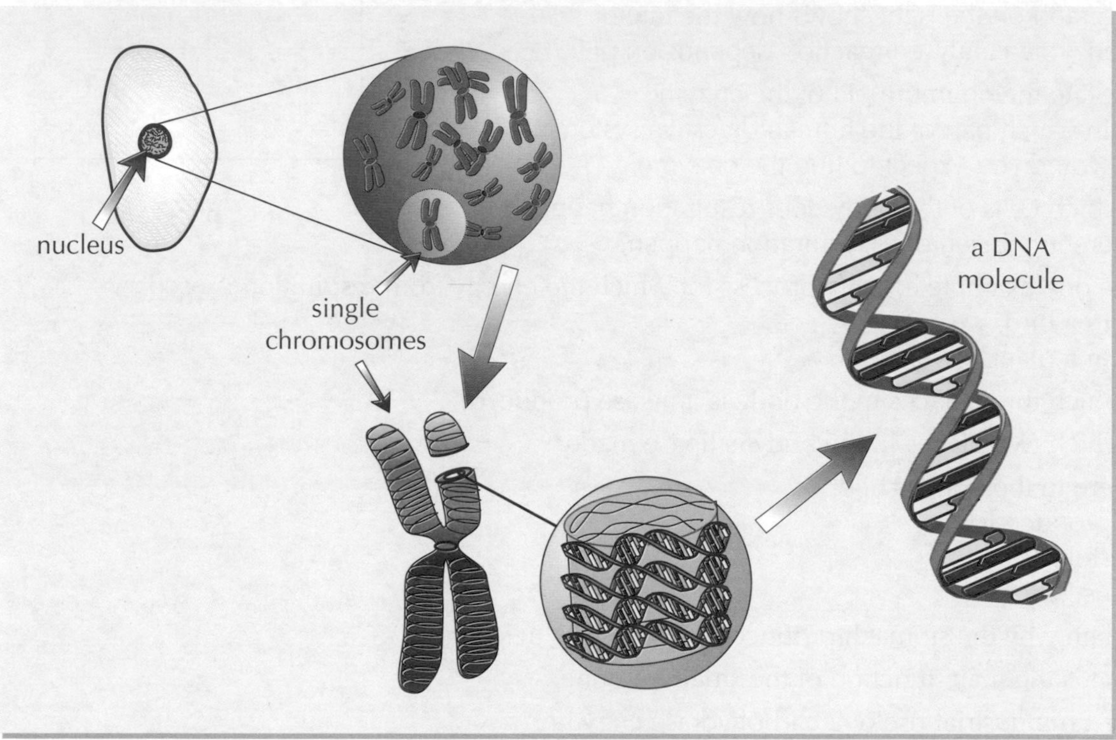

A *Gene* Codes for a *Specific Protein*

1) A gene is a section of DNA. It contains the instructions to make a specific protein.
2) Cells make proteins by stringing amino acids together in a particular order.
3) Only 20 amino acids are used, but they make up thousands of different proteins.
4) Genes simply tell cells in what order to put the amino acids together.
5) DNA also determines what proteins the cell produces, e.g. haemoglobin, keratin.
6) That in turn determines what type of cell it is, e.g. red blood cell, skin cell.

Your genes are what make you different from everyone else

You've got to make sure you know exactly what chromosomes and genes are. If you don't get that sorted out first, then anything else you read about them later on won't make a lot of sense.

DNA Fingerprinting

Now this is interesting — DNA is used to catch criminals and to identify the father of a child.

Everyone has Unique DNA

1) Almost everyone's DNA is unique. The only exceptions are identical twins, where the two people have identical DNA, and clones.

2) DNA fingerprinting (or genetic fingerprinting) is a way of cutting up a person's DNA into small sections and then separating them.

3) Every person's genetic fingerprint has a unique pattern (unless they're identical twins or clones of course). This means you can tell people apart by comparing samples of their DNA.

DNA fingerprinting is used in...

1) Forensic science — DNA (from hair, skin flakes, blood, semen etc.) taken from a crime scene is compared with a DNA sample taken from a suspect. In the diagram, suspect 1's DNA has the same pattern as the DNA from the crime scene — so suspect 1 was probably at the crime scene.

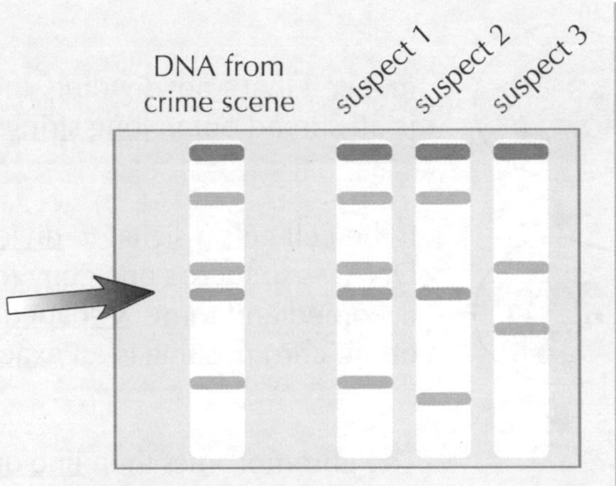

2) Paternity testing — to see if a man is the father of a particular child.

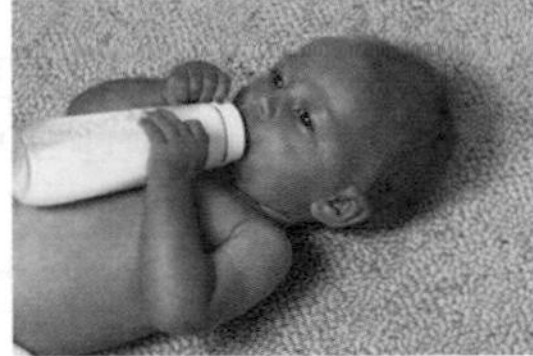

Some people would like there to be a national genetic database of everyone in the country. That way, DNA from a crime scene could be checked against everyone in the country to see whose it was. But others think this is a big invasion of privacy, and they worry about how safe the data would be and what else it might be used for. There are also scientific problems — false positives can occur if errors are made in the procedure or if the data is misinterpreted.

Forensic science is useful, but some people have concerns

In the exam you might have to interpret data on DNA fingerprinting for identification. They'd probably give you a diagram similar to the one that's on this page, and you'd have to say which of the known samples (if any) matched the unknown sample. Pretty easy — it's the two that look the same.

Mitosis

In order to survive and grow, our cells have got to be able to divide. And that means our DNA as well...

Mitosis Makes New Cells for Growth and Repair

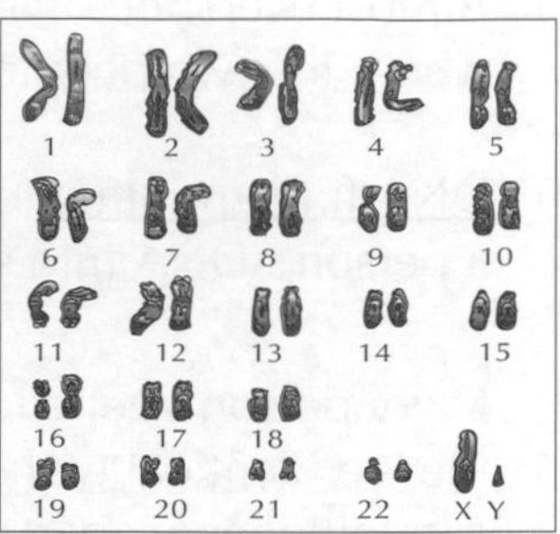

1) Body cells normally have two copies of each chromosome — one from the organism's 'mother', and one from its 'father'. So, humans have two copies of chromosome 1, two copies of chromosome 2, etc.
2) The diagram shows the 23 pairs of chromosomes from a human cell. The 23rd pair are a bit different — see page 119.
3) When a body cell divides it needs to make new cells identical to the original cell — with the same number of chromosomes.
4) This type of cell division is called mitosis. It's used when plants and animals want to grow or to replace cells that have been damaged.

"MITOSIS is when a cell reproduces itself by splitting to form two identical offspring."

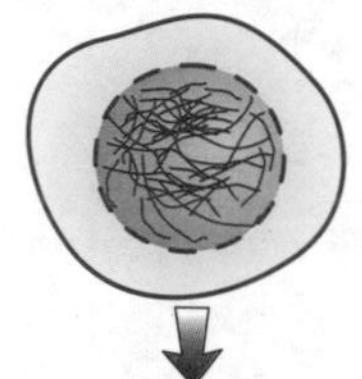

In a cell that's not dividing, the DNA is all spread out in long strings.

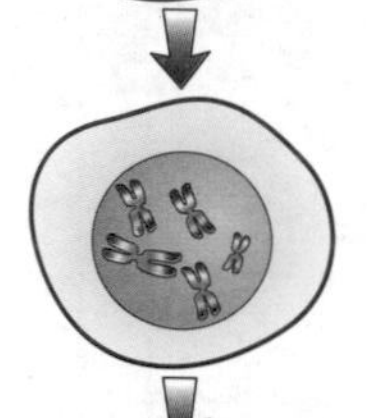

If the cell gets a signal to divide, it needs to duplicate its DNA — so there's one copy for each new cell. The DNA is copied and forms X-shaped chromosomes. Each 'arm' of the chromosome is an exact duplicate of the other.

The left arm of the chromosome has the same DNA as the right arm.

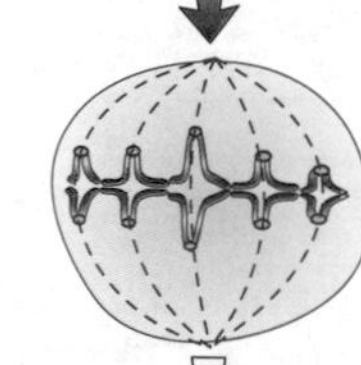

The chromosomes then line up at the centre of the cell and cell fibres pull them apart. The two arms of each chromosome go to opposite ends of the cell.

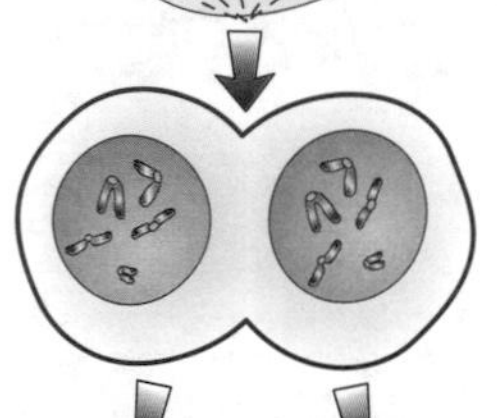

Membranes form around each of the sets of chromosomes. These become the nuclei of the two new cells.

Lastly, the cytoplasm divides.

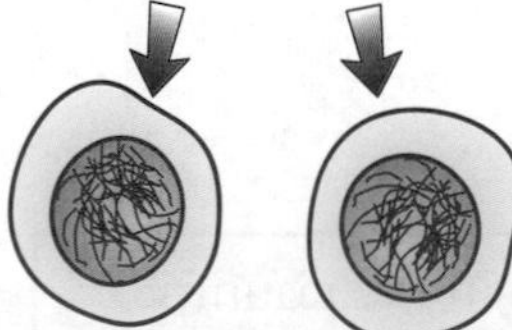

You now have two new cells containing exactly the same DNA — they're identical.

Asexual Reproduction Also Uses Mitosis

1) Some organisms also reproduce by mitosis, e.g. strawberry plants can form runners in this way, which become new plants.
2) This is an example of asexual reproduction.
3) The offspring have exactly the same genes as the parent — so there's no variation.

Mitosis happens in most organisms for growth and repair

This can seem tricky at first. But don't worry — just go through it slowly, one step at a time.

Meiosis

Mitosis produces identical cells, but there's another type of cell division which doesn't — it's called meiosis...

Gametes Have Half the Usual Number of Chromosomes

1) During sexual reproduction, two cells called gametes (sex cells) combine to form a new individual.
2) Gametes only have one copy of each chromosome. This is so that you can combine one sex cell from the 'mother' and one sex cell from the 'father' and still end up with the right number of chromosomes in body cells.
3) For example, human body cells have 46 chromosomes. The gametes have 23 chromosomes each, so that when an egg and sperm combine, you get 46 chromosomes again.

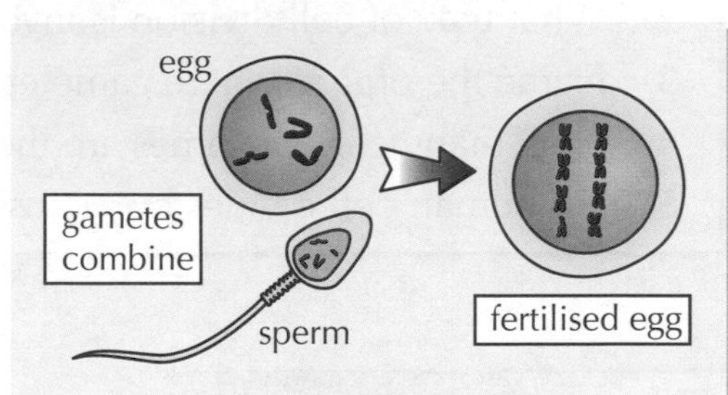

Meiosis Involves Two Divisions

To make new cells which only have half the original number of chromosomes, cells divide by meiosis. In humans it only happens in the reproductive organs (e.g. ovaries and testes).

"MEIOSIS produces cells which have half the normal number of chromosomes."

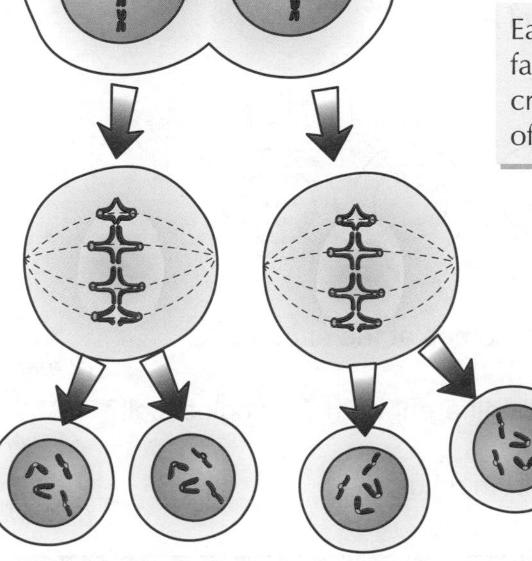

As with mitosis, before the cell starts to divide, it duplicates its DNA — one arm of each chromosome is an exact copy of the other arm.

In the first division in meiosis (there are two divisions) the chromosome pairs line up in the centre of the cell.

The pairs are then pulled apart, so each new cell only has one copy of each chromosome. Some of the father's chromosomes (shown in blue) and some of the mother's chromosomes (shown in red) go into each new cell.

Each new cell will have a mixture of the mother's and father's chromosomes. Mixing up the genes in this way creates variation in the offspring. This is a huge advantage of sexual reproduction over asexual reproduction.

In the second division the chromosomes line up again in the centre of the cell. It's a lot like mitosis. The arms of the chromosomes are pulled apart.

You get four gametes each with only a single set of chromosomes in it.

After two gametes join at fertilisation, the cell grows by repeatedly dividing by mitosis.

Warm-Up and Exam Questions

It's time to see how much you picked up about DNA and cell division, with the help of a few questions...

Warm-Up Questions

1) What does DNA stand for?
2) What type of cell division is involved in the regeneration of body parts?
3) Name the organs where gametes are formed.
4) How many chromosomes are there in a human liver cell?
5) If a human cell divides by meiosis, how many chromosomes do the new cells each have?

Exam Questions

1 Describe how a cell divides to form gametes.

(3 marks)

2 Mr X and Mr Y are both suspects in a burglary. A blood stain has been found on a crowbar at the crime scene. The police carry out a DNA fingerprint on Mr X, Mr Y and the blood from the crime scene.

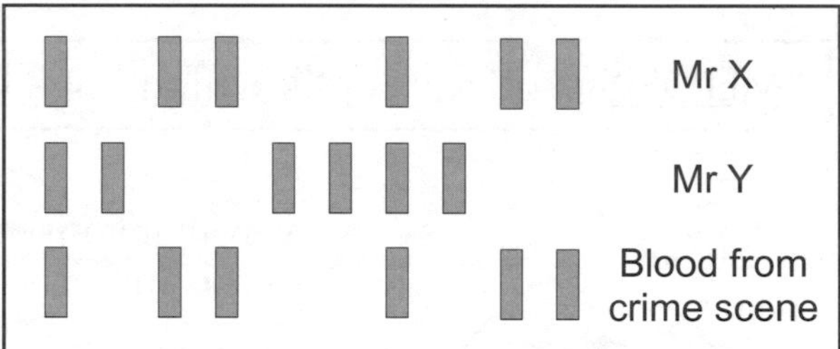

The diagram shows part of the test results.

(a) Do these results suggest that Mr X was at the crime scene? Explain your answer.

(2 marks)

(b) A police officer investigating the burglary says that no two people have exactly the same genetic fingerprint. Is he correct? Explain your answer.

(2 marks)

3 (a) The diagram below shows the chromosomes of a cell that is about to divide by meiosis.

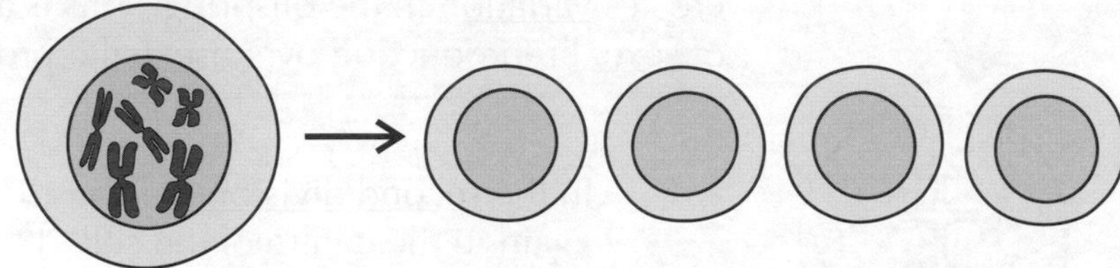

(i) Complete the diagram to show the chromosomes at the end.

(2 marks)

(ii) How is the genetic content of the new cells different from the original cell?

(1 mark)

(b) State three ways in which meiosis is different from mitosis.

(3 marks)

Stem Cells

Stem cell research has exciting possibilities, but it's also pretty controversial.

Embryonic Stem Cells Can Turn into ANY Type of Cell

1) Most cells in your body are specialised for a particular job. E.g. white blood cells are brilliant at fighting invaders but can't carry oxygen, like red blood cells.

2) Differentiation is the process by which a cell changes to become specialised for its job. In most animal cells, the ability to differentiate is lost at an early stage, but lots of plant cells don't ever lose this ability.

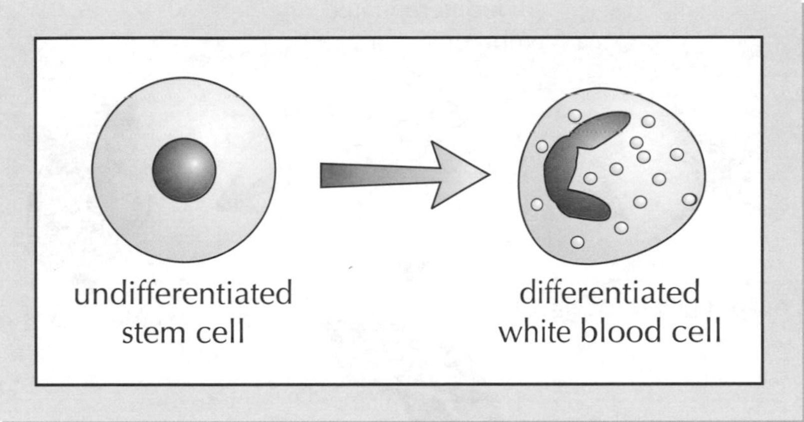

3) Some cells are undifferentiated. They can develop into different types of cell depending on what instructions they're given. These cells are called stem cells.

4) Stem cells are found in early human embryos. This makes sense if you think about it — all the different types of cell found in a human being have to come from those few cells in the early embryo.

5) These cells are exciting to doctors and medical researchers because they have the potential to turn into any kind of cell at all. This could be really useful in the treatment of all kinds of injuries and diseases (see next page).

6) Adults also have stem cells, but they're only found in certain places, like bone marrow. These aren't as versatile as embryonic stem cells — they can't turn into any cell type at all, only certain ones.

Stem Cells

Stem Cells May Be Able to **Cure** Many **Diseases**

1) Medicine already uses adult stem cells to cure disease. For example, people with some blood diseases (e.g. sickle cell anaemia) can be treated by bone marrow transplants. Bone marrow contains stem cells that can turn into new blood cells to replace the faulty old ones.
2) Scientists can also extract stem cells from very early human embryos and grow them.
3) These embryonic stem cells could be used to replace faulty cells in sick people — you could make beating heart muscle cells for people with heart disease, insulin-producing cells for people with diabetes, nerve cells for people paralysed by spinal injuries, and so on.
4) To get cultures of one specific type of cell, researchers try to control the differentiation of the stem cells by changing the environment they're growing in. So far, it's still a bit hit and miss — lots more research is needed.

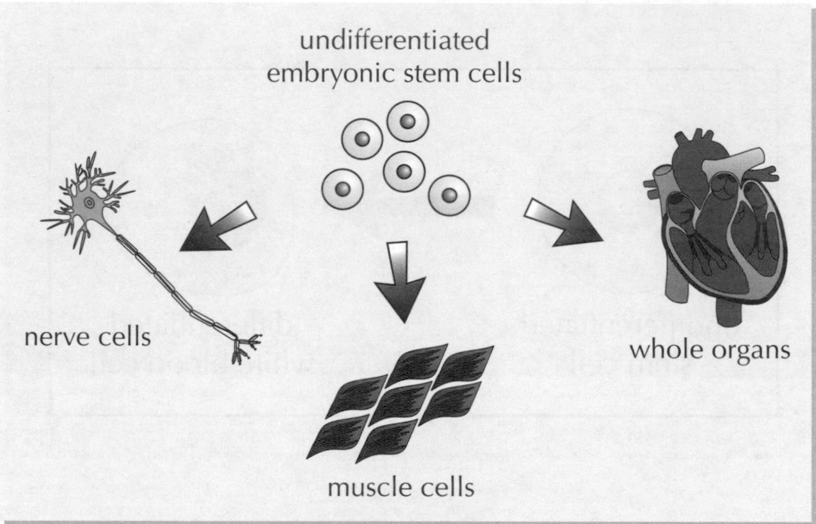

Some People Are **Against Stem Cell Research**

1) Some people are against stem cell research because they feel that human embryos shouldn't be used for experiments since each one is a potential human life.
2) Others think that curing patients who already exist and who are suffering is more important than the rights of embryos.
3) One fairly convincing argument in favour of this point of view is that the embryos used in the research are usually unwanted ones from fertility clinics which, if they weren't used for research, would probably just be destroyed. But of course, campaigners for the rights of embryos usually want this banned too.
4) These campaigners feel that scientists should concentrate more on finding and developing other sources of stem cells, so people could be helped without having to use embryos.
5) In some countries stem cell research is banned, but it's allowed in the UK as long as it follows strict guidelines.

Alternative sources of stem cells would avoid the controversy

The potential of stem cells is huge — but it's early days yet. Research has recently been done into getting stem cells from alternative sources. For example, umbilical cords may be one possible source.

X and Y Chromosomes

Now for a couple of very important little chromosomes...

*Your **Chromosomes** Control Whether You're **Male** or **Female***

1) There are 23 matched pairs of chromosomes in every human body cell.
2) The 23rd pair are labelled XX or XY.
3) They're the two chromosomes that decide whether you turn out male or female.

All men have an X and a Y chromosome: XY
The Y chromosome causes male characteristics.

All women have two X chromosomes: XX
The XX combination allows female characteristics to develop.

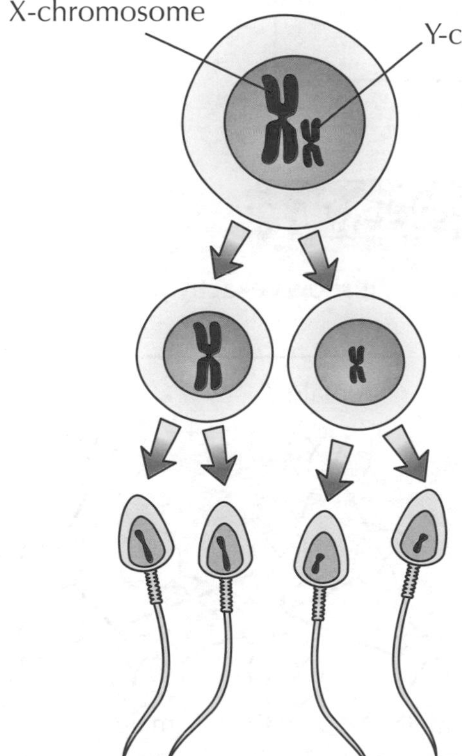

When making sperm, the X and Y chromosomes are drawn apart in the first division in meiosis. There's a 50% chance each sperm cell gets an X chromosome and a 50% chance it gets a Y chromosome.

A similar thing happens when making eggs. But the original cell has two X chromosomes, so all the eggs have one X chromosome.

The Y chromosome is physically smaller than the X chromosome

It's possible for people to have one X and two Y chromosomes, or even three X chromosomes, in their cells. But you don't really need to know this — just remember that it's XX for girls and XY for boys.

X and Y Chromosomes

You can work out the probability of offspring being male or female by using a genetic diagram. There are loads more examples of genetic diagrams on pages 123, 126 and 127.

Genetic Diagrams Show the Possible Combinations of Gametes

1) To find the probability of getting a boy or a girl, you can draw a genetic diagram.
2) Put the possible gametes from one parent down the side, and those from the other parent along the top.
3) Then in each middle square you fill in the letters from the top and side that line up with that square. The pairs of letters in the middle show the possible combinations of the gametes.
4) There are two XX results and two XY results, so there's the same probability of getting a boy or a girl.
5) Don't forget that this 50:50 ratio is only a probability — if you had four kids they could all be boys.

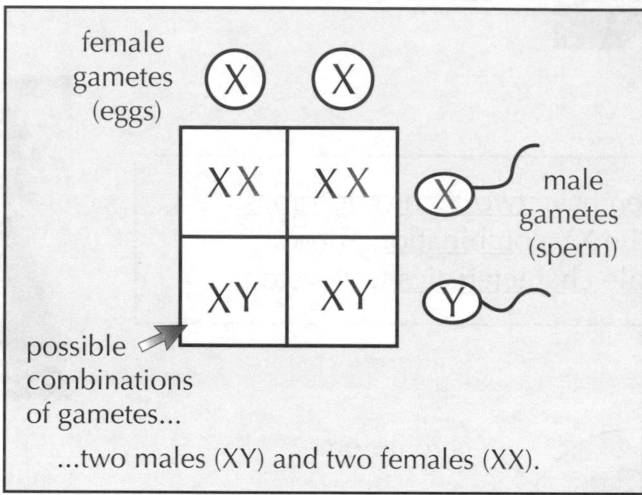

There's More Than One Type of Genetic Diagram

The other type of genetic diagram looks a bit more complicated, but it shows exactly the same thing.

1) At the top are the parents.
2) The middle circles show the possible gametes that are formed. One gamete from the female combines with one gamete from the male (during fertilisation).
3) The criss-cross lines show all the possible ways the X and Y chromosomes could combine.
4) The possible combinations of the offspring are shown in the bottom circles.
5) Remember, only one of these possibilities would actually happen for any one offspring.

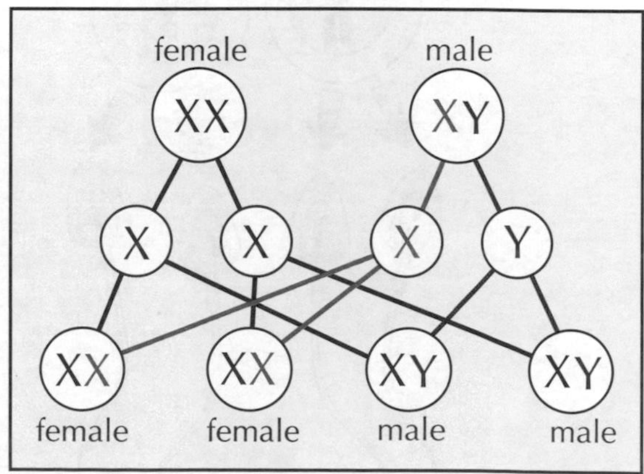

There's always 50% chance of having a boy or a girl

Most genetic diagrams you'll see in exams concentrate on a gene instead of an entire chromosome.

Warm-Up and Exam Questions

There's only one way to do well in the exam — learn the facts and then practise lots of exam questions to see what it'll be like on the big day. We couldn't have made it easier for you — so do it.

Warm-Up Questions

1) Give an example of a specialised cell.
2) What does cell 'differentiation' mean?
3) Give two examples of diseases that could be treated with embryonic stem cells.
4) What combination of X and Y chromosomes does: a) a male have? b) a female have?

Exam Questions

1 Read the passage below about stem cell research.

> Stem cell research has been widely debated over the past few years. Adult stem cells have already been used to cure disorders, and it is thought that embryonic stem cells have the potential to treat many more disorders.
>
> One of the most controversial issues surrounds the technique used to create embryonic stem cells. Current legislation in the UK means that production of stem cells by human reproductive cloning is illegal. Research can only be carried out on embryos produced in the laboratory and surplus embryos created for use in *in vitro* fertilisation (IVF).

(a) What are stem cells?

(2 marks)

(b) Describe how stem cells could be used to treat disorders.

(1 mark)

(c) Explain why embryonic stem cells have the potential to treat more disorders than adult stem cells.

(1 mark)

(d) Give one place where adult stem cells are found in the body.

(1 mark)

(e) Some people are opposed to the use of stem cells in medical research and want the government to ban their use. Give one argument for and one argument against embryonic stem cell research.

(2 marks)

2 Which of the following statements is **true**?

A Men have two X chromosomes. Women have an X and a Y chromosome.
B There is a 75% chance that a couple's first child will be a girl.
C Sperm cells (male gametes) can carry an X or a Y chromosome.
D If you have 4 children, you will always get 2 boys and 2 girls.

(1 mark)

The Work of Mendel

Mendel Did Genetic Experiments with Pea Plants

Gregor Mendel was an Austrian monk who trained in mathematics and natural history at the University of Vienna. On his garden plot at the monastery, Mendel noted how characteristics in plants were passed on from one generation to the next.

The results of his research were published in 1866 and eventually became the foundation of modern genetics.

The diagrams show two crosses for height in pea plants that Mendel carried out...

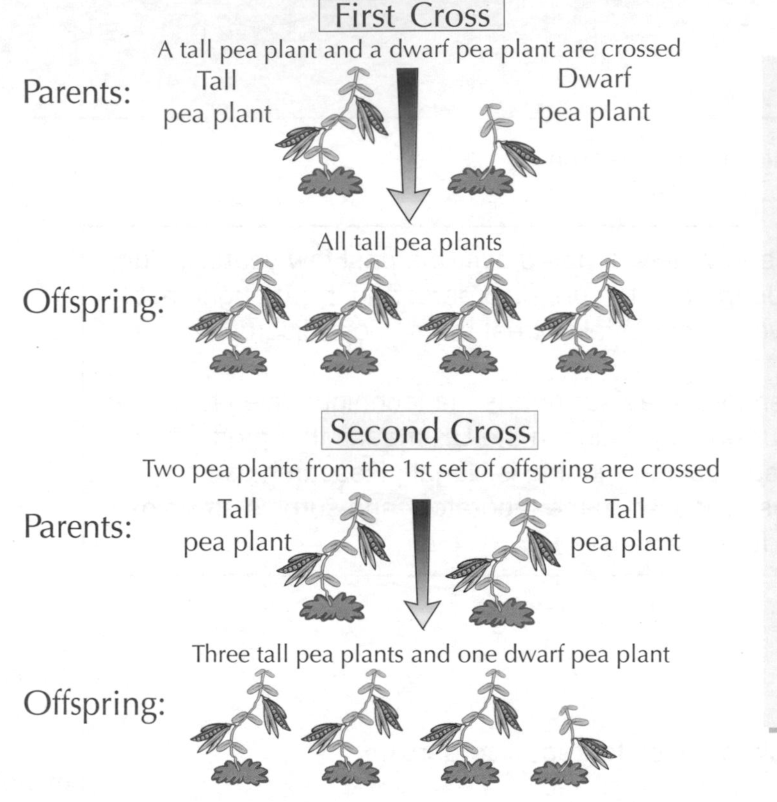

...explained nicely by a genetic diagram (see pages 123, 126 and 127):

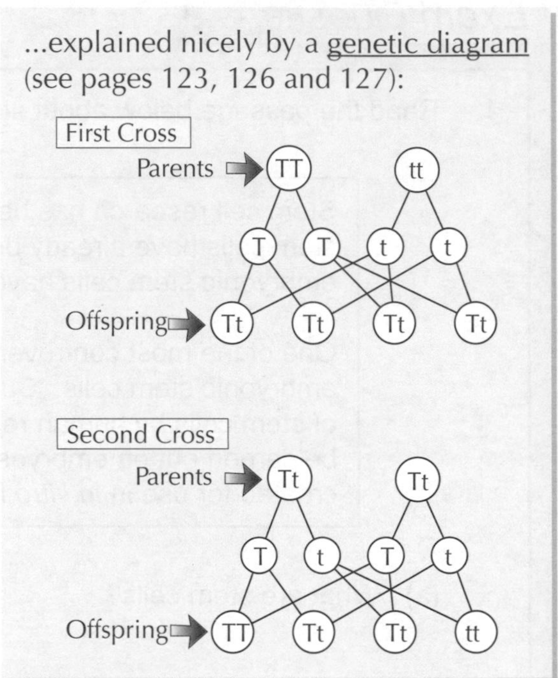

Mendel had shown that the height characteristic in pea plants was determined by separately inherited "hereditary units" passed on from each parent. The ratios of tall and dwarf plants in the offspring showed that the unit for tall plants, T, was dominant over the unit for dwarf plants, t.

Mendel Reached Three Important Conclusions

Mendel reached these three important conclusions about heredity in plants:

1) Characteristics in plants are determined by "hereditary units".
2) Hereditary units are passed on from both parents, one unit from each parent.
3) Hereditary units can be dominant or recessive — if an individual has both the dominant and the recessive unit for a characteristic, the dominant characteristic will be expressed.

We now know that the "hereditary units" are of course genes.
But in Mendel's time nobody knew anything about genes or DNA, and so the significance of his work was not to be realised until after his death.

Genetic Diagrams

When a single gene controls the inheritance of a characteristic, you can work out the odds of getting it...

Genetic Diagrams Show the Possible Genes of Offspring

1) Alleles are different versions of the same gene.
2) Most of the time you have two copies of each gene — one from each parent.
3) If they're different alleles, only one might be 'expressed' in the organism. The characteristic that appears is coded for by the dominant allele. The other one is recessive.
4) In genetic diagrams letters are used to represent genes. Dominant alleles are always shown with a capital letter, and recessive alleles with a small letter.

You Need to be Able to Interpret, Explain and Construct Them

Imagine you're cross-breeding hamsters, some with normal hair and a mild disposition and others with wild scratty hair and a leaning towards crazy acrobatics.

We'll use the letter 'B' (for boring) to represent the gene — always choose a letter whose capital looks different from the lower case one, so the examiners know exactly which one you're writing.

Let's say that the allele which causes the crazy nature is recessive, so we use a small "b" for it, whilst normal (boring) behaviour is due to a dominant allele, so we represent it with a capital "B".

1) For an organism to display a recessive characteristic, both its alleles must be recessive — so a crazy hamster must have the alleles 'bb'.
2) However, a normal hamster can have two possible combinations of alleles, BB or Bb, because the dominant allele overrules the recessive one.

Let's cross a thoroughbred crazy hamster, genetic type bb, with a thoroughbred normal hamster, BB:

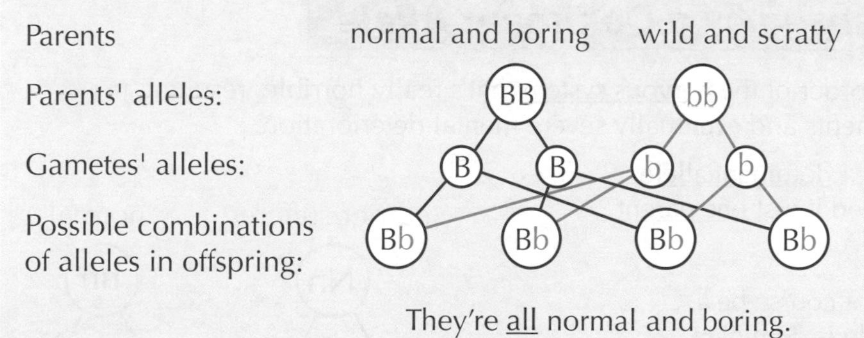

Remember, these results are only probabilities.

If two of these offspring now breed they will produce a new combination of kids:

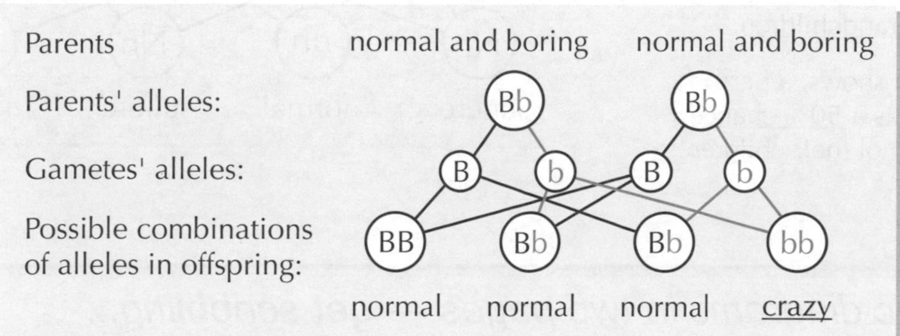

Genetic Disorders

Defective genes can cause serious problems — you need to know about two of them.

Cystic Fibrosis is Caused by a Recessive Allele

Cystic fibrosis is a genetic disorder of the cell membranes. It results in the body producing a lot of thick sticky mucus in the air passages and in the pancreas.

1) The allele which causes cystic fibrosis is a recessive allele, 'f', carried by about 1 person in 30.
2) Because it's recessive, people with only one copy of the allele won't have the disorder — they're known as carriers.
3) For a child to have the disorder, both parents must be either carriers or sufferers.
4) As the diagram shows there's a 1 in 4 chance of a child having the disease if both parents are carriers.

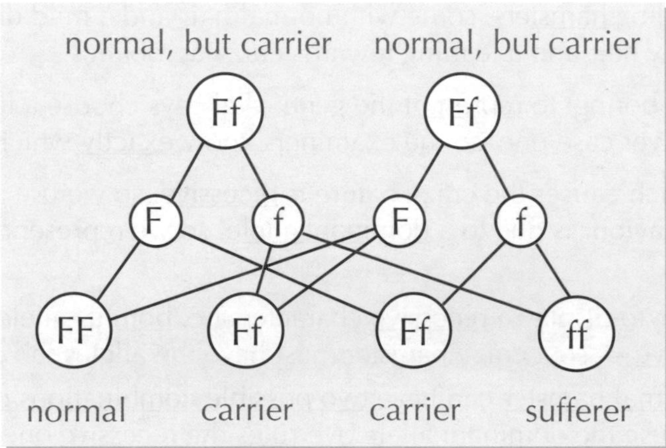

Huntington's is Caused by a Dominant Allele

Huntington's is a genetic disorder of the nervous system that's really horrible, resulting in shaking, erratic body movements and eventually severe mental deterioration.

1) The disorder is caused by a dominant allele, 'N', and so can be inherited if just one parent carries the defective gene.
2) The "carrier" parent will of course be a sufferer too since the allele is dominant, but the symptoms don't start to appear until after the person is about 40. By this time the allele might already have been passed on to children and even to grandchildren.
3) As the genetic diagram shows, a person carrying the N allele has a 50% chance of passing it on to each of their children.

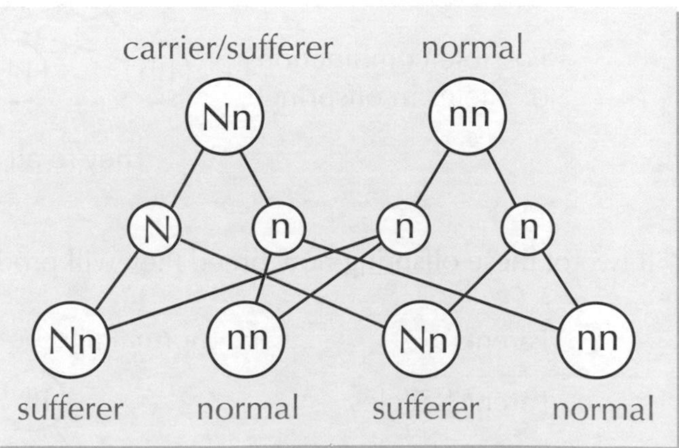

That's four genetic diagrams in two pages — get scribbling...

Genetic diagrams look pretty confusing at first, but they're really not. The important thing to get clear in your head is whether the characteristic is caused by a dominant or recessive allele.

Screening for Genetic Disorders

In vitro fertilisation (IVF) is quite widely used now by people who have problems conceiving naturally. Part of the process involves screening for genetic disorders, but some people are unhappy about this.

Embryos Can Be Screened for Genetic Disorders

1) During IVF, embryos are fertilised in a laboratory, and then implanted into the mother's womb. More than one egg is fertilised, so there's a better chance of the IVF being successful.
2) Before being implanted, it's possible to remove a cell from each embryo and analyse its genes.
3) Many genetic disorders could be detected in this way, such as cystic fibrosis and Huntington's.
4) Embryos with 'good' genes would be implanted into the mother — the ones with 'bad' genes destroyed.

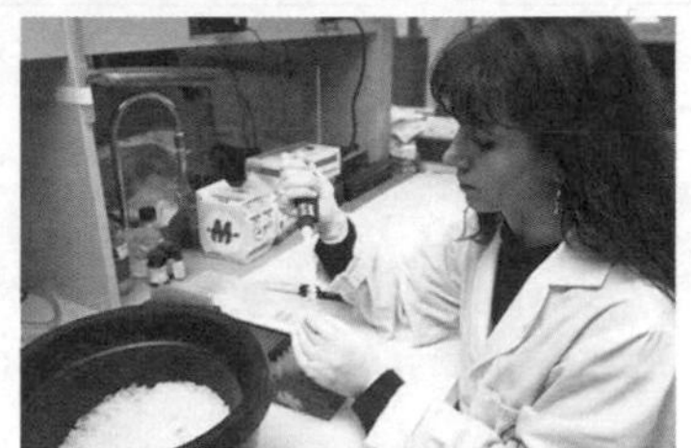

There is a huge debate raging about embryonic screening.
Here are some arguments for and against it:

Against Embryonic Screening

1) There may come a point where everyone wants to screen their embryos so they can pick the most 'desirable' one, e.g. they want a blue eyed, blonde haired, intelligent boy.
2) The rejected embryos are destroyed — they could have developed into humans.
3) It implies that people with genetic problems are 'undesirable' — this could increase prejudice.

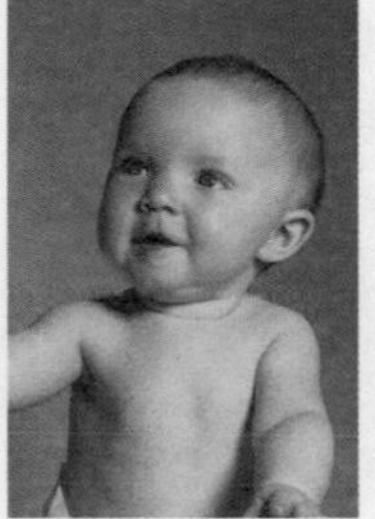

For Embryonic Screening

1) It will help to stop people suffering.
2) There are laws to stop it going too far. At the moment parents cannot even select the sex of their baby (unless it's for health reasons).
3) During IVF, most of the embryos are destroyed anyway — screening just allows the selected one to be healthy.
4) Treating disorders costs the Government (and the taxpayers) a lot of money.

Embryonic screening — it's a tricky one...

There's a nice moral argument for you to consider on this page. In the exam you may be asked your opinion — make sure you can back it up with good reasons, and consider other points of view.

More Genetic Diagrams

In the exam they could ask about the inheritance of any kind of characteristic that's controlled by a single gene, because the principle's always the same. So here's a bit more on genetic diagrams...

You Should be able to Predict and Explain the Outcomes of Crosses

If you've got your head round all this genetics lark you should be able to draw a genetic diagram and work out the outcomes of crosses between individuals for each possible combination of dominant and recessive alleles of a gene — but it'll make it easier if you've seen them all before. So here are some examples for you:

All the Offspring are *Normal*

Let's take another look at the crazy hamster example:

The crazy hamsters were introduced back on page 123.

In this cross, a hamster with two dominant alleles (BB) is crossed with a hamster with two recessive alleles (bb). All the offspring are normal and boring.

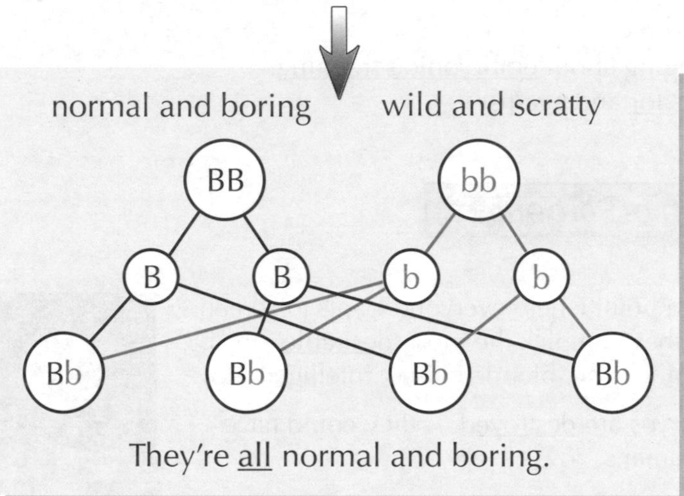

But, if you crossed a hamster with two dominant alleles (BB) with a hamster with a dominant and a recessive allele (Bb), you would also get all normal and boring offspring.

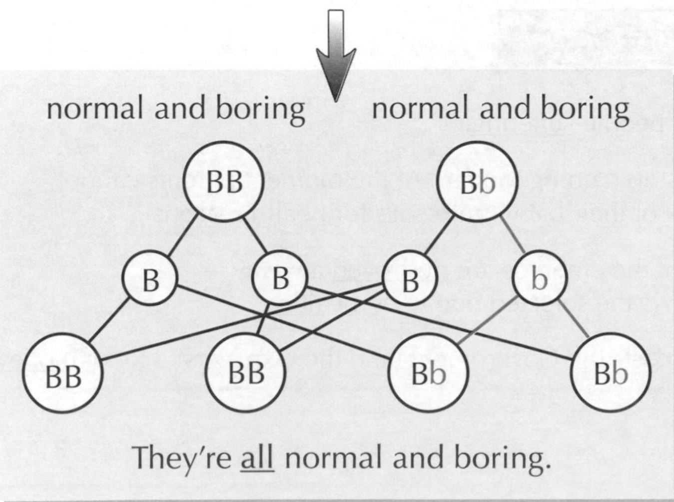

To find out which it was you'd have to breed the offspring together and see what kind of ratio you got that time — then you'd have a good idea. If it was 3:1, it's likely that you originally had BB and bb.

More Genetic Diagrams

There's a 3:1 Ratio in the Offspring

1) Sickle cell anaemia is a genetic disorder characterised by funny-shaped red blood cells.
2) It's caused by a recessive allele 'a' (for anaemia). The normal allele is represented by an 'A'.

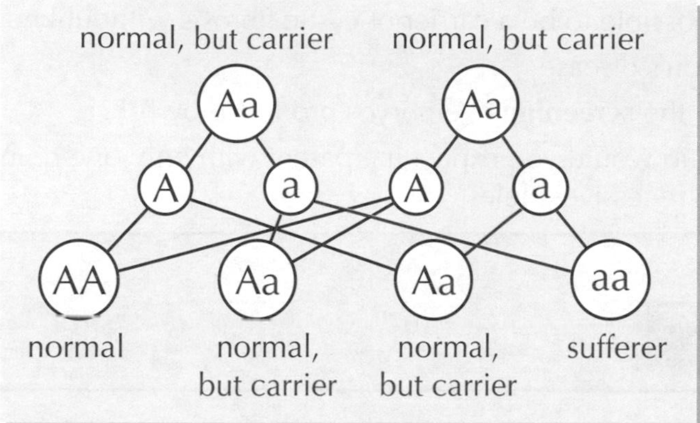

3) If two people who carry the sickle cell anaemia allele have children, the probability of each child suffering from the disorder is 1 in 4 — 25%.
4) The ratio you'd expect in the children is 3:1, non-sufferer:sufferer.
5) If you see this ratio in the offspring you know both parents must have the two different alleles.
6) Be careful with this one — it may be disguised as a 1:2:1 ratio (normal:carrier:sufferer), but it means the same thing.

There's a 1:1 Ratio in the Offspring

1) A cat with long hair was bred with another cat with short hair.
2) The long hair is caused by a dominant allele 'H', and the short hair by a recessive allele 'h'.

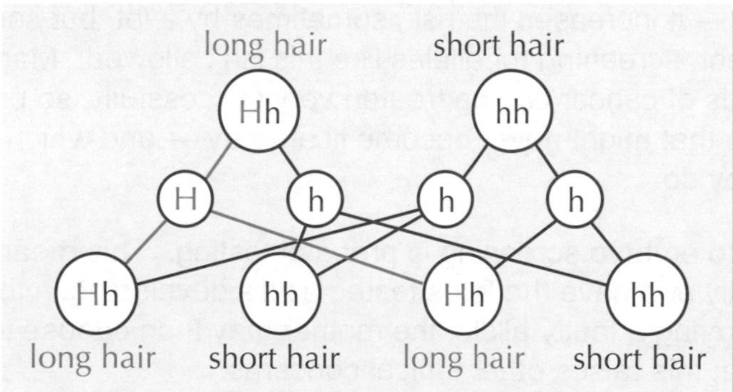

3) They had 8 kittens — 4 with long hair and 4 with short hair.
4) This is a 1:1 ratio — it's what you'd expect when a parent with only one dominant allele (Hh) is crossed with a parent with two recessive alleles (hh).

It's enough to make you go cross-eyed...

Remember that these are only probabilities, so you need loads of organisms in each generation to see a reliable ratio. That's why people tend to do genetic experiments with quick-breeding organisms like fruit flies. And of course it still won't be an exact ratio (just because of normal chance) — you might get 69 normal fruit flies and 31 crazy fruit flies out of 100. Not exact, but close enough to a 3:1 ratio.

Warm-Up and Exam Questions

There's no better preparation for exam questions than doing... err... practice exam questions. Hang on, what's this I see...

Warm-Up Questions

1) What are alleles?
2) Explain how it's possible to be a carrier of cystic fibrosis without knowing.
3) What is Huntington's disease?
4) What is meant by the **screening** of embryos produced by IVF?
5) What offspring ratio would you expect if a parent with only one dominant allele is crossed with a parent with two recessive alleles?

Exam Questions

1 Read this passage about embryo screening.

> Embryo screening already happens in the UK for genetic disorders like Huntington's disease. A genetic test can be done during IVF treatment — so that doctors can select a healthy embryo to implant in the mother. The other embryos are discarded.
>
> At the moment, regulations say that embryo screening is only allowed when there is "a significant risk of a serious genetic condition being present in the embryo." In other words, when the person carrying the faulty allele is certain (or almost certain) to get the disorder, and the disorder is serious. So screening for short-sightedness wouldn't be allowed, even if we knew that people with a faulty allele would definitely become short-sighted.
>
> Medical technology has made it possible to test for several genes that are linked to very serious illnesses, e.g. cancers. But, in many cases, the faulty allele isn't certain to cause cancer — it increases the risk, sometimes by a lot, but sometimes just slightly. So, at the moment, screening for alleles like this isn't allowed. Many people say this is right. Some kinds of cancer can be treated very successfully, so perhaps it's wrong to destroy embryos that might never become ill anyway — and which have a good chance of recovery if they do.
>
> One alternative to embryo screening is prenatal testing. This means that the parents conceive naturally and have the fetus tested as it's developing in the mother's womb. If the baby is carrying a faulty allele, the mother may then choose to have an abortion. For some people, this raises other ethical concerns.

(a) Could embryos be screened for colour-blindness under the current regulations? Explain your answer.

(2 marks)

(b) Cancer is a serious illness that kills thousands of people each year in the UK. Why is cancer not included in embryo screening?

(3 marks)

(c) Describe an alternative to embryo screening.

(2 marks)

Exam Questions

2 In one of Gregor Mendel's experiments, he crossed thoroughbred purple-flowered pea plants with thoroughbred white-flowered plants. The first generation of offspring were all purple-flowered.

(a) In Mendel's experiment, which characteristic is recessive?

(1 mark)

(b) Using the symbols F and f to represent the alleles for purple and white, write down the combination of alleles (genetic make-up) of each of the following:

(i) the original purple-flowered parent plant

(1 mark)

(ii) the original white-flowered parent plant

(1 mark)

(iii) the first generation of purple-flowered offspring

(1 mark)

3 Cystic fibrosis is a disease caused by recessive alleles.

F = the normal allele
f = the faulty allele that leads to cystic fibrosis

The genetic diagram below shows the possible inheritance of cystic fibrosis from one couple.

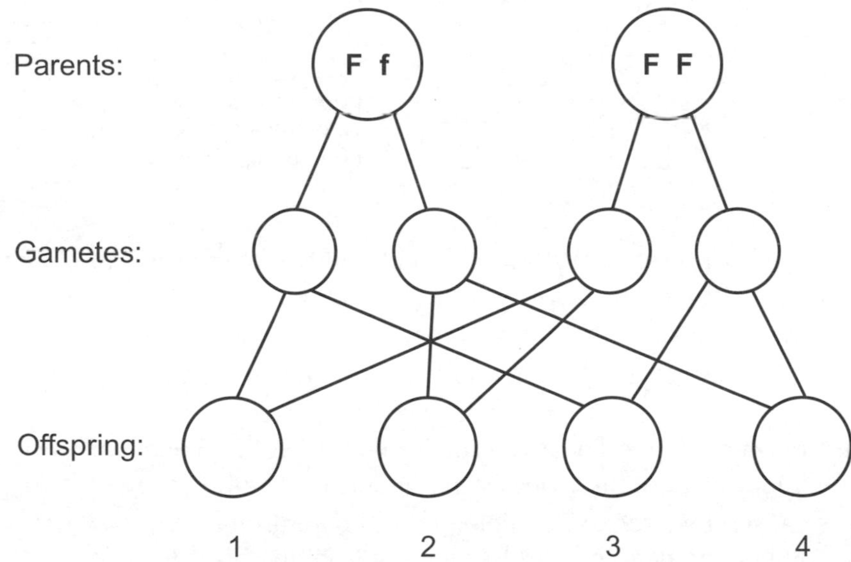

(a) Complete the genetic diagram.

(2 marks)

(b) Which of the possible offspring will be sufferers and which will be unaffected?

(1 mark)

(c) (i) What proportion of the possible offspring are homozygous (have two identical alleles)?

(1 mark)

(ii) Which of the possible offspring are carriers of the disease?

(1 mark)

Revision Summary for Biology 2(iii)

This section contains loads of new stuff all about genetics — it's even got a couple of moral dilemmas for you to ponder over. Your DNA contains all the instructions needed to make you. But your DNA can only account for so much, whether you can roll your tongue for example. You can't blame it for what colour you decide to dye your hair...

Use these questions to find out what you know about it all — and what you don't. Then look back and learn the bits you don't know. Then try the questions again, and again...

1) What is a gene?
2) Explain how DNA controls the activities of a cell.
3) Explain how DNA fingerprinting is used in forensic science.
4) Some people would like there to be a genetic database of everyone in the country. Discuss the advantages and disadvantages of such a database for use in forensic science.
5) Describe the four steps in mitosis.
6) Name the other type of cell division, and say where it happens in the body of a human male.
7) Explain why sexual reproduction produces more variation than asexual reproduction.
8) What type of cell division does a fertilised egg use to grow into a new organism?
9) Describe one way that adult stem cells are currently used to cure diseases.
10) Which chromosome in the human body causes male characteristics?
11) Copy and complete the diagrams below to show what happens to the X and Y chromosomes during reproduction.

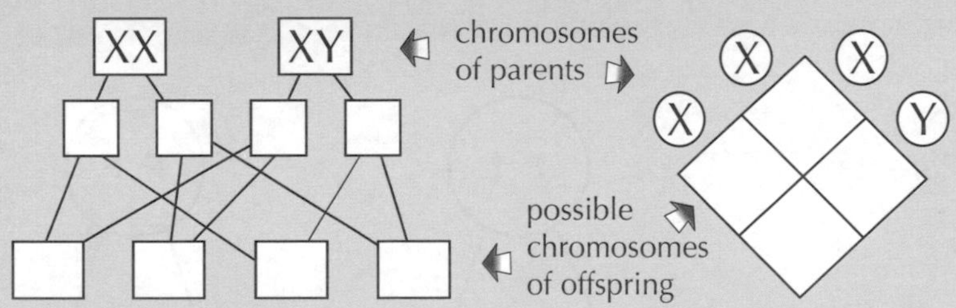

12)*A couple have three boys already. What is the probability that their fourth child will be a girl? (Hint: this may be a nasty trick question — don't be fooled.)
13) List three important conclusions that Mendel reached following his experiments with pea plants.
14) What were the "hereditary units" that Mendel concluded were controlling the characteristics of his pea plants?
15) The significance of Mendel's work was not realised until 1900, 16 years after Mendel died. Suggest why the importance of the work wasn't understood at the time.
16) Cystic fibrosis is caused by a recessive allele. If both parents are carriers, what is the probability of their child: a) being a carrier, b) suffering from the disorder?
17) Is Huntington's disease caused by a dominant or recessive allele?
18) During in vitro fertilisation, it is possible to screen embryos for various genetic disorders before they're implanted into the mother. Only the "good" embryos would be chosen for implantation. Summarise the main arguments for and against embryonic screening.
19)*Blue colour in a plant is carried on a recessive allele, b. The dominant allele, B, gives white flowers. In the first generation after a cross, all the flowers are white. These are bred together and the result is a ratio of 54 white : 19 blue. What were the alleles of the flowers used in the first cross?

* Answers on page 228

Gas and Solute Exchange

The processes that keep organisms alive won't happen without the right raw materials. And the raw materials have to get to the right places. It's like making chicken soup. You need the chicken in your kitchen. It's no good if it's still at the supermarket.

Substances Move by **Diffusion**, **Osmosis** and **Active Transport**

1) Life processes need gases or other dissolved substances before they can happen.

2) For example, for photosynthesis to happen, carbon dioxide and water have to get into plant cells. And for respiration to take place, glucose and oxygen both have to get inside cells.

3) Waste substances also need to move out of the cells so that the organism can get rid of them.

4) These substances move to where they need to be by diffusion, osmosis and active transport.

5) Diffusion is where particles move from an area of high concentration to an area of low concentration. For example, different gases can simply diffuse through one another, like when a weird smell spreads out through a room. Alternatively, dissolved particles can diffuse in and out of cells through cell membranes — see page 72.

6) Osmosis is similar, but it only refers to water. The water moves across a partially permeable membranc (c.g. a cell membrane) from an area of high water concentration to an area of low water concentration — see page 73.

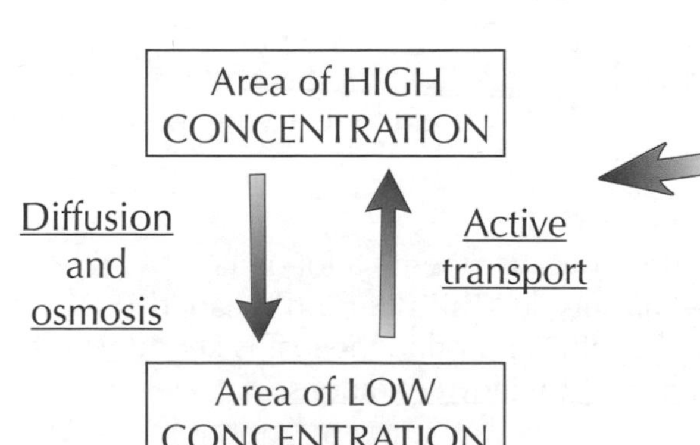

7) Diffusion and osmosis both involve stuff moving from an area where there's a high concentration of it, to an area where there's a lower concentration of it. Sometimes substances need to move in the other direction — which is where active transport comes in — see page 135.

8) In life processes, the gases and dissolved substances have to move through some sort of exchange surface. The exchange surface structures have to allow enough of the necessary substances to pass through.

Exchange surfaces are adapted to maximise effectiveness.

Gas and Solute Exchange

The *Structure of Leaves* Lets Gases *Diffuse* In and Out of Cells

Carbon dioxide diffuses into the air spaces within the leaf, then it diffuses into the cells where photosynthesis happens. The leaf's structure is adapted so that this can happen easily:

1) The underneath of the leaf is an exchange surface. It's covered in little holes called stomata which the carbon dioxide diffuses in through.

2) Water vapour and oxygen also diffuse out through the stomata. (Water vapour is actually lost from all over the leaf surface, but most of it is lost through the stomata.)

3) The size of the stomata are controlled by guard cells — see page 70. These close the stomata if the plant is losing water faster than it is being replaced by the roots. Without these guard cells the plant would soon wilt.

4) The flattened shape of the leaf increases the area of this exchange surface so that it's more effective.

5) The walls of the cells inside the leaf form another exchange surface. The air spaces inside the leaf increase the area of this surface so there's more chance for carbon dioxide to get into the cells.

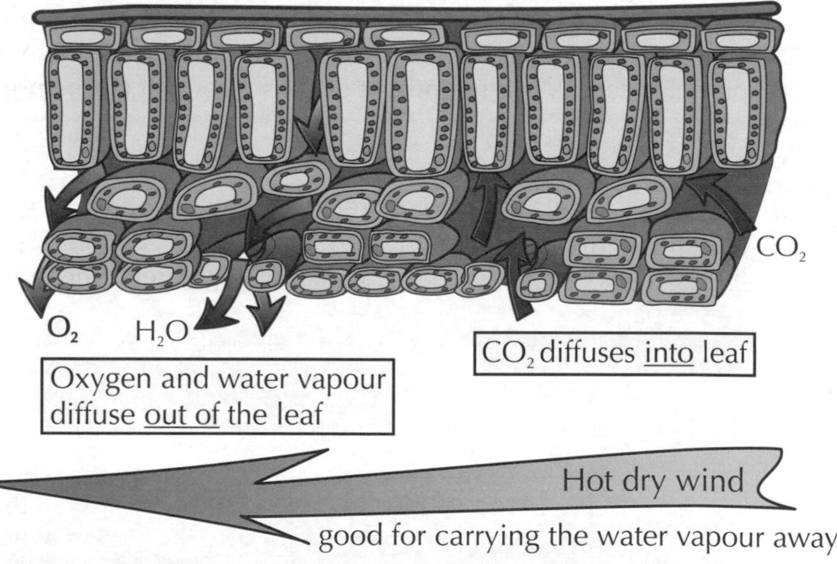

The water vapour escapes by diffusion because there's a lot of it inside the leaf and less of it in the air outside. This diffusion is called transpiration and it goes quicker when the air around the leaf is kept dry — i.e. transpiration is quickest in hot, dry, windy conditions.

Interesting fact — stomata is the plural of stoma...

The cells on the stem of a cactus photosynthesise and have stomata-like holes to let gases in. The cacti don't want to lose much water, so the holes only open at night when it's cooler. The cacti are adapted so that they can store the CO_2 that diffuses in at night until daylight when it's used for photosynthesis.

The Respiratory System

You need to get oxygen from the air into your bloodstream so that it can get to your cells for respiration. You also need to get rid of carbon dioxide in your blood. This all happens inside the lungs. Breathing is how the air gets in and out of your lungs, so it's definitely a useful skill to have.

The Lungs Are in the **Thorax**

1) The thorax is the top part of your 'body'.
2) It's separated from the lower part of the body by the diaphragm.
3) The lungs are like big pink sponges and are protected by the ribcage.
4) The air that you breathe in goes through the trachea. This splits into two tubes called 'bronchi' (each one is 'a bronchus'), one going to each lung.
5) The bronchi split into progressively smaller tubes called bronchioles.
6) The bronchioles finally end at small bags called alveoli where the gas exchange takes place.

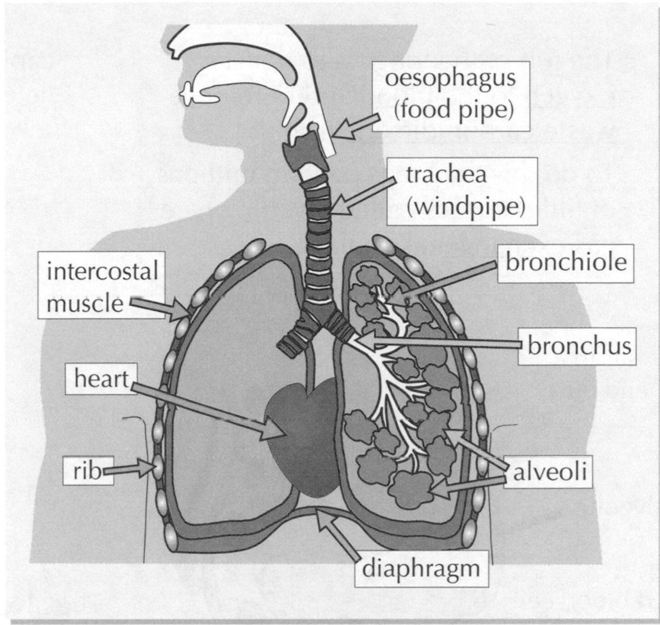

*Breathing **In**...*

1) Intercostal muscles and diaphragm contract.
2) Thorax volume increases.
3) This decreases the pressure, drawing air in.

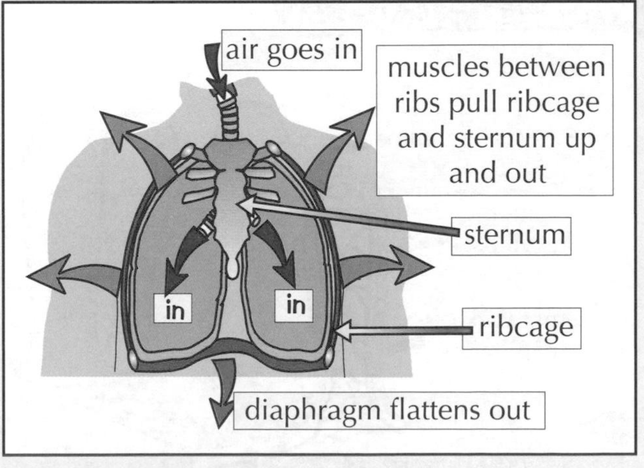

*...and Breathing **Out***

1) Intercostal muscles and diaphragm relax.
2) Thorax volume decreases.
3) Air is forced out.

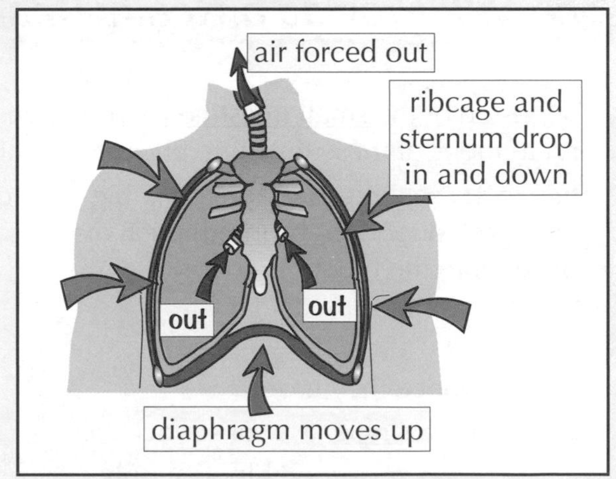

Remember — breathing in and out is different from respiration

When you breathe in, you don't suck the air in. You make the space in your lungs bigger and air rushes in to fill it. The small bags called alveoli at the ends of the air passages are the interesting bit — it's here that oxygen gets into the blood supply and waste carbon dioxide gets out of the blood supply.

Diffusion Through Cell Membranes

This page is about how two different parts of the human body are adapted so that substances can diffuse through them most effectively. The first bit is about how gases in the lungs get into and out of the blood. The second is about how digested food gets from the gut to the blood.

Gas Exchange Happens in the Lungs

The job of the lungs is to transfer oxygen to the blood and to remove waste carbon dioxide from it.

To do this the lungs contain millions of little air sacs called alveoli where gas exchange takes place.

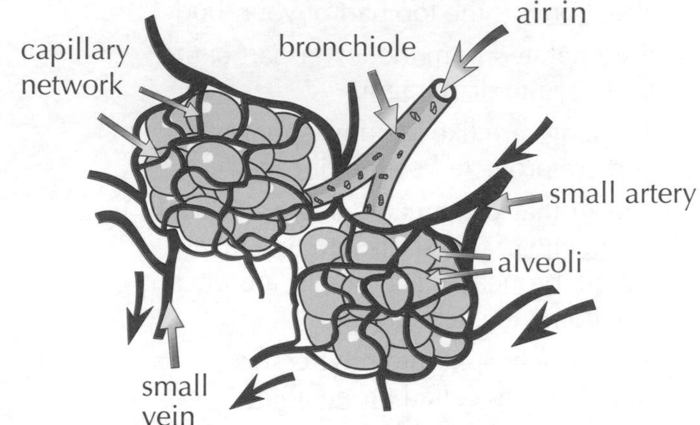

Blue = blood with carbon dioxide.

Red = blood with oxygen.

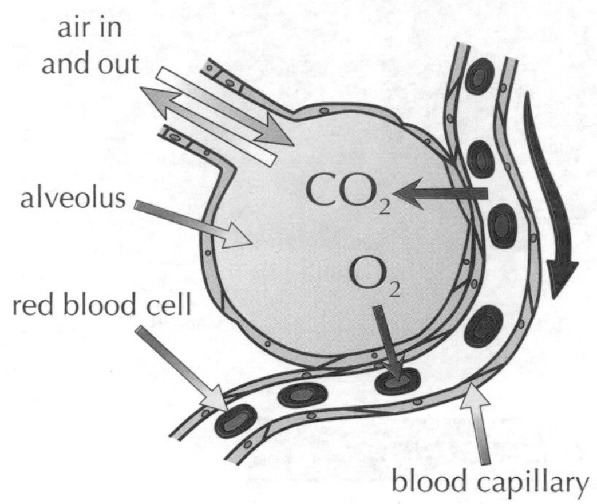

The alveoli are specialised to maximise the diffusion of oxygen and CO_2. They have:

- An enormous surface area (about 75 m^2 in humans).
- A moist lining for dissolving gases.
- Very thin walls.
- A copious blood supply.

The Villi Provide a Really Really Big Surface Area

The inside of the small intestine is covered in millions and millions of these tiny little projections called villi. They increase the surface area in a big way so that digested food is absorbed much more quickly into the blood.

Notice they have:

- a single layer of surface cells
- a very good blood supply to assist quick absorption.

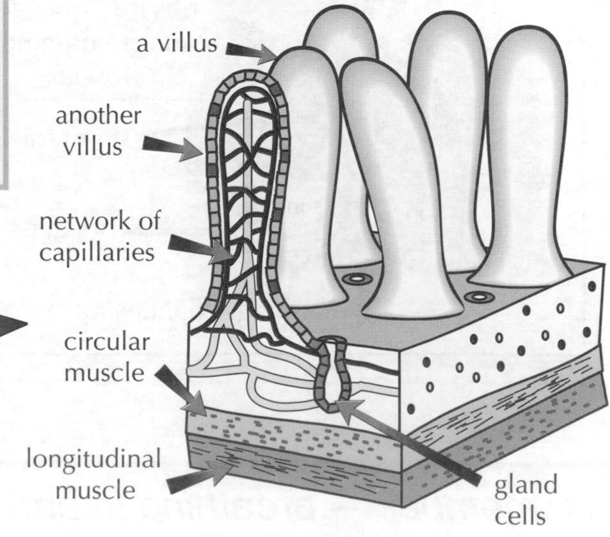

The digested food moves into the blood by diffusion and by active transport (see page 135).

Active Transport

Sometimes substances need to be absorbed against a concentration gradient, i.e. from a lower to a higher concentration. This process is referred to as active transport.

Root Hairs are Specialised for Absorbing Water and Minerals

Root hair cell

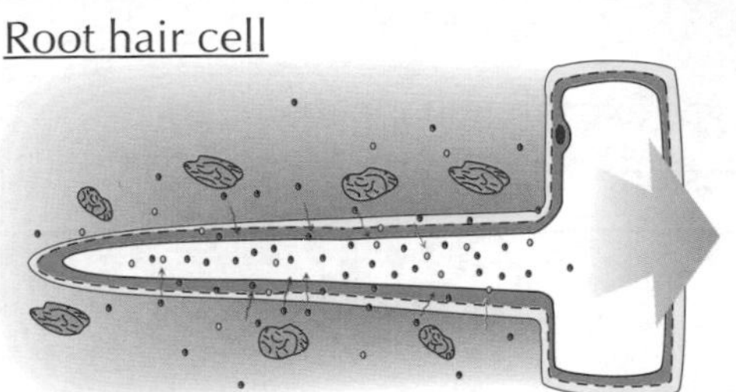

1) The cells on the surface of plant roots grow into long "hairs" which stick out into the soil.
2) This gives the plant a big surface area for absorbing water and mineral ions from the soil.
3) Most of the water and mineral ions that get into a plant are absorbed by the root hair cells.

Root Hairs Take in Minerals Using Active Transport

1) The concentration of minerals is usually higher in the root hair cell than in the soil around it.
2) So normal diffusion doesn't explain how minerals are taken up into the root hair cell.
3) They should go the other way if they followed the rules of diffusion.
4) The answer is that a different process called 'active transport' is responsible.
5) Active transport allows the plant to absorb minerals against a concentration gradient. This is essential for its growth. But active transport needs energy from respiration to make it work.
6) Active transport also happens in humans, for example in taking glucose from the gut (see below), and from the kidney tubules (see page 142).

We Need Active Transport to Stop Us Starving

Active transport is used in the gut when there is a low concentration of nutrients in the gut, but a high concentration of nutrients in the blood.

1) When there's a higher concentration of glucose and amino acids in the gut they diffuse naturally into the blood.
2) BUT — sometimes there's a lower concentration of nutrients in the gut than there is in the blood.
3) This means that the concentration gradient is the wrong way.
4) The same process used in plant roots is used here — active transport.
5) Active transport allows nutrients to be taken into the blood, despite the fact that the concentration gradient is the wrong way.

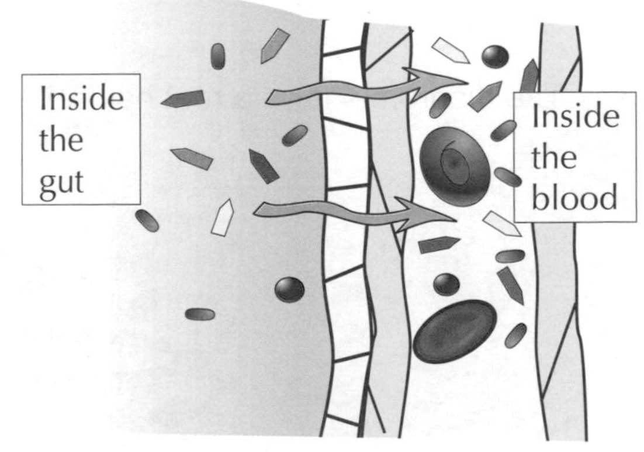

Active transport uses energy

An important difference between active transport and diffusion is that active transport uses energy. Imagine a pen of sheep in a field. If you open the pen, the sheep will happily diffuse from the area of high sheep concentration into the field, which has a low sheep concentration — you won't have to do a thing. To get them back in the pen though, you'll have to put in quite a bit of energy.

Warm-Up and Exam Questions

Question time again — Warm-Up first, then Exam (or the other way round if you want to be different).

Warm-Up Questions

1) Through what structure do carbon dioxide and oxygen get in and out of a leaf?
2) Describe what happens when you breath out.
3) What name is given to the air sacs in the lungs where gas exchange happens?
4) Give two differences between active transport and diffusion.

Exam Questions

1 Describe the changes that take place in the thorax when breathing air into the lungs. You should use the following words in your description:

diaphragm intercostal muscles pressure volume

(4 marks)

2 The diagram shows a villus from the small intestine. Glucose and other products of digestion are absorbed into the blood through the villi.

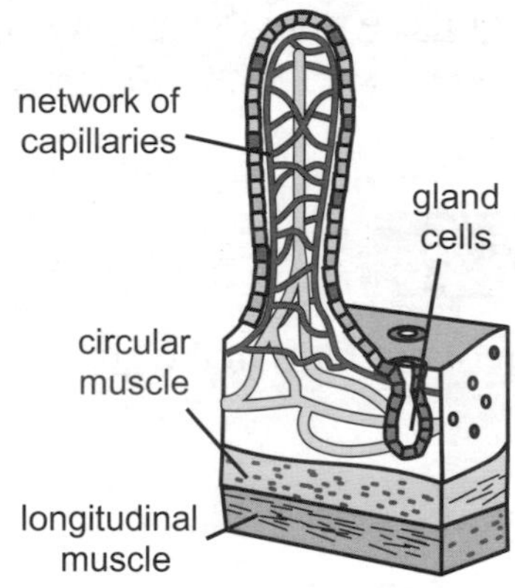

(a) Describe how the products of digestion move into the blood.

(2 marks)

(b) Explain, as fully as you can, how the structure of a villus is related to its function.

(3 marks)

3 The diagram shows a root hair cell.

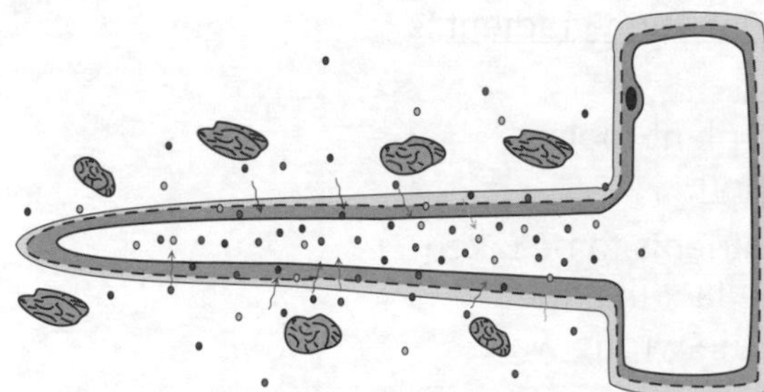

(a) Describe how the structure of a root hair cell is adapted to carry out its function.

(1 mark)

(b) Explain how mineral ions are absorbed into the root hair cell.

(3 marks)

The Circulation System

The circulation system's main function is to get food and oxygen to every cell in the body. As well as being a delivery service, it's also a waste collection service — it carries waste products like carbon dioxide and urea to where they can be removed from the body.

The DOUBLE Circulation System, Actually

1. The heart is actually two pumps. The right side pumps deoxygenated blood to the lungs to collect oxygen and remove carbon dioxide. Then the left side pumps this oxygenated blood around the body.

2. Arteries carry blood away from the heart at high pressure.

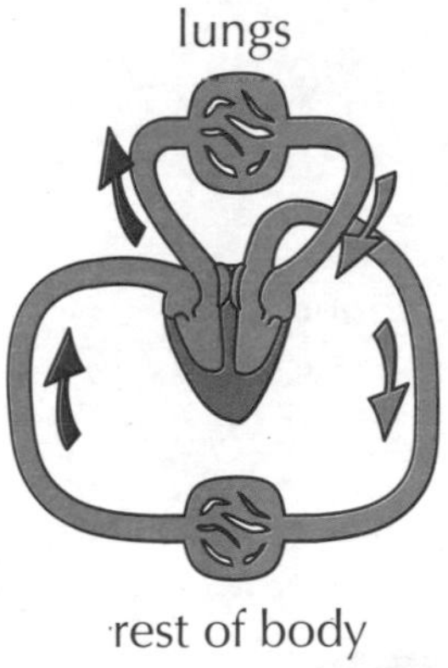

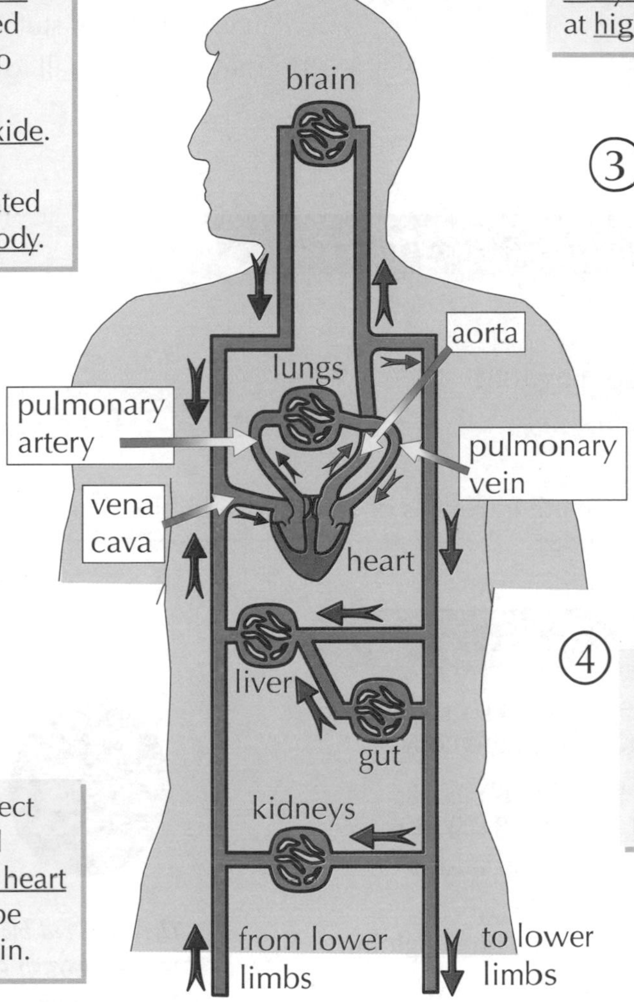

3. Normally, arteries carry oxygenated blood and veins carry deoxygenated blood. The pulmonary artery and pulmonary vein are the big exceptions to this rule (see diagram).

4. The arteries eventually split off into thousands of tiny capillaries which take blood to every cell in the body.

5. The veins then collect the used blood and carry it back to the heart at low pressure to be pumped round again.

lungs

rest of body

brain

lungs

aorta

pulmonary artery

pulmonary vein

vena cava

heart

liver

gut

kidneys

from lower limbs

to lower limbs

All mammals and birds have a double circulation system, while fish only have a single circulation system — the blood goes straight from the heart to the gills (their lungs), then to the rest of the body.

And there are some even more curious circulation systems, e.g. worms have five pairs of hearts, and flat worms don't actually have any circulation system.

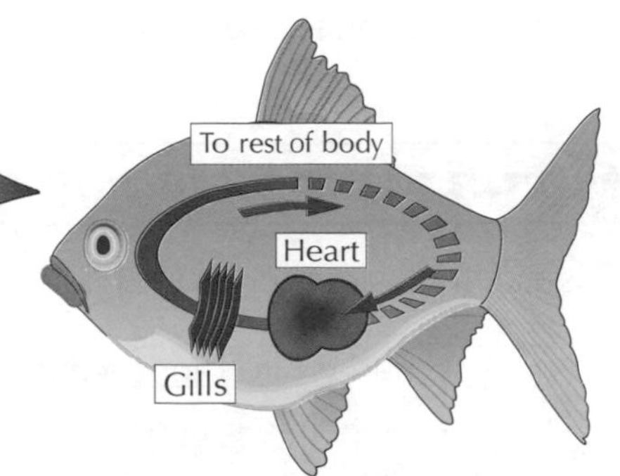

One system goes to the lungs — the other to the rest of the body

The diagram above only shows the basic layout. There are loads of blood vessels. If you laid all your arteries, capillaries and veins end to end, they'd go around the world about three times. These vessels vary from hose-pipe width arteries to capillaries that are a tenth of the thickness of a human hair.

Capillaries and Blood

This stuff's the nitty gritty about capillaries and blood. Make sure you learn it all.

Capillaries Deliver Food and Oxygen to Each Cell

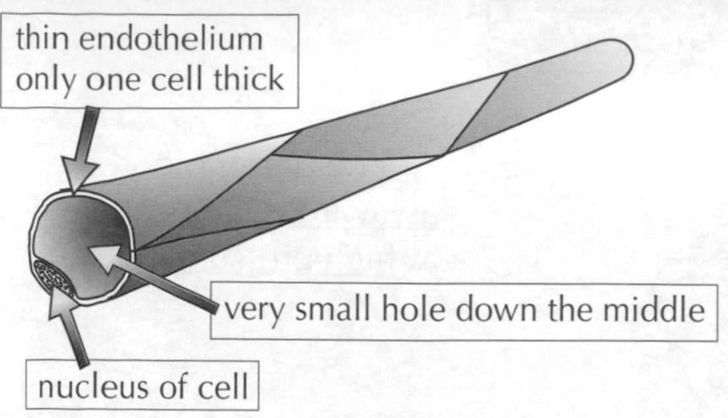

1) Capillaries use diffusion to deliver food and oxygen direct to body tissues and take carbon dioxide and other waste materials away.
2) Their walls are usually only one cell thick to make it easy for stuff to pass in and out of them.
3) They are too small to see without a microscope.

Blood is Made Up of Four Main Parts

Blood consists of:

- white blood cells (see page 33)
- red blood cells (see below)
- plasma (see below)
- platelets — these are small fragments of cells that help blood to clot at a wound.

Red Blood Cells Carry Oxygen

1) The job of red blood cells is to carry oxygen from the lungs to all the cells in the body.
2) They have a doughnut shape to give a large surface area for absorbing oxygen.
3) They don't have a nucleus — this allows more room to carry oxygen.
4) They contain a substance called haemoglobin.
5) In the lungs, haemoglobin combines with oxygen to become oxyhaemoglobin. In body tissues the reverse happens to release oxygen to the cells.

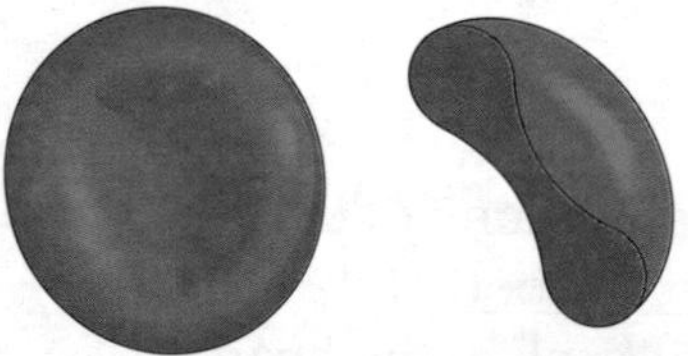

The more red blood cells you've got, the more oxygen can get to your cells. At high altitudes there's less oxygen in the air — so people who live there produce more red blood cells to compensate.

Plasma is the Liquid That Carries Everything in Blood

This is a pale straw-coloured liquid which carries just about everything:

1) Red and white blood cells and platelets.
2) Nutrients like glucose and amino acids. These are the soluble products of digestion which are absorbed from the gut and taken to the cells of the body.
3) Carbon dioxide from the organs to the lungs.
4) Urea from the liver to the kidneys.
5) Hormones (see page 11).
6) Antibodies and antitoxins produced by the white blood cells.

Exercise

When you exercise, your body adapts so that your muscles get more oxygen and glucose to supply energy.

Exercise Increases the Heart Rate

1) Muscles are made of muscle cells. These use oxygen to release energy from glucose (this process is called respiration), which is used to contract the muscles.

See page 95 for more on respiration.

2) An increase in muscle activity requires more glucose and oxygen to be supplied to the muscle cells. Extra carbon dioxide needs to be removed from the muscle cells. For this to happen the blood has to flow at a faster rate.

3) This is why physical activity:

- increases your breathing rate and makes you breathe more deeply to meet the demand for extra oxygen.
- increases the speed at which the heart pumps.
- dilates (makes wider) the arteries which supply blood to the muscles.

Glycogen is Used During Exercise

1) Some glucose from food is stored as glycogen.

2) Glycogen's mainly stored in the liver, but each muscle also has its own store.

3) During vigorous exercise, muscles use glucose rapidly, and have to draw on their glycogen stores to provide more energy. If the exercise goes on for a while the glycogen stores get used up.

4) When the glycogen stores run low, the muscles don't get the energy they need to keep contracting, and they get tired.

Glucose is stored as glycogen in the liver and muscles

I bet you're exhausted after reading this page. But nonetheless, you need to know about the changes to your body that exercise causes — it increases your breathing rate, your breathing depth and your heart rate. It also makes your arteries get wider. All this helps loads of glucose and oxygen get to your muscles, which is just what you need to keep them working.

Exercise and Anaerobic Respiration

If your body can't get enough oxygen or glucose to your muscles, it has a back-up plan ready...

Anaerobic Respiration is Used if There's Not Enough Oxygen

1) When you do vigorous exercise and your body can't supply enough oxygen to your muscles, they start doing anaerobic respiration instead of aerobic respiration.
2) Anaerobic just means without oxygen. It's the incomplete breakdown of glucose, which produces lactic acid.

$$\text{glucose} \rightarrow \text{energy} + \text{lactic acid}$$

3) This is NOT the best way to convert glucose into energy because lactic acid builds up in the muscles, which gets painful. This also causes the muscles to get tired.
4) Another downside is that anaerobic respiration does not release nearly as much energy as aerobic respiration — but it's useful in emergencies.
5) The advantage is that at least you can keep on using your muscles for a while longer.

Anaerobic Respiration Leads to an Oxygen Debt

1) After resorting to anaerobic respiration, when you stop exercising you'll have an oxygen debt.
2) In other words you have to repay the oxygen that you didn't get to your muscles in time, because your lungs, heart and blood couldn't keep up with the demand earlier on.
3) This means you have to keep breathing hard for a while after you stop, to get oxygen into your muscles to oxidise the painful lactic acid to harmless CO_2 and water.
4) While high levels of CO_2 and lactic acid are detected in the blood (by the brain), the pulse and breathing rate stay high to try and rectify the situation.

These rowers have finished rowing, but they're still breathing hard to replace their oxygen debt.

An oxygen debt needs to be repaid

Yeast also respire anaerobically, but they produce ethanol (and carbon dioxide) — see page 149. It's just as well humans produce lactic acid instead — or after a bit of vigorous exercise we'd all be drunk.

Warm-Up and Exam Questions

You know what to do — get those brain cells working on these warm-up and exam questions.

Warm-Up Questions

1) What is unusual about the pulmonary artery, compared to other arteries in the body?
2) Explain why the heart is thought of as two pumps rather than a single pump.
3) List four things that are carried around the body in the blood plasma.
4) State three changes that take place in the body during vigorous exercise.
5) What substance, stored mainly in the liver, is broken down during exercise to release glucose?

Exam Questions

1 Which of the following statements about red blood cells is **not** true.

A Red blood cells are doughnut shaped to give them a large surface area.
B Red blood cells transport oxygen from the lungs to the organs.
C Each red blood cell is packed with haemoglobin.
D Red blood cells have a large nucleus.

(1 mark)

2 In the human body, respiration may be aerobic or anaerobic at different times.

(a) Explain why the body uses anaerobic respiration during vigorous exercise.
(2 marks)

(b) Write down the word equation for anaerobic respiration.
(1 mark)

(c) Give two disadvantages of anaerobic respiration.
(2 marks)

3 The graph below shows the rate of oxygen use by a person before, during and after a period of exercise.

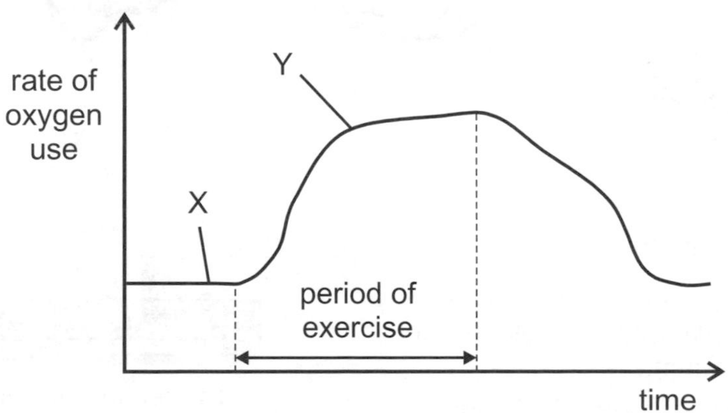

(a) Explain why the rate of oxygen consumption is higher at Y than at X.
(1 mark)

(b) Mark on the graph the point at which the person's blood lactic acid concentration will be highest.
(1 mark)

(c) Why does oxygen use remain high even after the exercise ends?
(1 mark)

Kidneys

The kidneys are really important organs. They get rid of toxic waste like urea as well as adjusting the amount of dissolved ions and water in the blood. The kidneys were introduced on page 103, but here's the rest of the stuff you need to know.

Nephrons Are the *Filtration Units* in the *Kidneys*

1) Ultrafiltration:

1) A high pressure is built up which squeezes water, urea, ions and sugar out of the blood and into the Bowman's capsule.
2) The membranes between the blood vessels and the Bowman's capsule act like filters, so big molecules like proteins and blood cells are not squeezed out. They stay in the blood.

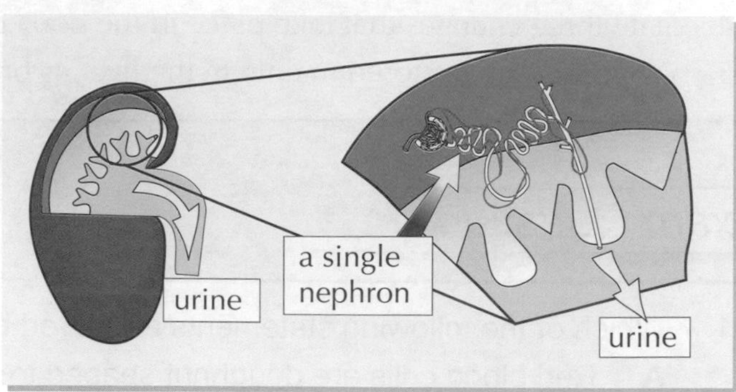

Enlarged View of a Single Nephron

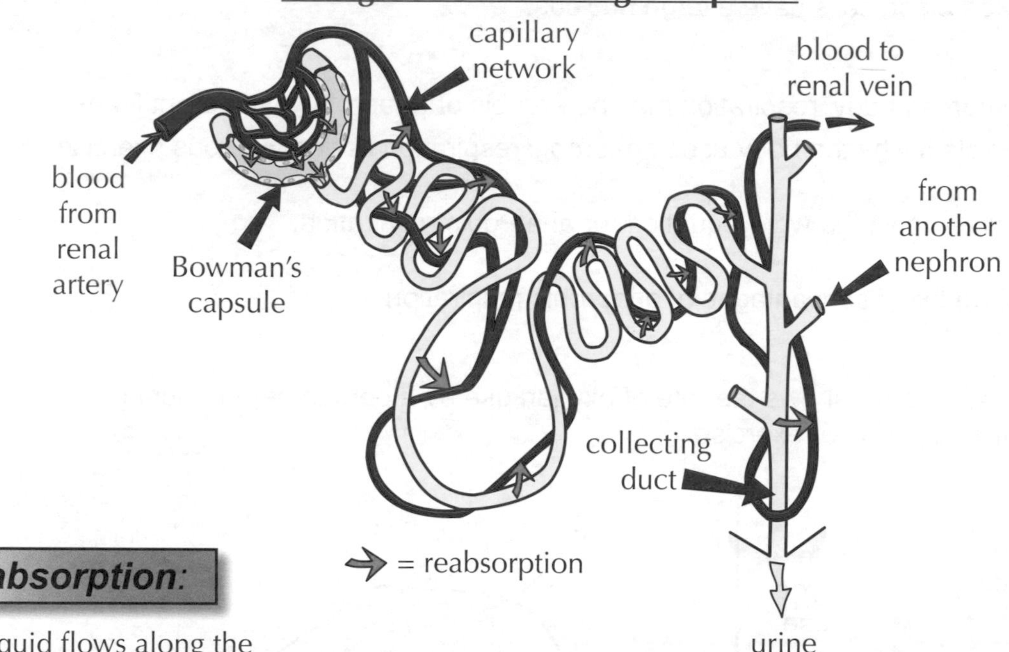

2) Reabsorption:

As the liquid flows along the nephron, useful substances are reabsorbed back into the blood:

1) All the sugar is reabsorbed. This involves the process of active transport against the concentration gradient.
2) Sufficient ions are reabsorbed. Excess ions are not. Active transport is needed.
3) Sufficient water is reabsorbed.

3) Release of wastes:

The remaining substances (including urea) continue out of the nephron, into the ureter and down to the bladder as urine.

Each kidney contains about one million nephrons

The kidneys are pretty complicated organs as you can see. Luckily you don't have to learn all the ins and outs of the diagram — but you do have to make sure you know exactly what happens in each of the three stages. Learn what's filtered, what's reabsorbed and what's released as urine.

Kidney Failure

If someone's kidneys stop working, there are basically two treatments — regular dialysis or a transplant.

The Kidneys Remove **Waste Substances** from the Blood

1) If the kidneys don't work properly, waste substances build up in the blood and you lose your ability to control the levels of ions and water in your body. Eventually, this results in death.

2) People with kidney failure can be kept alive by having dialysis treatment — where machines do the job of the kidneys. Or they can have a kidney transplant.

The kidneys are incredibly important — if they don't work as they should, you can get problems in the heart, bones, nervous system, stomach, mouth, etc.

Dialysis Machines **Filter** the Blood

1) Dialysis has to be done regularly to keep the concentrations of dissolved substances in the blood at normal levels, and to remove waste substances.

2) In a dialysis machine the person's blood flows alongside a selectively permeable barrier, surrounded by dialysis fluid. It's permeable to things like ions and waste substances, but not big molecules like proteins (just like the membranes in the kidney).

3) The dialysis fluid has the same concentration of dissolved ions and glucose as healthy blood.

4) This means that useful dissolved ions and glucose won't be lost from the blood during dialysis.

5) Only waste substances (such as urea) and excess ions and water diffuse across the barrier.

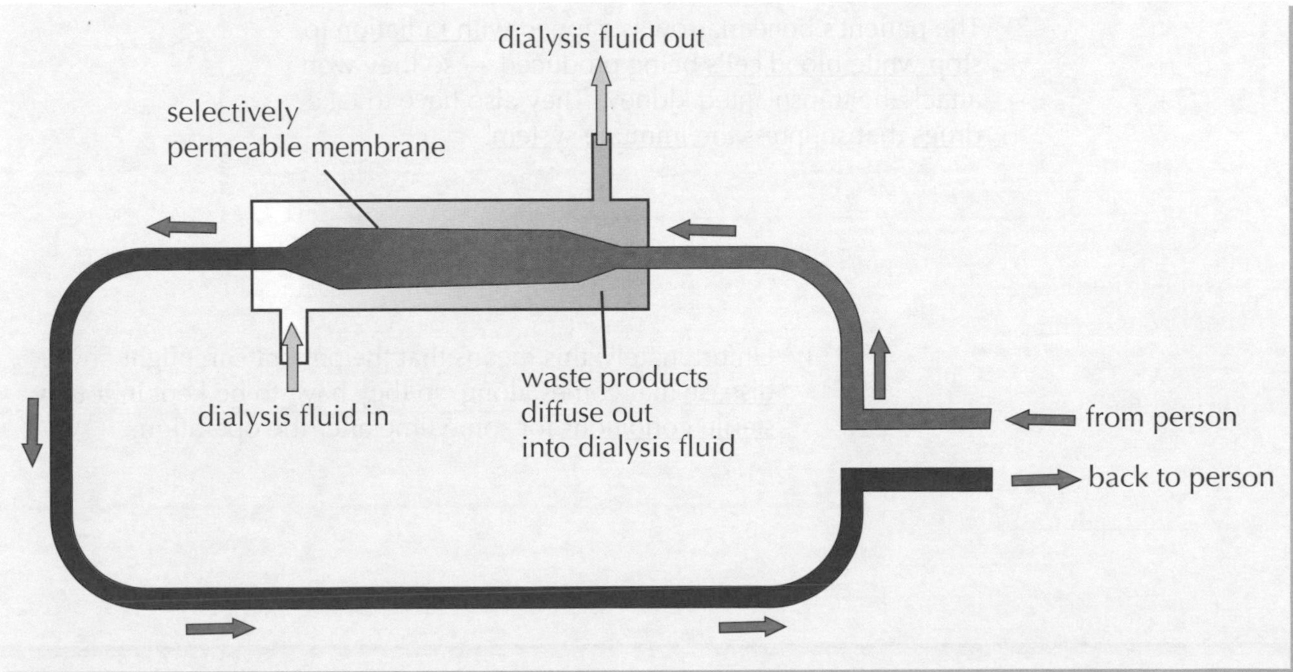

6) Many patients with kidney failure have to have a dialysis session three times a week. Each session takes 3-4 hours — not much fun.

Kidney Failure

Getting a kidney transplant sounds like the ideal treatment for kidney failure — but it's not that simple.

Transplanted Organs can be Rejected by the Body

1) At the moment, the only cure for kidney disease is to have a kidney transplant.
2) Healthy kidneys are usually transplanted from people who have died suddenly, say in a car accident, and who are on the organ donor register or carry a donor card (provided their relatives give the go-ahead).
3) But kidneys can also be transplanted from people who are still alive — as we all have two of them.

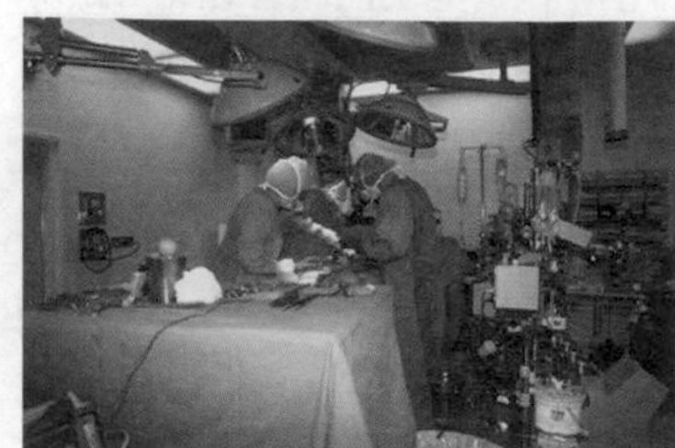

The first successful kidney transplant was carried out in 1954.

The donor kidney can be rejected by the patient's immune system — treated like a foreign body and attacked by antibodies. To help prevent this happening, precautions are taken:

1) A donor with a tissue type that closely matches the patient is chosen. Tissue type is based on the antigens (see page 33) that are on the surface of most cells.

2) The patient's bone marrow is zapped with radiation to stop white blood cells being produced — so they won't attack the transplanted kidney. They also have to take drugs that suppress the immune system.

3) Unfortunately, this means that the patient can't fight any disease that comes along, so they have to be kept in totally sterile conditions for some time after the operation.

Dialysis or transplant — both have their downsides...

Kidney dialysis machines are expensive things for the NHS to run — and dialysis is not a pleasant experience. Transplants can put an end to the hours spent on dialysis, but there are long waiting lists for kidneys. Even if one with a matching tissue type is found, there's the possibility that it'll be rejected. And taking drugs that suppress the immune system means the person is vulnerable to other illnesses.

Warm-Up and Exam Questions

You've nearly reached the end of the section — just a few simple Warm-Up Questions and a few slightly harder Exam Questions stand between you and the Revision Summary...

Warm-Up Questions

1) What is a nephron?
2) By which process are ions reabsorbed back into the blood?
3) Explain what happens if a person's kidneys don't work properly.

Exam Questions

1 Put the following stages in order to describe how the kidneys work.

1. Wastes such as urea, are carried out of the nephron to the bladder, whilst reabsorbed materials leave the kidneys in the renal vein.
2. Small molecules are squeezed into the Bowman's capsule. Large molecules remain in the blood.
3 Useful products are reabsorbed from the nephron and enter the capillaries.
4. Molecules travel from the Bowman's capsule along the nephron.
5. Blood enters the kidney through the renal artery.

(1 mark)

2 The table shows the concentrations of some different substances in the fluid inside a nephron of a kidney — in the Bowman's capsule, and in the collecting duct.

Substance	Conc. in Bowman's capsule (g/100 ml)	Conc. in urine (g/100 ml)
water	99	96
protein	0	0
glucose	0.10	0
urea	0.04	2.0
salt	0.70	0.30

(a) Explain why there is a difference in the concentrations of glucose.

(1 mark)

(b) Explain why the liquid in the Bowman's capsule does not contain any proteins.

(2 marks)

3 Mary has kidney failure. She has dialysis three times a week.

(a) (i) Explain how the dialysis machine removes urea from Mary's blood.

(2 marks)

(ii) Explain why Mary does not lose glucose from her blood during dialysis.

(2 marks)

(b) Mary is hoping that she will soon have a kidney transplant.
Suggest one reason why this form of treatment may be preferable to dialysis.

(1 mark)

Revision Summary for Biology 3(i)

It's no good just reading the section through and hoping you've got it all — it'll only stick if you've learned it properly. These questions are designed to really test whether you know all your stuff — ignore them at your peril. OK, rant over — I'll leave it to you...

1) What's the name for the process that's happening when water moves across a partially permeable membrane to equalise the concentrations on either side?
2) Explain how leaves are adapted to maximise the amount of carbon dioxide that gets to their cells.
3) Why do the leaves care if carbon dioxide gets to their cells or not?
4) What are the pores in the leaves called?
5) Name the main substances that diffuse out of leaves.
6) What conditions does transpiration happen most quickly in?
7) Cacti, which grow in the desert, have spikes instead of flat leaves. Why is this?
8) Name the chest cavity that's above the diaphragm.
9) Describe the gas exchange that happens between the alveoli and the blood.
10) Give four ways that the alveoli's structure is ideal for gas exchange.
11) Why can't most mineral ions get into roots by diffusion?
12) Draw a diagram of a root hair cell. Why is it this shape?
13) Does glucose only get into the blood from the gut by active transport?
14) Explain why our circulation system is called a *double* circulation system.
15) Describe the pressure and oxygen content of the blood in veins and arteries. What are the words for saying if the blood has oxygen in or not?
16) Sketch a red blood cell. Why is it this shape?
17) What's the substance in red blood cells called? What is it called when it combines with oxygen?
18)*Some companies sell special tents for athletes to sleep in. These tents have a lower oxygen concentration than the air at sea level has.
    a) Explain why an athlete might buy one of these tents.
    b) How could an athlete achieve the same effect without buying one of these tents?
19) Why does your heart beat faster when you do exercise?
20)*The table below shows the oxygen consumption of an athlete as her heart beats at different rates.

Heart rate (BPM)	85	105	118	125	143	148	152	163
Oxygen consumption (ml/kg/min)	13	26	30	33	40	47	53	56

    a) Draw a scattergraph of the data and a line of best fit.
    b) What does this graph show?
    c) Explain why this relationship exists.
21) What is "anaerobic respiration"?
22) Give two reasons why anaerobic respiration isn't the best way to release energy.
23) Explain how you repay an oxygen debt.
24) How does kidney dialysis work?
25) What are the advantages and disadvantages of a kidney transplant over dialysis?
26) Why do transplant patients have their immune systems suppressed?

* Answers on page 229

The Theory of Biogenesis

We've not always known where living things come from — a few hundred years ago people had a very different opinion about it...

The Theory of Biogenesis Has Been Developed Over the Years

1) People used to think that life could spontaneously generate (just appear) from non-living material.
2) But then evidence showed that this couldn't be the case. The evidence supported the theory that living things are created from other living organisms — this is the theory of biogenesis.
3) Here's how the accepted theory was changed to fit the available evidence:

Before 1765 it was believed that substances in food were changed into microbes, which caused the food to go off.

A scientist called Lazzaro Spallanzani boiled two sets of broth to kill the microbes, then sealed one flask and left the other open. Only the open one went off (although the broth in the sealed flask did go off when it was left open later).

This showed that microbes got into the food from the air, but opponents just thought that it meant air from outside the flask was necessary to start the change.

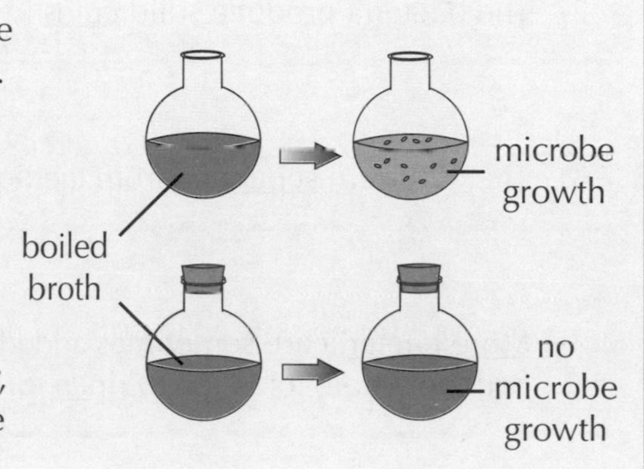

The theory that 'fresh' air caused substances in food to change into microbes was disproved by Theodor Schwann in 1837. He showed that meat would not go off in air, provided the air was heated first to kill microorganisms.

A more conclusive experiment was carried out by the famous scientist Louis Pasteur in 1859.

He heated broth in two flasks, both of which were left open to the air. However, one of the flasks had a curved neck so that bacteria in the air would settle in the loop, and not get through to the broth.

The broth in the flask with the curved neck stayed fresh, proving that it was the microbes and not the air causing it to go off.

Flask 1: Air and microbes get in

Flask 2: Air gets in, but microbes can't

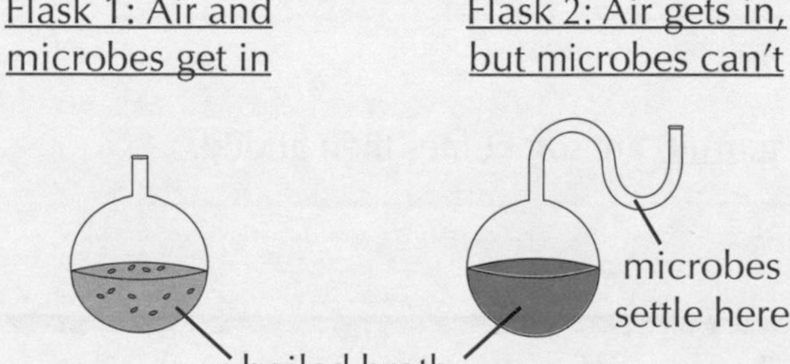

Food and Drink from Microorganisms

Microorganisms, such as bacteria, cause changes in food — often the changes are bad, but sometimes they're useful and mean we can have foods that we wouldn't have otherwise.

Most **Cheese** is Made Using **Bacteria**...

Here's what happens:

1) A culture of bacteria is added to milk.

2) The bacteria produce solid curds in the milk.

3) The curds are separated from the liquid whey.

4) More bacteria are sometimes added to the curds, and the whole lot is left to ripen for a while.

5) Moulds are added to give blue cheese (e.g. Stilton) its colour and taste.

Yoghurt is Made Using **Bacteria** Too

Bacteria are used to clot milk during the manufacture of yoghurt.

1) The milk is often heat treated first to kill off any bacteria that may be in it, then cooled.

2) A starter culture of bacteria is then added. The bacteria ferment the lactose sugar (present in the milk) to lactic acid.

3) The acid causes the milk to clot and solidify into yoghurt.

4) Sterilised flavours (e.g. fruit) are sometimes then added.

So bacteria aren't always the bad guys...

It seems weird. Microorganisms in food can make you ill — that's why you should wash your hands before touching food and the reason you have to make sure meat is cooked thoroughly. Yet some foods are made with microorganisms, and as you'll see on page 151, some food is microorganisms.

Using Yeast

There's nothing newfangled about yeast. It's been used for donkey's years to make bread and alcohol.

Yeast is a Single-Celled Fungus

Yeast is a microorganism. A yeast cell has a nucleus, cytoplasm, a vacuole, and a cell membrane surrounded by a cell wall.

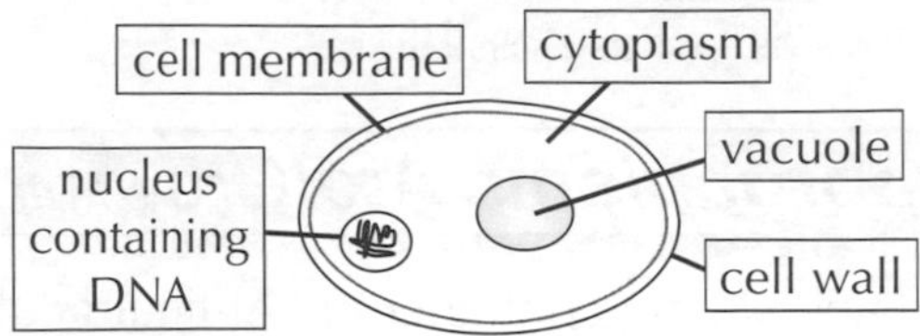

Yeast Can Respire With or Without Oxygen

Learn the equation for anaerobic respiration (i.e. without oxygen) of glucose by yeast (this process is called fermentation):

glucose → ethanol + carbon dioxide + energy

Yeast can also respire aerobically (i.e. with oxygen). This produces much more energy, and is needed to grow and reproduce:

glucose + oxygen → carbon dioxide + water + energy

This is the same respiration process that releases energy in animals and plants.

Yeast is Used to Make Bread

Holes in the bread, which make it nice and light, are made by carbon dioxide bubbles in the dough.

1) Yeast is used in dough to produce nice, light bread.
2) The yeast converts sugars to carbon dioxide and some ethanol. It is the carbon dioxide that makes the bread rise.
3) As the carbon dioxide expands, it gets trapped in the dough, making it lighter.

Yeast is Used to Make Alcoholic Drinks

Here's how beer is brewed:

1) Beer is made from grain — usually barley.
2) The barley grains are allowed to germinate for a few days, during which the starch in the grains is broken down into sugar by enzymes. Then the grains are dried in a kiln. This process is called malting.
3) The malted grain is mashed up and water is added to produce a sugary solution with lots of bits in it. This is then sieved to remove the bits.
4) Hops are added to the mixture to give the beer its bitter flavour.
5) The sugary solution is then fermented by yeast, turning the sugar into alcohol.

In wine-making, the yeast use the natural sugars in the grape juice as their energy source.

Microorganisms in Industry

Shedloads of microorganisms are grown in huge vats called fermenters to make things like antibiotics, fuels and proteins. It's really important to control the conditions in fermenters so that just the stuff you want grows as fast as possible.

Microorganisms Are Grown in Fermenters on a Large Scale

A fermenter is a big container full of liquid culture medium which microorganisms can grow and reproduce in. The fermenter needs to give the microorganisms the conditions they need to grow and produce their useful product. The diagram shows a typical fermenter.

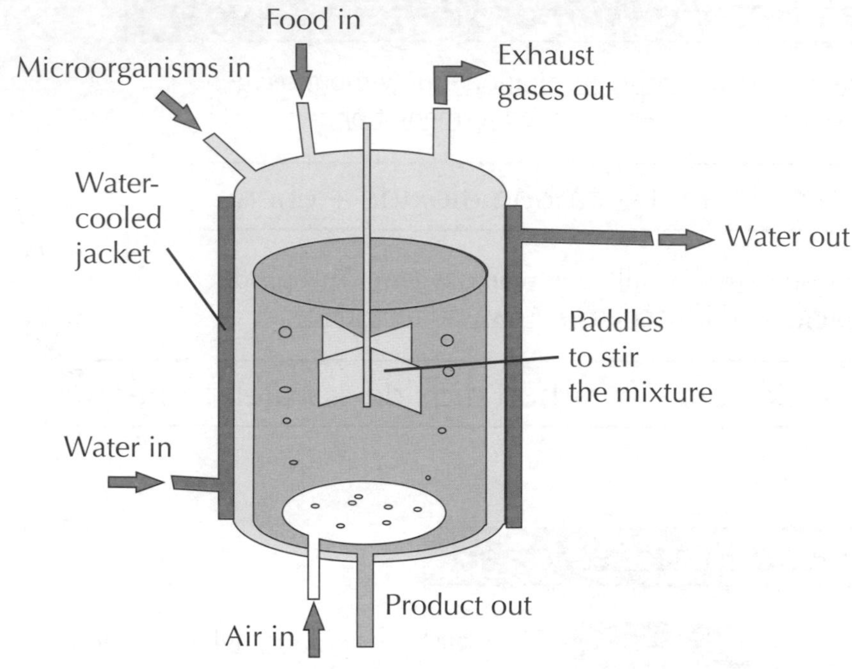

1) Food is provided in the liquid culture medium. More can be pumped in if needed.

2) Air is piped in to supply oxygen to the microorganisms.

3) The microorganisms need to be kept at the right temperature. The microorganisms produce heat by respiration, so the fermenters must be cooled. This is usually done with water in a water-cooled jacket. The temperature is monitored by instruments.

4) The right pH is needed for the microorganisms to thrive. Instruments will monitor this.

5) Sterile conditions are needed to prevent contamination from other microorganisms.

6) The microorganisms need to be kept from sinking to the bottom. A motorised stirrer keeps them moving around and maintains an even temperature.

Make sure you know the main parts of a fermenter

Industrial fermenters come in loads of different sizes — some are so big that they have to be stored outside. But all fermenters have the same basic parts, and it's these that you need to know about — an air supply, some sort of stirrer, a water-cooled jacket and instruments to monitor pH and temperature.

Microorganisms in Industry

Mycoprotein is a very useful kind of edible biomass. The meat substitutes it is used to make tend to be lower in fat, so often healthier than meat itself. Some non-vegetarians prefer it to meat because of this.

Mycoprotein — Food from Fermenters

1) Mycoprotein means protein from fungi. It's a type of single-celled protein.

2) Mycoprotein is used to make meat substitutes for vegetarian meals — Quorn™, for example.

3) A fungus called *Fusarium* is the main source of mycoprotein.

4) The fungus is grown in fermenters, using glucose syrup as food. The glucose syrup is obtained by digesting maize starch with enzymes.

5) The fungus respires aerobically, so oxygen is supplied, together with nitrogen (as ammonia) and other minerals.

6) It's important to prevent other microorganisms growing in the fermenter. So the fermenter is initially sterilised using steam. The incoming nutrients are heat sterilised and the air supply is filtered.

Penicillin is Made by Growing Mould in Fermenters

1) Penicillin is an antibiotic made by growing the mould *Penicillium chrysogenum* in a fermenter.
2) The mould is grown in a liquid culture medium containing sugar and other nutrients (for example, a source of nitrogen).
3) The sugar is used up as the mould grows.
4) The mould only starts to make penicillin after using up most of the nutrients for growth.

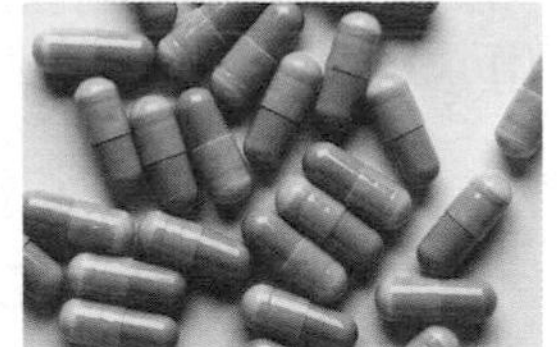

Alexander Fleming discovered Penicillin accidentally in 1928. A culture of bacteria became contaminated with a mould. This mould wiped out areas of bacteria. No one took much notice of Fleming's findings until the Second World War, when the huge number of injuries made it important to find something that would heal infected wounds.

Microorganisms are used to make food and medicines

Food made from microorganisms might not sound very appetising, but it has its advantages. In some developing countries it's difficult to find enough protein. Meat is a big source of protein, but animals need lots of space to graze, plenty of nice grass, etc. Single-celled protein grown in a fermenter is an efficient way of producing protein to feed people. The microorganisms grow very quickly, and don't need much space — they can even feed on waste material that would be no good for feeding animals.

Warm-Up and Exam Questions

You'll be glad to know that this is the penultimate page of warm-up and exam questions, but there'll be no slacking — if you get any wrong, go back and learn the page you're stuck on and try again.

Warm-Up Questions

1) What is the theory of biogenesis?
2) Describe how yoghurt is made.
3) Explain the process of malting in making beer.
4) Name the fungus that is the main source of mycoprotein.

Exam Questions

1 The diagram to the right shows a yeast cell.

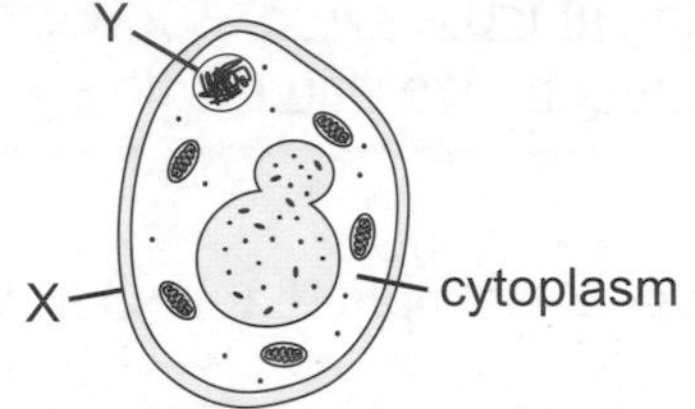

(a) Name the structures labelled X and Y.

(2 marks)

(b) Yeast is used in wine-making. The diagram to the right shows some of the apparatus involved in this process.

(i) Describe the role of yeast in wine-making.

(2 marks)

(ii) One of the functions of the airlock is to prevent any air from entering the demijohn. Explain why this is important.

(1 mark)

(iii) Write down the equation for anaerobic respiration in yeast.

(1 mark)

(c) Name a product, other than wine, that is made with the help of yeast.

(1 mark)

2 A fermenter is used for growing mycoprotein.

(a) What is mycoprotein used for?

(1 mark)

(b) Explain why it is necessary to control the temperature of the fermenter.

(2 marks)

(c) Name two conditions, apart from the temperature, that need to be controlled in the fermenter.

(2 marks)

Fuels from Microorganisms

Food and antibiotics aren't the only things microorganisms can be used for — the stuff they produce can also be used as fuel. And with the world's oil and gas supplies running low, other fuel sources, such as this, are going to become really important.

Fuels Can Be Made by Fermentation

1) Fuels can be made by fermentation of natural products — luckily enough, waste products can often be used.
2) Fermentation is when bacteria or yeast break sugars down by anaerobic respiration.

Anaerobic respiration does not use oxygen.

Ethanol is Made by Anaerobic Fermentation of Sugar

1) Yeast make ethanol when they break down glucose by anaerobic respiration.

Glucose → Ethanol + Carbon dioxide + Energy

This is the same as the reaction used in wine-making.

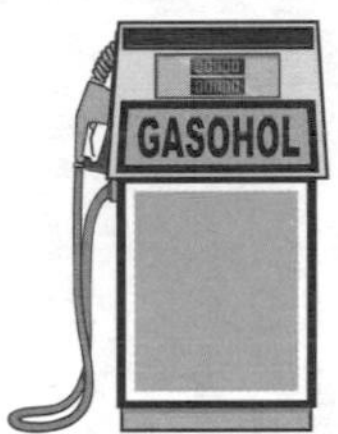

2) Sugar cane juices can be used, or glucose can be derived from maize starch by the action of carbohydrase (an enzyme).
3) The ethanol is distilled to separate it from the yeast and remaining glucose before it's used.
4) In some countries, e.g. Brazil, cars are adapted to run on a mixture of ethanol and petrol — this is known as gasohol.

Biogas is Made by Anaerobic Fermentation of Waste Material

1) Biogas is usually about 70% methane (CH_4) and 30% carbon dioxide (CO_2).
2) Lots of different microorganisms are used to produce biogas. They ferment plant and animal waste, which contains carbohydrates. Sludge waste from, e.g. sewage works or sugar factories, is used to make biogas on a large scale.
3) It's made in a simple fermenter called a digester or generator (see the next page).
4) Biogas generators need to be kept at a constant temperature to keep the microorganisms respiring away.
5) There are two types of biogas generators — batch generators and continuous generators. These are explained on the next page.
6) Biogas can't be stored as a liquid (it needs too high a pressure), so it has to be used straight away — for heating, cooking, lighting, or to power a turbine to generate electricity.

Biogas was used to power street lights in London

Fascinating stuff, this biogas. It makes a lot of sense, I suppose, to get energy from rubbish, sewage and pig poop instead of leaving it all to rot naturally — which would mean all that lovely methane just wafting away into the atmosphere. Remember — anaerobic respiration makes biofuels.

Fuels from Microorganisms

Here's more than you could ever have wanted to know about that magic stuff, biogas.

Fuel Production Can Happen on a **Large** or **Small Scale**

1) Large-scale biogas generators are now being set up in a number of countries. Also, in some countries, small biogas generators are used to make enough gas for a village or a family to use in their cooking stoves and for heating and lighting.

2) Human waste, waste from keeping pigs, and food waste (e.g. kitchen scraps) can be digested by bacteria to produce biogas.
3) By-products are used to fertilise crops and gardens.

Not All **Biogas Generators** Are the Same

There are two main types of biogas generator — batch generators and continuous generators.

Batch Generators

Batch generators make biogas in small batches. They're manually loaded up with waste, which is left to digest, and the by-products are cleared away at the end of each session.

Continuous Generators

Continuous generators make biogas all the time. Waste is continuously fed in, and biogas is produced at a steady rate. Continuous generators are more suited to large-scale biogas projects.

The diagram below shows a simple biogas generator.
Whether it's a continuous or batch generator, it needs to have the following:

1) an inlet for waste material to be put in
2) an outlet for the digested material to be removed through
3) an outlet so that the biogas can be piped to where it is needed

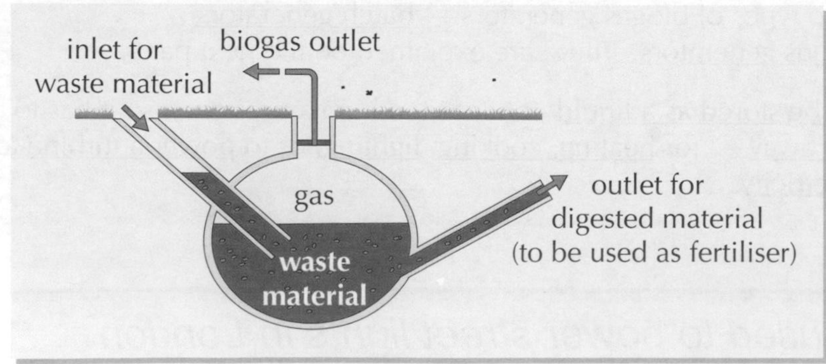

Fuels from Microorganisms

Four Factors to Consider When Designing a Generator:

When biogas generators are being designed, the following factors need to be considered:

COST: Continuous generators are more expensive than batch ones, because waste has to be mechanically pumped in and digested material mechanically removed all the time.

CONVENIENCE: Batch generators are less convenient because they have to be continually loaded, emptied and cleaned.

EFFICIENCY: Gas is produced most quickly at about 35 °C. If the temperature falls below this the gas production will be slower. Generators in some areas will need to be insulated or kept warm, e.g. by solar heaters. The generator shouldn't have any leaks or gas will be lost.

POSITION: The waste will smell during delivery, so generators should be sited away from homes. The generator is also best located fairly close to the waste source.

Using Biofuels Has **Economic** and **Environmental** Effects

1) Biofuels are a greener alternative to fossil fuels. The carbon dioxide released into the atmosphere was taken in by plants which lived recently, so they're carbon neutral.
2) The use of biofuels doesn't produce significant amounts of sulfur dioxide or nitrogen oxides, which cause acid rain.
3) Methane is a greenhouse gas and is one of those responsible for global warming. It's given off from untreated waste, which may be kept in farmyards or spread on agricultural land as fertiliser. Burning it as biogas means it's not released into the atmosphere.
4) The raw material is cheap and readily available.
5) The digested material is a better fertiliser than undigested dung — so people can grow more crops.
6) In some developing rural communities people have to spend hours each day collecting wood for fuel. Biogas saves them from having to do this task.
7) Biogas generators act as a waste disposal system, getting rid of human and animal waste that'd otherwise lie around, causing disease and polluting water supplies.

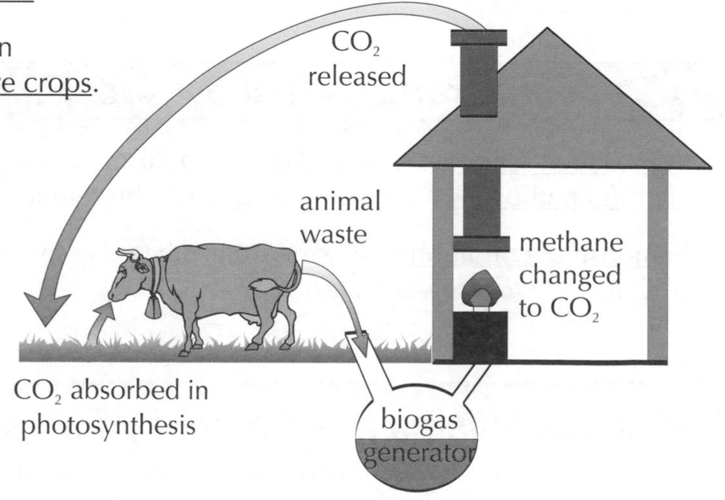

Using Microorganisms Safely

Microorganisms can be grown in a lab, but they need certain conditions to flourish.
Also, precautions must be taken to stop unwanted microorganisms growing as well.

Microorganisms Are Grown on **Agar Jelly** in a **Petri Dish**

1) Microorganisms are grown (cultured) in a culture medium.
2) They need carbohydrates as an energy source, plus mineral ions, and sometimes supplementary proteins and vitamins.
3) These nutrients are usually added to the agar jelly.
4) Agar jelly can be poured when hot, and sets when cold. It's poured into shallow round plastic dishes called Petri dishes.

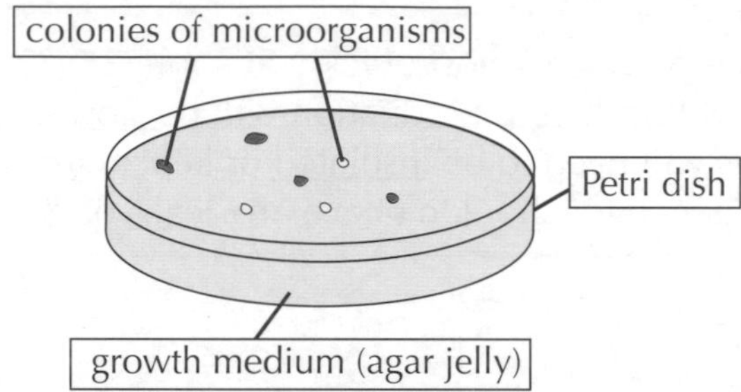

Equipment is **Sterilised** to Prevent **Contamination**

1) If equipment isn't sterilised, unwanted microorganisms in the growth medium will grow and contaminate the end product.
2) The unwanted microorganisms might make harmful substances, or cause disease.
3) Petri dishes and the growth medium must be sterilised before use.
4) Inoculating loops (used for transferring microorganisms to the growth medium) are sterilised by passing them through a flame.
5) The Petri dish must have a lid to stop any microorganisms in the air contaminating the culture. The lid should be taped on.

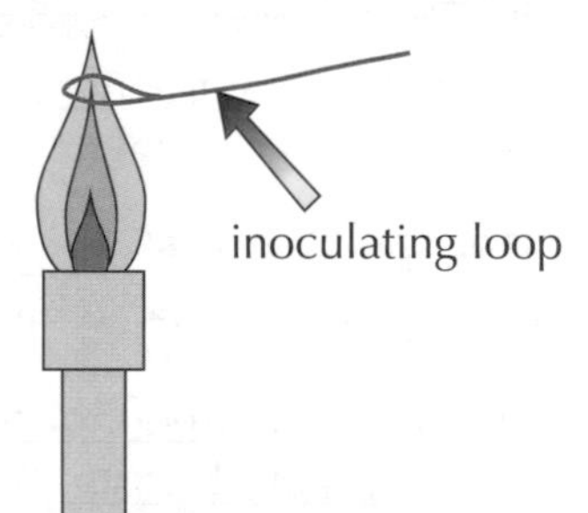

The **Temperature** Must be Kept **Fairly Low** in **School Labs**

In the lab at school, cultures of microorganisms are kept at about 25 °C. Harmful pathogens aren't likely to grow at this temperature.

In industrial conditions, cultures are incubated at higher temperatures so that they can grow a lot faster.

Pathogens are microorganisms which cause disease.

Microorganisms need carbohydrates and other nutrients to grow

Culture medium = growth medium = liquid or jelly that the microorganisms are grown in. Sorted. And with that, you've come to the end of the biology stuff that you need to know for your exam — speaking of exams, head over to the next page for your last lot of warm-up and exam questions...

Warm-Up and Exam Questions

Would you believe it, these are the last Warm-Up and Exam Questions in the book — congratulations... Unless for some reason you started with this section, in which case, welcome to the book.

Warm-Up Questions

1) How is ethanol made?
2) What is gasohol and what is it used for?
3) Name three things that a biogas generator needs to have.
4) Name four things that are commonly found in a culture medium to help microorganisms grow.
5) Name two pieces of lab equipment that must be sterilised when growing microorganism cultures.
6) Why are microorganism cultures kept at around 25 °C in schools?

Exam Questions

1 (a) What is the main gas found in biogas?

(1 mark)

(b) Biogas can be made in continuous or batch generators.
Give one advantage and one disadvantage of continuous generators.

(2 marks)

(c) The table below shows the average temperatures in January and July for four countries.

	Average temperature (°C)	
	January	July
Nigeria	27	26
Brazil	27	26.5
England	4	18
Denmark	0	18

Use the data in the table to explain why the rate of biogas production, in a generator placed above ground, would be greater in Nigeria and Brazil than in England and Denmark.

(1 mark)

2 Some Chinese villages use biogas generators to provide energy.

(a) What sort of waste material can be used in a biogas generator?

(1 mark)

(b) Villagers usually site their generators some way from their houses and close to their agricultural fields. Suggest why:

(i) the generator is positioned away from the houses.

(1 mark)

(ii) the generator is sited close to the agricultural area.

(1 mark)

(c) Give two benefits of using a biogas generator instead of burning coal for energy.

(2 marks)

Revision Summary for Biology 3(ii)

So you think you've learnt these pages on microorganisms... Well, there's only one way to really find out. Just write down the answers to all these questions. Then go back over the section and see if you got any wrong. If you did, then you need a bit more revision, so go back and have another read of the section and then have another go. It's the best way to make sure you actually know your stuff.

1) What's the difference between spontaneous generation and biogenesis?
2) Describe three experiments that helped develop the theory of biogenesis.
3) What kind of microorganism is used in the manufacture of cheese?
4) In yoghurt-making, what's produced when the bacteria ferment the lactose in milk?
5) What type of microorganisms are yeasts?
6) What does "anaerobic" mean? Write an equation for the anaerobic respiration of glucose by yeast.
7) Write an equation for the aerobic respiration of glucose by yeast.
8)* Some yeast is added to 100 ml of water. Half of this is cooled to 0 °C for 2 hours and the other half is placed in a water bath at 90 °C for 2 hours.
   Each sample is then placed in a flask as shown in the diagram and brought to 40 °C. 20 g of sugar is added to each flask and the amount of carbon dioxide produced by each is measured after an hour.
   The sample that had been cooled to 0 °C produced 18 cm^3 of carbon dioxide. The sample that had been heated did not produce any carbon dioxide.
   What conclusions can you draw from these results?
   How could you check the reliability of your results?

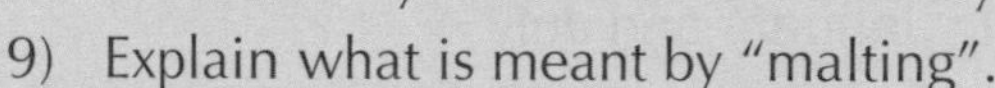

9) Explain what is meant by "malting".
10) Give four examples of conditions that are controlled inside an industrial fermenter.
11) What microorganism is used to make penicillin?
12) What is ethanol used for in some countries (apart from the obvious)?
13) What are the two main components of biogas?
14)*Loompah is a small village. It's very hot in the summer but freezing cold in winter. The villagers keep goats and cows. They also try to grow crops, but the soil isn't very fertile, so it's difficult. The villagers currently rely on wood for fuel for heating and cooking. There's not much of this around, so they spend a lot of time collecting it.
   a) How suitable do you think biogas would be for this village? Explain the advantages that using biogas would have for the village. What disadvantages or problems might there be?
   b) Loompah starts using biogas and uses the digested material as fertiliser. They compare their crops to the crops grown by the village of Moompah, which uses normal manure as a fertiliser. Loompah's crops are bigger, so they conclude that the digested material is a better fertiliser than manure.
   What do you think of the conclusion they've drawn?
15)*The data below shows the rate of biogas produced by a generator at various temperatures.
   a) Draw a graph showing the temperature against biogas produced. Join the points with a smooth curve.
   b) Using your graph, estimate the optimum temperature for biogas production.
   c) How much biogas would you expect to be produced in 24 hours at 25 °C?

Temperature (°C)	10	20	30	40	50	60
Biogas produced in 1 hour (cm^3)	6	32	54	78	50	18

16) What is a culture medium?
17) Why is it important to sterilise laboratory equipment before using it to culture microorganisms?

* Answers on page 230

Thinking in Exams

In the old days, it was enough to learn a whole bunch of facts while you were revising and just spew them onto the paper come exam day. If you knew the facts, you had a good chance of doing well, even if you didn't really understand what any of those facts actually meant. But those days are over. Rats.

Remember — You Might Have to Think During the Exam

1) Nowadays, the examiners want you to be able to apply your scientific knowledge to situations you've never seen before. Eeek.
2) The trick is not to panic. They're not expecting you to show Einstein-like levels of scientific insight (not usually, anyway).
3) They're just expecting you to use the science you know in an unfamiliar setting — and usually they'll give you some extra info too that you should use in your answer.

So to give you an idea of what to expect come exam-time, use the new CGP Exam Simulator (below). Read the article, and have a go at the questions. It's guaranteed to be just as much fun as the real thing.

Underlining or making notes of the main bits as you read is a good idea.

1. Blood glucose levels controlled by insulin.

2. Insulin added → liver removes glucose.

3. Not enough insulin → high blood glucose → death?

4. Carbohydrates cause problems for diabetics. So carbohydrates and glucose linked...

All cells need energy to function, and this energy is supplied by glucose carried in the blood. The level of glucose in the blood is controlled by the hormone insulin — if the blood glucose level gets too high, insulin is introduced into the bloodstream, which in turn makes the liver remove glucose.

Diabetes (type I) is where not enough insulin is produced, meaning that a person's blood glucose level can rise to a level that can kill them. The problem can be controlled in two ways:

a) Avoiding foods rich in carbohydrates. It can also be helpful to take exercise after eating carbohydrates.

b) Injecting insulin before meals (especially if high in carbohydrates).

Dave Edwards, a director of InsulinProducts plc, said: "We recommend controlling diabetes via insulin injections for its ease and safety."

Questions:
1. Why can it be helpful for a diabetic to take exercise after eating carbohydrates?
2. Suggest why a diabetic person should make sure they eat sensibly after injecting insulin.
3. Why might some people suspect Dave Edwards of being biased?

Clues — don't read unless you need a bit of a hand...
1. More complex carbohydrates are broken down to make glucose. What would normally happen if lots of glucose is suddenly put into the blood? How would this normally be controlled? And what happens in a diabetic?
2. Think about what insulin causes to happen.
3. What's his job?

Answers
1) Eating carbohydrates puts a lot of glucose into the blood. Exercising can use up extra glucose, which helps stop blood glucose levels getting too high.
2) If they don't, blood glucose levels can drop dangerously low.
3) He's a director of a firm that probably makes insulin — so he'll want to make that sound as good as possible.

Answering Experiment Questions (i)

You'll definitely get some questions in the exam about experiments. They can be about any topic under the Sun — but if you learn the basics and throw in a bit of common sense, you'll be fine.

Read the Question Carefully

The question might describe an experiment, e.g. —

Ellie had three different powdered fertilisers: A, B and C.
She investigated which fertiliser was most effective when growing pea plants.
Ellie planted a seed in each of 12 pots. She then added fertiliser A to three pots, fertiliser B to three pots and fertiliser C to three. She did not add any fertiliser to the remaining three pots.

Fertiliser A

Fertiliser B

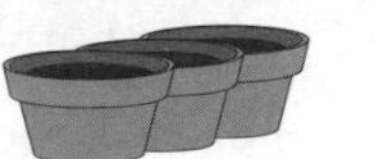
Fertiliser C

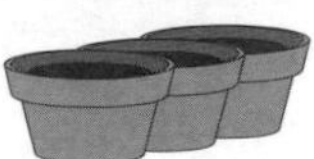
No fertiliser

She watered each pot daily and after three weeks she measured the heights of each seedling.

1. What is the independent variable?
   The type of fertiliser.

The independent variable is the thing that is changed.
The dependent variable is the thing that's measured.

2. What is the dependent variable?
   The heights of the seedlings.

To make it a fair test, you've got to keep all the other variables the same. Or else you won't know if the only thing affecting the dependent variable is the independent variable.
There are loads of other things that must be kept the same for each pot in this experiment. You could also have put temperature or the type of soil, etc.
It's easy to keep the variables the same in this experiment as it's in a laboratory. But it can sometimes be trickier. For example, if the seeds were growing in fields, it'd be hard to make sure that they all had exactly the same soil conditions, and got the same amount of water and light, etc.

3. Give two variables that must be kept the same to make it a fair test.
   1. The amount of fertiliser.
   2. The amount of light.

It's even harder to make investigations involving people fair.
If, say, the effect of a person's age on their blood pressure was being investigated, there'd be loads of other variables to consider — weight, diet and whether someone's a smoker could make a big difference to their blood pressure.
To make it a fairer test, it would be better if just nonsmokers with a similar weight and diet were used.

4. What is the control group in this investigation?
   The group of pots with no fertiliser.

A control group isn't really part of the experiment, but it's kept in the same conditions as the rest of the experiment. You can compare changes in the experiment with those that happened to the control group, and see if the changes might have happened anyway. Control groups make results more meaningful.
In this experiment the seeds might grow better without any fertiliser — with a control group you can check for this.

Control groups are used when testing drugs. People can feel better just because they've been given a drug that they believe will work. To rule this out, researchers give one group of patients dummy pills (called placebos) — but they don't tell them that their pills aren't the real thing. This is the control group. By doing this, they can tell if the real drug is actually working.

Answering Experiment Questions (ii)

5. Why was each type of fertiliser added to three pots, instead of just one?

To check for anomalous results and make the results more reliable.

Sometimes unusual results are produced — repeating an experiment gives you a better idea what the correct result should be.

6. The table below shows the heights of the seedlings in each pot.

When an experiment is repeated, the results will usually be slightly different each time.

The mean (or average) of the measurements is usually used to represent the values.

The more times the experiment is repeated the more reliable the average will be.

To find the mean:

Add together all the data values and divide by the total number of values in the sample.

The range is how far the data spreads.

You just work out the difference between the highest and lowest numbers.

	First pot	Second pot	Third pot	Mean
Fertiliser A	4.4 cm	5.2 cm	4.2 cm	
Fertiliser B	8.3 cm	7.9 cm	8.7 cm	8.3 cm
Fertiliser C	6.7 cm	5.7 cm	(0 cm)	6.2 cm
No fertiliser	2.4 cm	1.9 cm	2.6 cm	2.3 cm

a) Calculate the mean height of the seedlings grown with fertiliser A.

Mean = (4.4 + 5.2 + 4.2) ÷ 3 = 4.6 cm

b) What is the range of the heights of the seedlings grown with fertiliser A?

5.2 – 4.2 = 1.0 cm

If one of the results doesn't seem to fit in, it's called an anomalous result. You should usually ignore an anomalous result. It's been ignored when the mean was worked out.

This is a random error — it only happens occasionally.

7. One of the results in the table is anomalous. Circle the result and suggest why it may have occurred.

The seed may have had something genetically wrong with it.

If the same mistake is made every time, it's a systematic error, e.g. if you measured from the very end of your ruler instead of from the 0 cm mark every time, meaning all your measurements would be a bit small.

8. What conclusion can you draw from these results?

Fertiliser B makes pea plants grow taller over the first three weeks than fertilisers A or C, given daily watering.

Be careful that your conclusions match the data you've got, and don't go any further.

You can't say that fertiliser B will always be better than fertilisers A or C, because:

- The results may be totally different with another type of plant.
- After four weeks, the plants grown with fertiliser B may all drop dead, while the others keep growing. Etc.

Mistakes happen...

NASA made a bit of a mistake once. They muddled up measurements in pounds and newtons and caused the Mars Climate Orbiter to burn up in the Martian atmosphere. It just goes to show that anyone can make a mistake, even a bunch of brainy boffins. So always double-check everything.

Answering Experiment Questions (iii)

Use Sensible Measurements for Your Variables

Pu-lin did an experiment to see how the mass of a potato changed depending on the sugar solution it was in.

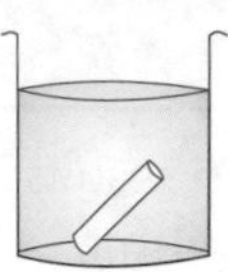

She started off by making potato tubes 5 cm in length, 1 cm in diameter and 2.0 g in mass. She then filled a beaker with 500 ml of pure water and placed a potato tube in it for 30 minutes. She repeated the experiment with different amounts of sugar dissolved in the water. For each potato tube, she measured the new mass. She did the experiment using Charlotte, Desiree, King Edward and Maris Piper potatoes.

Before she started, she did a trial run, which showed that most of the potato tubes shrunk to a minimum of 1 g (in a really strong sugar solution) or grew to a maximum of 3 g (in pure water).

1. What kind of variable was the list of potatoes?

   A A continuous variable ☐

   B A categoric variable ☑

   C An ordered variable ☐

   D A discrete variable ☐

2. Pu-lin should add sugar in intervals of...

   A a pinch ☐

   B a teaspoon ☑

   C a cupful ☐

   D a bucketful ☐

3. The balance used to find the mass of the potato should be capable of measuring...

   A to the nearest 0.01 gram ☑

   B to the nearest 0.1 gram ☐

   C to the nearest gram ☐

   D to the nearest 10 grams ☐

Categoric variables are variables that can't be related to size or quantity — they're types of things. E.g. names of potatoes or types of fertiliser.

Continuous data is numerical data that can have any value within a range — e.g. length, volume, temperature and time.

Note: You can't measure the exact value of continuous data. Say you measure a height as 5.6 cm to the nearest mm. It's not exact — you get a more precise value if you measure to the nearest 0.1 mm or 0.01 mm, etc.

Ordered variables are things like small, medium and large lumps, or warm, very warm and hot.

Discrete data is the type that can be counted in chunks, where there's no in-between value. E.g. number of people is discrete, not continuous, because you can't have half a person.

It's important to use sensible values for variables. It's no good using loads of sugar or really weedy amounts like a pinch at a time cos you'd be there forever and the results wouldn't show any significant difference. (You'd get different amounts of sugar in each pinch anyway.)

A balance measuring only to the nearest gram, or bigger, would not be sensitive enough — the changes in mass are likely to be quite small, so you'd need to measure to the nearest 0.01 gram to get the most precise results.

The sensitivity of an instrument is the smallest change it can detect, e.g. some balances measure to the nearest gram, but really sensitive ones measure to the nearest hundredth of a gram.

For measuring tiny changes — like from 2.00 g to 1.92 g — the more sensitive balance is needed.

You also have to think about the precision and accuracy of your results.

Precise results are ones taken with sensitive instruments, e.g. volume measured with a burette will be more precise than volume measured with a 100 ml beaker. Really accurate results are those that are really close to the true answer. It's possible for results to be precise but not very accurate, e.g. a fancy piece of lab equipment might give results that are precise, but if it's not calibrated properly those results won't be accurate.

Answering Experiment Questions (iv)

Once you've collected all your data together, you need to analyse it to find any relationships between the variables. The easiest way to do this is to draw a graph, then describe what you see...

Graphs Are Used to Show Relationships

These are the results Pu-lin obtained with the King Edward potato.

Number of teaspoons of sugar	0	2	4	6	8	10	12	14	16	18	20
Mass of potato tube (g)	2.50	2.40	2.23	2.10	2.02	1.76	1.66	1.25	1.47	1.3	1.15

4. a) Nine of the points are plotted below. Plot the remaining **two** points on the graph.

To plot the points, use a sharp pencil and make a neat little cross.

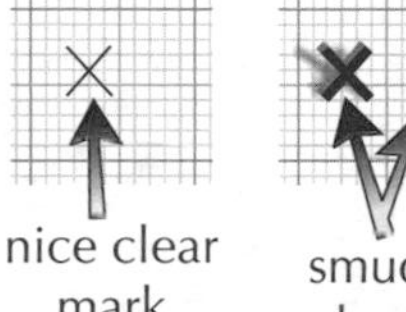

b) Draw a straight line of best fit for the points.

A line of best fit is drawn so that it's easy to see the relationship between the variables. You can then use it to estimate other values.

When drawing a line of best fit, try to draw the line through or as near to as many points as possible, ignoring any anomalous results.

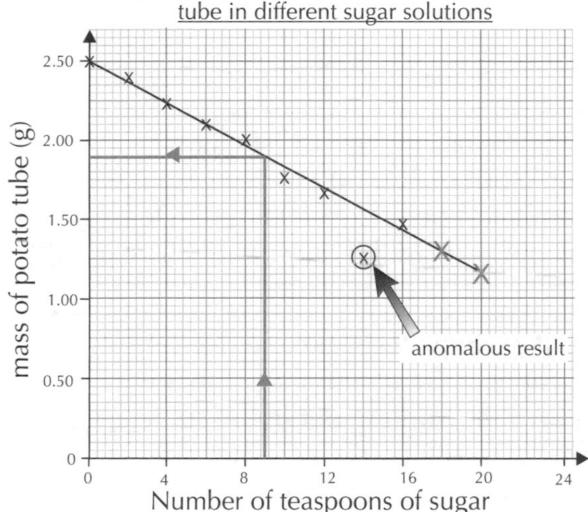

This is a scattergram — they're used to see if two variables are related.

5. Estimate the mass of the potato tube if you added nine teaspoons of sugar.

Estimate of mass = 1.90 g (see graph)

This graph shows a negative correlation between the variables. This is where one variable increases as the other one decreases.

The other correlations you could get are:

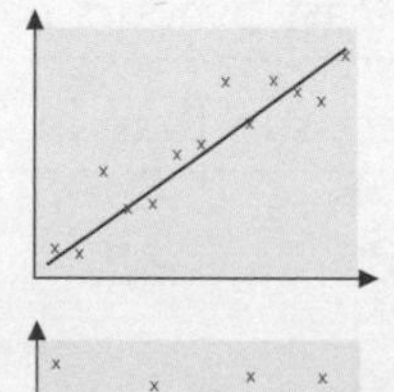

Positive correlation — this is where as one variable increases so does the other one.

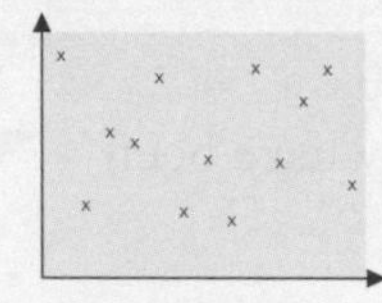

No correlation — this is where there's no obvious relationship between the variables.

6. What can you conclude from these results?

There is a negative correlation between the number of teaspoons of sugar and the mass of potato tube. Each additional teaspoon causes the potato tube to lose mass.

In lab-based experiments like this one, you can say that one variable causes the other one to change. The extra sugar causes the potato to lose mass. You can say this because everything else has stayed the same — nothing else could be causing the change.

Answering Experiment Questions (v)

Not all experiments can be carefully controlled in a laboratory. Some have to be done in the real world. Unfortunately, this creates complications of its own.

Relationships Do *NOT* Always Tell Us the *Cause*

Melanomas are a dangerous form of skin cancer. It's thought that UV damage may increase the risk of getting skin cancer later in life, so people are advised to avoid being in direct sunlight for long periods at a time.

The graph shows the number of new cases of melanoma found per year in people who spend at least 5 hours of each working day exposed to direct sunlight.

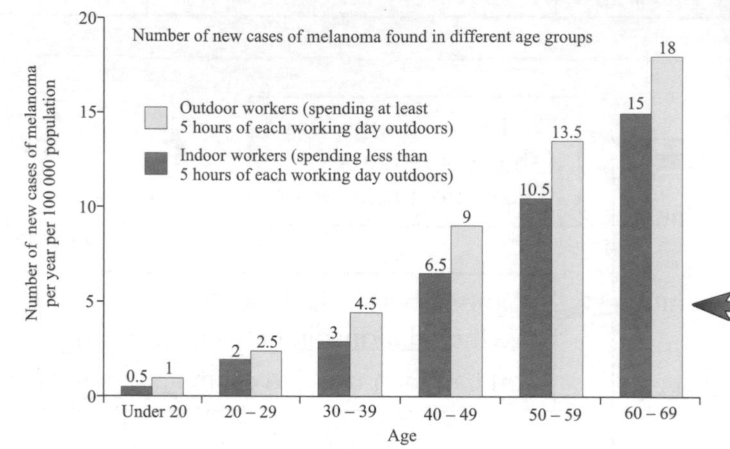

In large studies done outside a lab it's really difficult to keep all the variables the same and to make sure the control group are kept in the same conditions.

In this study the control group are people who work indoors.

This is a bar chart. It contains a key to tell you which colour bars relate to which group.

1. The graph is representative of a country that has 500 000 people aged between 40 and 49 who work outdoors.

   Using the graph, estimate how many of these people will get melanomas in a given year.

   $9 \times 5 = 45$ people

Here they're asking you to estimate the number of people out of 500 000 — the graph tells you the number of people in 100 000. Don't get caught out — read the question really carefully.

2. What conclusion can you draw from these results?

   Melanomas are found more frequently in people who spend at least 5 hours of each working day in direct sun than in people who work indoors.

When describing the data and drawing conclusions it's really important that you don't say that working out in the sun causes melanomas. The graph only shows that there's a positive correlation between the two.

In studies like this where you're unable to control everything, it's possible a third variable is causing the relationship. For example, many people who work outside are farm labourers or builders. Pesticides and other toxic chemicals that you might be exposed to in these professions could cause the increased rate of melanomas.

3. Suggest how the data may have been collected.

   e.g. from medical records

Use your common sense to find a sensible answer.

Try to suggest a method to get reliable results. For example, it's very unlikely that the data would have been collected by a telephone survey or an internet search.

A relationship doesn't necessarily imply cause and effect

It's really difficult to prove what causes what in science, especially with all the things you've got to control. The experiments are usually done in a lab first so you can control as much as possible. Then they're done in the real world to see if the same thing happens, and to find any unexpected results.

ıce you've been through all the questions in this book, you should feel pretty confident about the exams. As final preparation, ıre is a set of practice exams to really get you set for the real thing. The papers are designed to give you the best possible ɘparation for the AQA specification. If you're doing Foundation then you won't have learnt every bit — but it's still good practice.

General Certificate of Secondary Education

AQA GCSE Biology (Objective Test)

Unit Biology 1a – *Human Biology*

Higher Tier

Centre name					
Centre number					
Candidate number					

Surname
Other names
Candidate signature

Time allowed: 30 minutes.

Instructions to candidates

- Write your name and other details in the spaces provided above.
- Answer all questions on a separate sheet of paper.
- Do all rough work on this question paper.

Information for candidates

- Marks will not be deducted for incorrect answers.
- In calculations show clearly how you worked out your answers.
- You may use a calculator.
- There are 9 questions in this paper.
- The maximum mark for this paper is 36.

Advice to candidates

- Do not choose more responses than you are asked to.
- Work steadily through the paper.
- Don't spend too long on one question.
- If you have time at the end, go back and check your answers.

SECTION ONE

Questions **ONE** and **TWO**.
In these questions, match the letters **A**, **B**, **C** and **D** with the numbers **1** – **4**.
Use **each** answer only **once**.
Mark your choices on a separate sheet of paper.

QUESTION ONE

Your lifestyle can affect your health. Below is some data from four patients who attended a health clinic for a medical check-up.

Patient	Body weight	Smoking habit	Blood pressure	Blood sugar level
A	normal	non-smoker	normal	normal
B	normal	light smoker	normal	high
C	normal	heavy smoker	normal	normal
D	obese	moderate smoker	high	normal

Match patients, **A**, **B**, **C** and **D** with numbers **1 - 4** in the sentences.

The patient most likely to have diabetes is ...**1**....

The patient most likely to be in good health is ...**2**....

The patient most likely to get heart disease is ...**3**....

The patient most likely to get lung cancer is ...**4**....

QUESTION TWO

The table gives conditions that are controlled by the body and describes how the body regulates them. Match each condition, **A**, **B**, **C** and **D** with how the body regulates it **1 - 4** in the table.

A Water content

B Ion content

C Temperature

D Blood sugar levels

Condition	How the body regulates it
1	Regulated by hormones, including insulin
2	Regulated by the kidneys (also lost in breath and sweat)
3	Regulated by the skin and muscles (to maintain the conditions at which enzymes work best)
4	Regulated by the kidneys (also lost in sweat)

SECTION TWO

Questions **THREE** to **NINE**.
Each of these questions has four parts.
In each part choose only **one** answer.
Mark your choices on a separate sheet of paper.

QUESTION THREE

In vitro fertilisation (IVF) involves collecting eggs from the woman's ovaries and fertilising them in a laboratory using the man's sperm. The embryos produced are then transplanted into the woman's uterus. Throughout this process different hormones are used to improve the chances of success. The hormones can sometimes cause abdominal pain and dehydration.

3A What are hormones?

1 Chemicals that are secreted by the pituitary gland and act on the nervous system.

2 Chemicals that are secreted by the reproductive system and act on neurones.

3 Chemicals that are secreted by organs and are transported to other organs by the nervous system.

4 Chemicals that are secreted by glands and are transported to their target organ by the bloodstream.

3B What is the advantage of using IVF?

1 Some women can get pregnant that previously couldn't.

2 Some women can have twins that previously couldn't.

3 Women can choose babies who will have blue eyes.

4 Women can choose who to have a child with.

3C What is the advantage of giving FSH to women during IVF?

1 To stimulate the release of oestrogen from the ovaries.

2 To stimulate eggs to mature so lots can be collected.

3 To stimulate the pituitary gland.

4 To stimulate the release of LH.

3D What is a disadvantage of using hormones during IVF?

1 They reduce the chance of a successful pregnancy.

2 They stimulate egg production in the ovaries.

3 They can cause side-effects.

4 They can harm the embryo.

Turn over➤

QUESTION FOUR

Antibiotics can be used to kill bacteria and help a patient fight disease. Scientists developing antibiotics were testing the effectiveness of three different antibiotics, X, Y and Z, against a bacterium. They grew the bacteria on agar jelly in 20 Petri dishes — forming a 'bacterial lawn' on the top of the agar. They took four identical discs of paper and soaked each of them in a different liquid (see table). The discs were then placed onto the agar in each dish.

Disc	Liquid soaked in
1	Antibiotic X
2	Antibiotic Y
3	Antibiotic Z
4	None

The dishes were kept in an incubator at 35 °C for two days, and then they were examined. A typical dish is shown below.

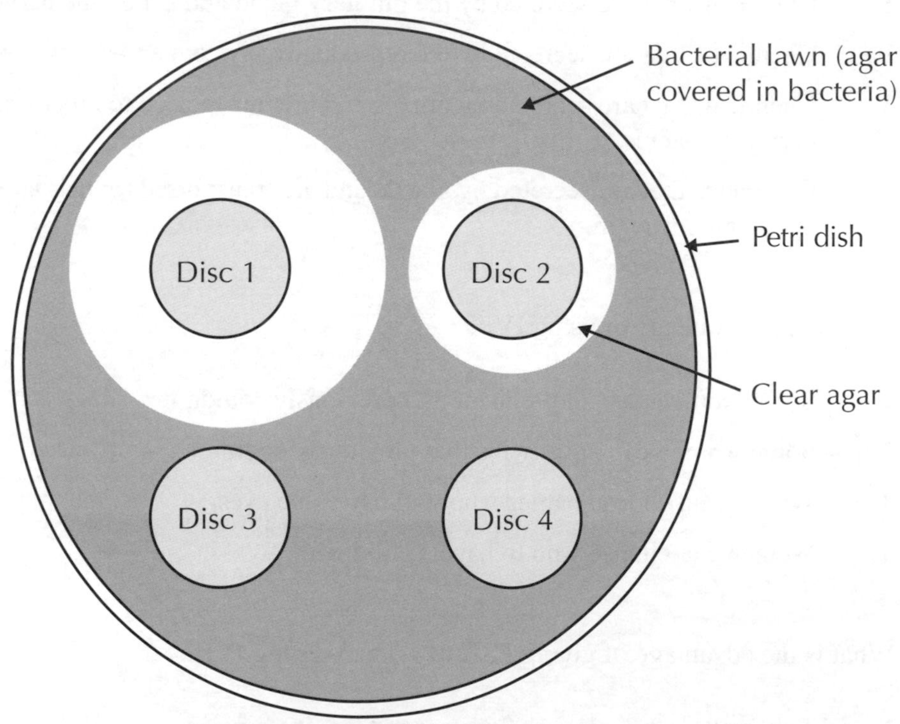

4A Which antibiotic was the most effective in killing the bacteria?

1 Antibiotic X

2 Antibiotic Y

3 Antibiotic Z

4 None of them were effective

4B What was the dependent variable in this experiment?

1. The type of antibiotic
2. The type of bacterium
3. The concentration of the antibiotic
4. The diameter of the clear zone in the agar

4C The scientists did not add anything to disc four to make sure that the paper disc was not having an effect. What is this sort of procedure called?

1. An independent variable
2. A base-line
3. A control
4. A standard

4D The most effective antibiotic was manufactured and prescribed to patients. Two years later scientists repeated the experiment with a fresh sample of the bacteria and found that no clear zone was produced around the disc soaked in this antibiotic. What is the most likely reason for this?

1. The bacteria were squashed by the paper disc.
2. The bacteria have developed resistance to the antibiotic.
3. The antibiotic was contaminated with another chemical.
4. Antibiotic X affected the results.

Turn over for the next question

Turn over➤

QUESTION FIVE

Alcohol affects a person's ability to drive safely. The graph shows the effects of drinking a certain number of 250 ml glasses of an average strength wine on the percentage of alcohol in the blood, for people weighing 75 kg.

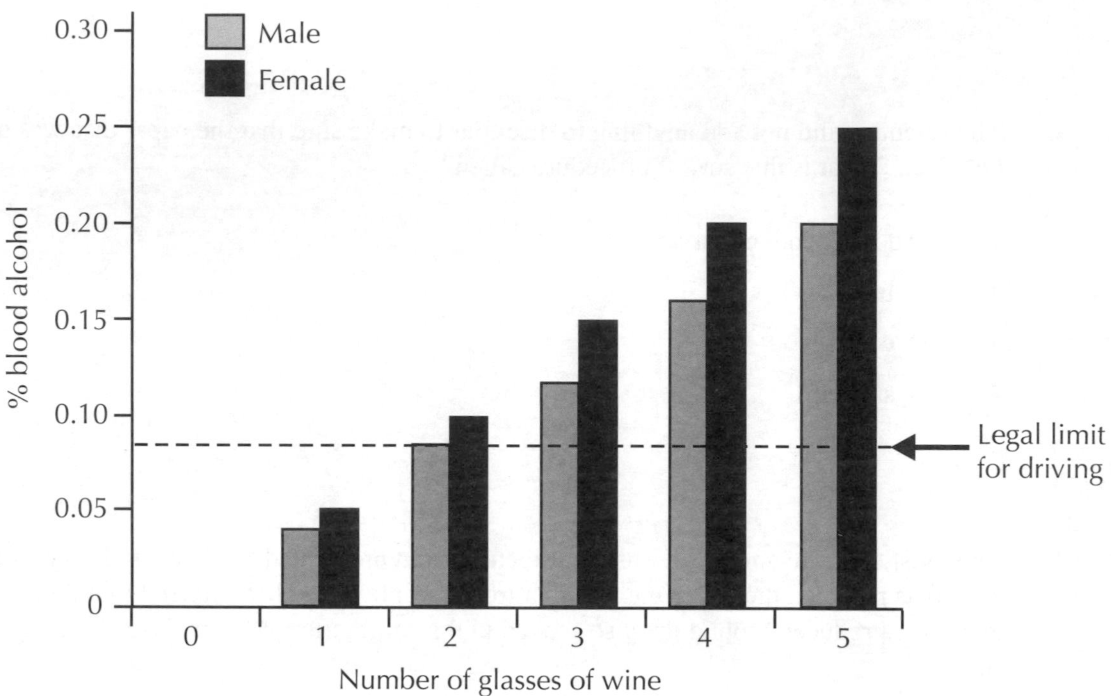

5A Why does drinking alcohol affect your ability to drive safely?

1 It speeds up your reaction time.

2 It is a poison.

3 It slows down your nervous system reactions.

4 It makes you more talkative.

5B Which of the following conclusions can **not** be drawn from the data?

1 Heavier people are less affected by alcohol than lighter people.

2 After one glass of wine, women generally have a higher blood alcohol level than men.

3 The more alcohol you drink, the higher your blood alcohol percentage becomes.

4 There is a correlation between the volume of alcohol drunk and % blood alcohol.

5C From this data, how many 250 ml glasses of wine would a 75 kg woman need to drink to be over the legal limit for driving?

1 1

2 2

3 3

4 4

5D People are warned not to use data like that shown in the graph to predict how many drinks they can have before they are over the legal limit for driving. What is the best scientific explanation for this warning?

1 The data could be incorrect.

2 Some wines have a higher alcohol content per 250 ml than the average wine.

3 It will depend on whether you are male or female.

4 It is best not to drink at all if you are going to drive.

Turn over for the next question

Turn over➤

QUESTION SIX

Exercise helps to keep your body fat low and strengthens your heart. The table lists some different activities and how much energy (in kJ per minute) they use up.

Activity	kJ/min
Sleeping	4.5
Active office work	16
Watching TV	7
Cycling (5 mph)	21
Aerobics	43
Swimming	35
Slow walking	14
Jogging (5 mph)	40

6A Why does exercise help you to reduce body fat?

1 It is part of a healthy lifestyle.

2 It makes your muscles less efficient.

3 It makes you sweat.

4 It increases your metabolic rate.

6B Jim watches TV for half an hour and then slowly walks to his friend's house, which takes him 10 minutes. How much energy will he use up during these activities?

1 400 kJ

2 375 kJ

3 350 kJ

4 325 kJ

6C Jim eats a packet of crisps that contains 760 kJ of energy. How many minutes will he have to jog (at 5 mph) for to burn off the same amount of energy?

1 190

2 152

3 19

4 1.9

6D Jim eats a lot of processed food and very little fruit and vegetables. His daily food intake has a total energy content of 12 500 kJ. His daily activities use 11 000 kJ per day. Which of the following may this diet lead to?

1 Deficiency diseases only.

2 Being overweight only.

3 Being underweight and suffering from deficiency diseases.

4 Being overweight and suffering from deficiency diseases.

Turn over for the next question

QUESTION SEVEN

Based on the results of a study, a nutritionist claims that a high protein, low carbohydrate diet helps people to lose weight. Two hundred people took part in the six month long study — half followed a high protein, low carbohydrate diet and half continued their normal diet. The participants were weighed before and after the study and were also asked general questions on their lifestyle. The following results were obtained.

	Normal diet	**Study diet**
Percent overweight after study	35	26
Percent obese after study	10	9
Percent taking regular exercise throughout study	30	48
Percent with heart disease after study	8	10
Percent that are smokers	22	18

On average, the people who continued their normal diet lost -1% of their body weight.
On average, those that followed the study diet lost 4% of their body weight.

7A Around 10% of the people that took part in the study were obese.
Which of the following health problems is **not** more likely to occur in obese people?

1 Heart disease

2 Diabetes

3 High blood pressure

4 Meningitis

7B Do you think the nutritionist's claim is valid?

1 Yes, a lower percent of people on the high protein, low carbohydrate diet were obese or overweight at the end of the study.

2 Yes, the people on the high protein, low carbohydrate diet lost more weight on average.

3 No, there were fewer overweight and obese people on the study diet.

4 No, quite a lot more people on the study diet took regular exercise throughout the study, which could have caused them to lose more weight.

7C Other nutritionists did not recommend the diet as they thought the high protein diet could increase the person's intake of saturated fat (from eating more meat). What is the effect of saturated fat on the level of cholesterol in the blood?

1 Saturated fat increases the level of cholesterol in the blood.

2 Saturated fat decreases the level of cholesterol in the blood.

3 Saturated fat does not affect the level of cholesterol in the blood.

4 Saturated fat combines with the cholesterol in the blood.

7D How does a high level of blood cholesterol affect your health?

1 It increases the risk of stomach cancer.

2 It decreases the risk of liver disease.

3 It increases the risk of blood disorders.

4 It increases the risk of diseases of the heart and blood vessels.

Turn over for the next question

QUESTION EIGHT

Scientists are trying to develop a new vaccine against virus Z. Twenty people trial the vaccine. The results are shown in the table.

Number that became immune to virus Z	18
Number that contracted the illness in the next year	1
Number that suffered side-effects	7

8A What are the disadvantages of the vaccine against virus Z?

1 Not everyone becomes immune and about 50% suffer from side-effects.

2 It can make people ill and about 50% suffer from side-effects.

3 Not everyone becomes immune and some people suffer from side-effects.

4 The majority of people suffer from side-effects.

8B The following sentences describe how the vaccine against virus Z can protect you from getting ill from the virus in the future. What is the correct order of the sentences?

1 Virus Z infects the body.

2 The vaccine containing an inactive form of virus Z is injected.

3 The cells of the immune system can rapidly produce the correct antibodies against the virus, which destroy it before any symptoms appear.

4 This stimulates the immune system to produce antibodies against the virus.

1 2, 4, 1, 3

2 2, 3, 1, 4

3 1, 4, 2, 3

4 1, 3, 2, 4

8C How do viruses make us feel ill?

1. They produce antibodies that attach to our cells.
2. They damage the cells in which they reproduce.
3. They decrease our body temperature.
4. They engulf our cells and destroy them.

8D Scientists now know more about the action of drugs used to treat infectious diseases. They recommend that patients suffering from virus Z are not given antibiotics. Why is this?

1. Antibiotics help viruses to infect more cells.
2. Antibiotics are expensive.
3. Antibiotics should only be given to those who are very ill.
4. Antibiotics do not kill viruses.

Turn over for the next question

Turn over➤

QUESTION NINE

Scientists tested the reaction times of eight volunteers. Each person was touched on the back of the neck and had to press a button as soon as they felt the touch. Each person did the test 20 times, and an average reaction time was calculated. The results are shown in the table.

Name	Average reaction time (s)
Mary	0.5
Tom	0.3
Phillip	0.4
Sarah	0.6
Christopher	0.4
Isobelle	0.6
Lucy	0.4
Ben	0.5

9A In this experiment, what was the stimulus?

1 The skin of the neck.

2 The neck being touched.

3 Pressing the button.

4 Reacting as quickly as possible.

9B The response of the volunteers was not a reflex. How do you know?

1 It was quick.

2 It was voluntary.

3 It was timed.

4 The touch was not painful.

9C Why did the scientists test each subject twenty times?

1 To make the results more precise.

2 To increase the size of the sample.

3 To make the average more reliable.

4 The test can be done very quickly.

9D Below is a diagram of the parts of the nervous system involved in this response.

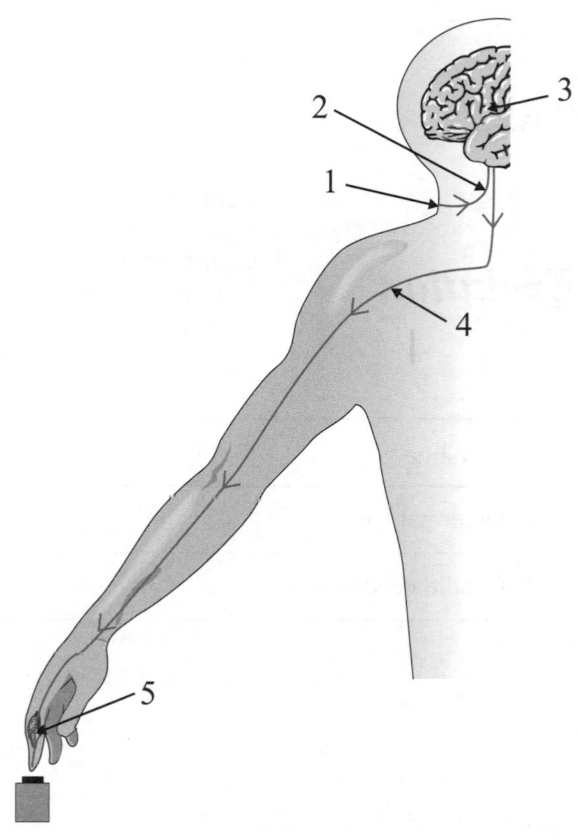

Label	A	B	C	D
1	receptor	receptor	receptor	receptor
2	motor neurone	sensory neurone	brain	sensory neurone
3	brain	brain	sensory neurone	effector
4	sensory neurone	motor neurone	effector	brain
5	effector	effector	motor neurone	motor neurone

Which column in the table shows the correct labels?

1 Column A

2 Column B

3 Column C

4 Column D

END OF TEST

General Certificate of Secondary Education

AQA GCSE Biology
(Objective Test)
Unit Biology 1b – *Evolution and Environment*
Higher Tier

Centre name					
Centre number					
Candidate number					

Surname
Other names
Candidate signature

Time allowed: 30 minutes.

Instructions to candidates
- Write your name and other details in the spaces provided above.
- Answer all questions on a separate sheet of paper.
- Do all rough work on this question paper.

Information for candidates
- Marks will not be deducted for incorrect answers.
- In calculations show clearly how you worked out your answers.
- You may use a calculator.
- There are 9 questions in this paper.
- The maximum mark for this paper is 36.

Advice to candidates
- Do not choose more responses than you are asked to.
- Work steadily through the paper.
- Don't spend too long on one question.
- If you have time at the end, go back and check your answers.

SECTION ONE

Questions **ONE** and **TWO**.
In these questions, match the letters **A, B, C** and **D** with the numbers **1 – 4**.
Use **each** answer only **once**.
Mark your choices on a separate sheet of paper.

QUESTION ONE

Match the terms **A**, **B**, **C** and **D** with the environmental effects **1** - **4** listed in the table.

A Deforestation

B Cattle rearing

C Fertilisers

D Car exhausts

Factor	Environmental Effect
1	release carbon dioxide into the atmosphere
2	adds methane to the atmosphere
3	reduces the amount of carbon dioxide absorbed from the atmosphere
4	can pollute lakes and rivers

Turn over for the next question

Turn over➤

QUESTION TWO

A survey was carried out on the air pollution in a town. The students counted the number of four different types of lichen found on trees in four different areas. Lichens can be used as indicator species for air pollution.

Lichen	Condition
W	nitrogen dioxide tolerant
X	ozone tolerant
Y	sulfur tolerant
Z	clean air only

Match the descriptions **A**, **B**, **C** and **D** with the areas **1 - 4** given in the results table.

A Unpolluted area

B Area polluted with sulfur dioxide but not nitrogen dioxide

C Area polluted with ozone

D Area polluted with sulfur dioxide and nitrogen dioxide

	Numbers of each lichen species found			
Area	**W**	**X**	**Y**	**Z**
1	10	15	44	0
2	32	4	16	37
3	10	34	7	0
4	17	5	25	0

SECTION TWO

Questions **THREE** to **NINE**.
Each of these questions has four parts.
In each part choose only **one** answer.
Mark your choices on a separate sheet of paper.

QUESTION THREE

An experiment was carried out to discover the best growth medium for the tissue culture of a certain species of plant. Four different growth media, **1** - **4**, were used.

The scientists weighed ten blocks of stem tissue, each measuring 1 mm × 1 mm × 1 mm. These were placed onto growth medium 1, as shown in the diagram.

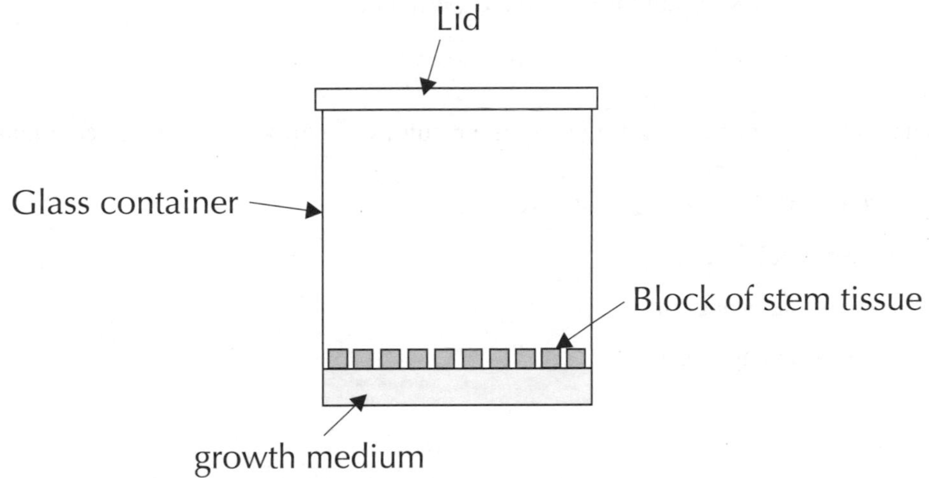

The container was then incubated at 35 °C for two days. At the end of that time, the blocks were taken out and weighed again to see how much they had grown. This was repeated with the other three growth media.

The whole experiment was repeated twice again, using leaf tissue and then using root tissue instead of stem tissue.

The results of the experiments are shown in the table.

	Average % increase in mass		
Growth medium	**Stem tissue**	**Leaf tissue**	**Root tissue**
1	120	33	77
2	85	21	62
3	65	17	58
4	98	25	102

Question 3 continues on the next page

Turn over➤

3A The data shows that the best combination for growing plant tissue is:

1 Stem tissue with growth medium 1

2 Stem tissue with growth medium 2

3 Leaf tissue with growth medium 3

4 Root tissue with growth medium 4

3B Which of the following variables does not need to be controlled to make it a fair experiment?

1 The amount of growth medium used.

2 The starting mass of the blocks of stem tissue.

3 The temperature in the incubator.

4 The species of plant used in the experiment.

3C What is the scientific term for using tissue cultures to grow lots of identical plants?

1 Cloning

2 Reproduction

3 Artificial selection

4 Genetic engineering

3D Which of the following statements is **not** a reason why plants are grown using this technique?

1 Plants can be produced quickly.

2 The gene pool is reduced.

3 Plants can be grown all year round.

4 Plants with desired characteristics can be copied.

QUESTION FOUR

A type of snail exists in two varieties, one brown, the other greenish-yellow.

Ecologists studied the numbers of each variety in an area of woodland. During the second year of the study, the woodland was cut down and the area became grassland used for grazing sheep. The table shows the ecologists' results

Year	Number of brown snails in 100 m²	Number of greenish-yellow snails in 100 m²
1	178	17
2	163	29
3	144	77
4	109	89
5	98	104
6	75	143
7	43	158
8	22	176
9	24	197
10	23	189

Question 4 continues on the next page

Turn over➤

4A What is the most likely explanation for the decrease in the number of brown snails?

1 The snails were changing colour from brown to greenish-yellow.

2 The brown snails weren't as well camouflaged in grassland so were more likely to get eaten.

3 The greenish-yellow snails were eating the brown ones.

4 The decrease is a natural variation in population size.

4B The change in the number of each colour of snail in this area is due to a change in environment. This is an example of:

1 Genetic modification

2 Global warming

3 Environmental variation

4 Natural selection

4C The total number of snails in the area remained roughly constant throughout the time of the study. What is the most likely reason for this?

1 The food resources of the area remained the same.

2 The brown snails replace the greenish-yellow snails.

3 The ecologists only looked at 10 m^2.

4 The method of sampling was always the same.

4D The snails are eaten by birds. This is an example of:

1 Competition

2 Equilibrium

3 Nutrition

4 Predation

QUESTION FIVE

A maize plant was genetically modified to be resistant to a herbicide. Herbicides are used by farmers to kill weeds.

5A When unmodified crops were sprayed with the herbicide, only 25% survived. Which of the following is the most likely reason that the herbicide did not kill all the unmodified crops?

1 Some had a natural genetic resistance to the herbicide.

2 The herbicide was not very effective.

3 The modified plants had passed on their resistance.

4 Some genetically modified plants had accidentally got mixed with the unmodified ones.

5B How would the plants have been genetically modified?

1 By treating them with a low dose of the herbicide.

2 By dosing them with radiation.

3 By inserting a herbicide resistance gene into them.

4 By breeding them from plants that were naturally resistant to the herbicide.

5C There are concerns about the use of genetically modified plants. Which of the following statements is an opinion rather than a scientifically valid concern?

1 The gene could be passed on to unmodified crops.

2 It is wrong for human beings to interfere with natural processes.

3 People might develop allergies to the new crops.

4 Having herbicide-resistant crops could increase the use of herbicides by farmers.

5D Which of the following is used to cut out genes for genetic engineering?

1 Enzymes

2 Hormones

3 Insulin

4 DNA

Turn over➤

QUESTION SIX

The red squirrel is the 'native' squirrel of Great Britain. The grey squirrel arrived from America during the last century, and ever since, the numbers of red squirrels have been going down while the number of grey squirrels have been going up. The data below shows the numbers of red and grey squirrels in an area of woodland over the last 25 years.

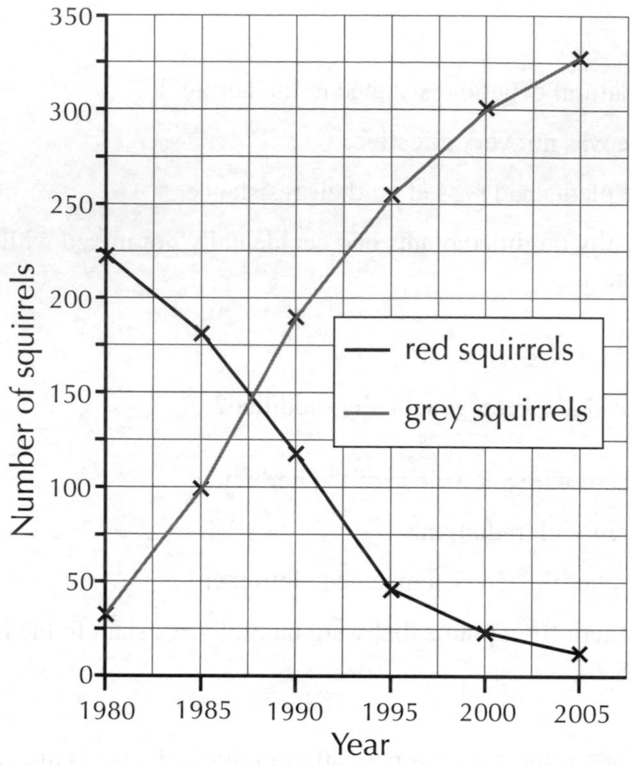

6A In 2000, approximately how many more grey squirrels than red squirrels were there?

1 150

2 200

3 275

4 300

6B Red squirrels and grey squirrels eat very similar food. When two organisms need the same resource, it is called:

1 Competition

2 Predation

3 Natural selection

4 Fighting for survival

6C Which of the following is the correct conclusion to draw from the data?

1 The grey squirrels are killing the red ones.

2 Red squirrels are not suited to their environment.

3 There is a correlation between the numbers of red and grey squirrels.

4 Grey squirrels eat the same food as red squirrels.

6D In which year were the numbers of red and grey squirrels approximately equal?

1 1985

2 1987

3 1989

4 1991

Turn over for the next question

Turn over➤

QUESTION SEVEN

Environmental officers studied a river that was polluted by sewage. They measured the amount of dissolved oxygen in the river at different points along its length. The flow of water is from point 1 towards point 15. The graph shows their results.

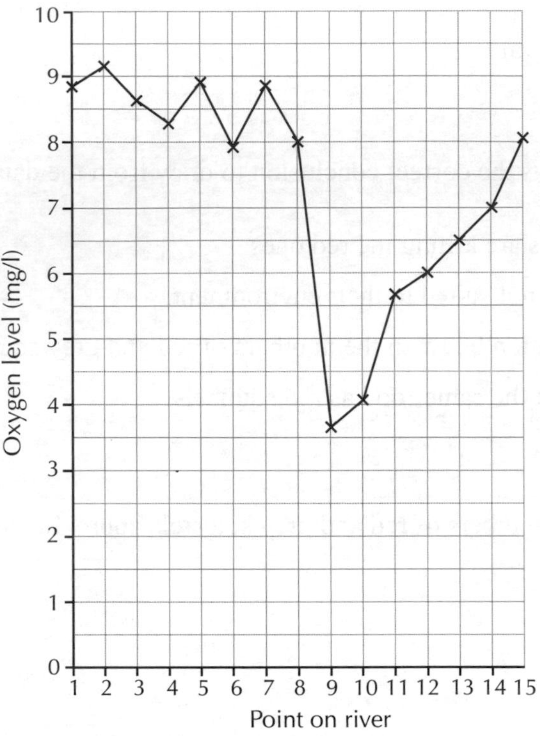

7A Where is the source of the pollution?

1 At point 9.

2 Somewhere between points 7 and 8.

3 Somewhere between points 8 and 9.

4 At points 8.

7B What is the approximate oxygen level at point 9?

1 3.6 mg/l

2 4.0 mg/l

3 3.8 mg/l

4 4.2 mg/l

QUESTION NINE

The diagram shows the possible evolution of modern humans and Neanderthals from a common ancestor.

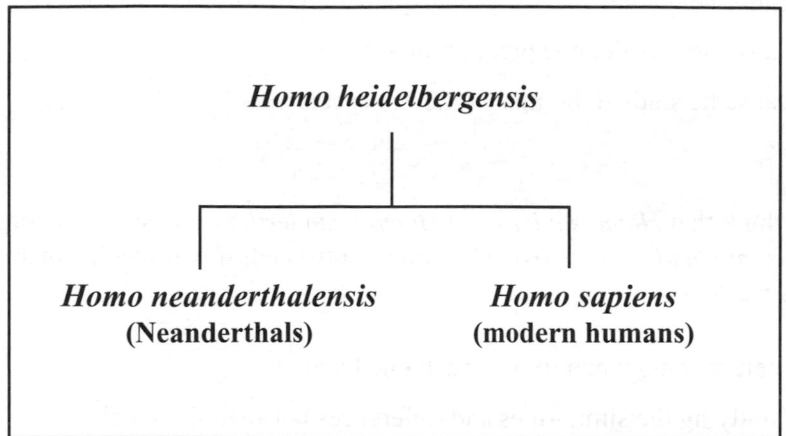

9A Neanderthals are now extinct. Which of the following could extinction **not** be caused by?

1 Changes in the environment.

2 Variation within a population.

3 Introduction of new competitors.

4 Introduction of new diseases.

9B *Homo sapiens* evolved a bigger brain than their ancestor, *Homo heidelbergensis*. Put the statements in order to explain how this occurred by natural selection.

A Those individuals with bigger brains were more likely to survive and to breed successfully.

B This process is repeated and over many generations until a new species is formed.

C Variation in brain size existed in the *Homo heidelbergensis* population because of differences in their genes.

D The genes that increased the survival of those bigger-brained individuals are passed on to their offspring.

1 A, D, B, C

2 A, C, D, B

3 C, A, D, B

4 C, D, A, B

Question 9 continues on the next page

Turn over➤

9C Darwin developed the theory of Evolution by Natural Selection. However, natural selection was not immediately accepted as a mechanism for evolution. Why was this?

1 Because he had no evidence.

2 Because he couldn't give a good explanation of why new characteristics appeared.

3 Because he wasn't an expert in biology.

4 Because he studied too many different species.

9D Scientists think that *Homo sapiens* and *Homo neanderthalensis* shared a common ancestor (*Homo heidelbergensis*). How do scientists tell if two species share a common ancestor?

1 By determining when in time each one lived.

2 By studying the similarities and differences between the species.

3 By studying what other species lived at the same time.

4 By studying how many were in the population.

END OF TEST

General Certificate of Secondary Education

AQA GCSE Biology

Set A

Unit Biology 2

Higher Tier

Centre name					
Centre number					
Candidate number					

Surname	
Other names	
Candidate signature	

Time allowed: 45 minutes.

Instructions to candidates

- Write your name and other details in the spaces provided above.
- Answer all questions in the spaces provided.
- Do all rough work on this question paper.
- Write your answers in black or blue ink or ball-point pen.

Information for candidates

- The marks available are given in brackets at the end of each question or part-question.
- In calculations show clearly how you worked out your answers.
- You may use a calculator.
- There are 7 questions in this paper.
- The maximum mark for this paper is 45.

Advice to candidates

- Work steadily through the paper.
- Don't spend too long on one question.
- If you have time at the end, go back and check your answers.

Answer **all** questions in the spaces provided.

1 Dan and Jenny carried out an experiment to investigate the effects of different minerals on plant growth. Their teacher has given them three plants of the same type, all of a similar height. The method they used is described below.

1. Measure the height of the three plants.
2. Add a solution containing minerals to three beakers as follows:
   Beaker A: solution high in magnesium and nitrates.
   Beaker B: solution high in magnesium and low nitrates.
   Beaker C: solution high in nitrates and low in magnesium.
3. Place a plant into each of the beakers A, B and C.
4. Leave the plants to grow for one week.
5. Measure the height of each of the plants at the end of the week.

The results of Dan and Jenny's experiment are shown below.

Beaker	Height at start (cm)	Height at end (cm)	Change in height (cm)
A	4	9	5
B	5	7	2
C	4	8	4

a) Explain why the growth in dish B, which lacked nitrates, was poor.

....

....

(2 marks)

b) Describe how you would expect the plants in dish C, which lacked magnesium, to look at the end of the week. Explain your answer.

....

....

(2 marks)

c) State one factor that Dan and Jenny would have had to keep the same in each dish to make the experiment fair.

....

....

(1 mark)

d) What conclusion can you draw from this experiment?

....

....

(1 mark)

6

Turn over for the next question

Turn over➤

2 Genes contain instructions to make specific proteins.
They are made of a chemical called DNA (deoxyribose nucleic acid).

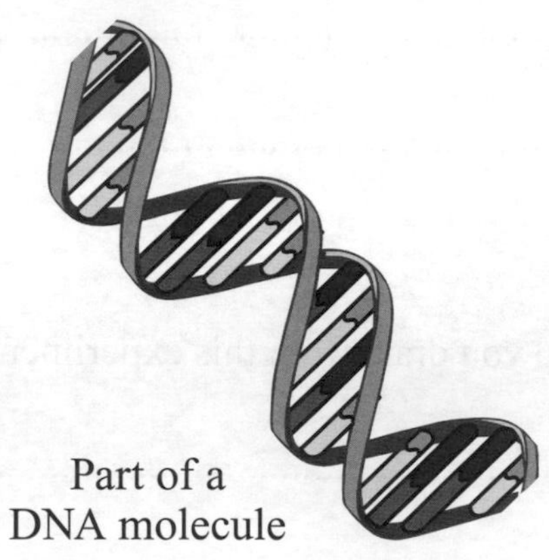

Part of a
DNA molecule

a) A single gene may exist in different forms.
What name is given to these different forms?

....
(1 mark)

b) In criminal investigations, forensic scientists may analyse DNA left at the scene of a crime, using DNA fingerprinting.

i) Why can DNA provide strong evidence that a particular suspect was at a crime scene?

....

....

....
(2 marks)

ii) Why would DNA fingerprinting be less useful if two of the suspects were identical twins?

....

....
(1 mark)

iii) Some people think it would be a good idea to store details of everybody's DNA, so that DNA from a crime scene could be checked against everyone in the country to see whose it is.

Suggest a reason why some people might be against this idea.

....

....

(1 mark)

5

Turn over for the next question

Turn over➤

3 The diagram shows the apparatus used in an experiment investigating photosynthesis. A lamp is used to provide light energy.

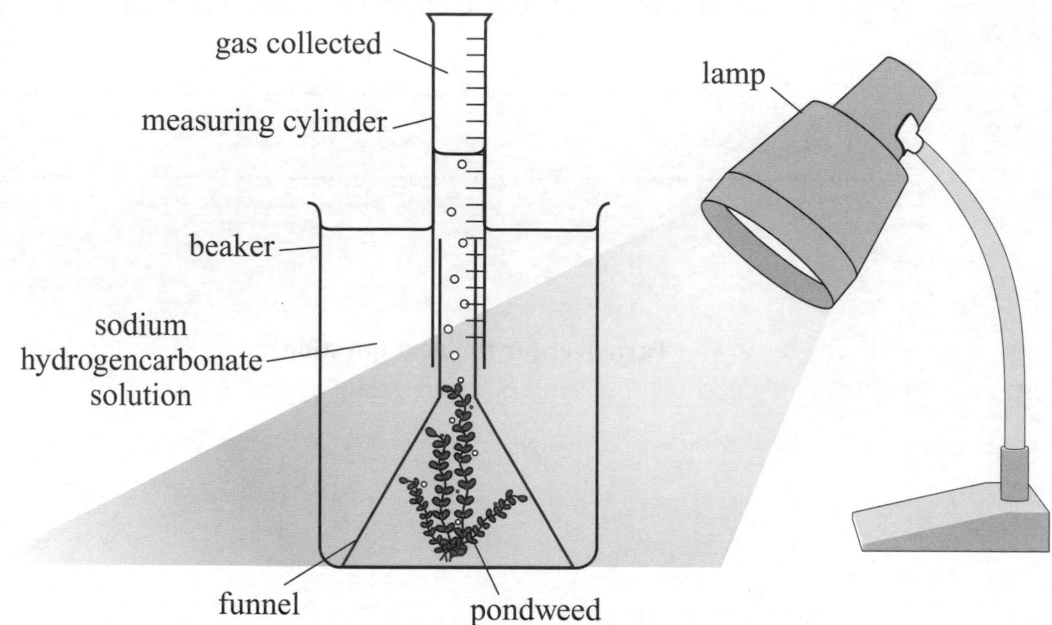

a) What gas is being collected in the measuring cylinder?

....

(1 mark)

b) What would happen to the volume of gas collected if the lamp was turned off? Give a reason for your answer.

....

....

....

(2 marks)

c) How do plants trap the light energy?

....
(1 mark)

d) Describe how the plant uses the light energy.

....

....
(1 mark)

e) Sodium hydrogencarbonate dissolves in water and releases carbon dioxide.
Suggest why sodium hydrogencarbonate was added to the water in this experiment.

....

....
(2 marks)

—
7

Turn over for the next question

Turn over➤

4 The diagram below shows the amount of energy in each trophic level in a food chain.

plant seeds	→	grasshoppers	→	mice	→	snakes
11 000 J		1100 J		130 J		12 J

a) Where does the energy stored in the seeds originally come from?

....

(1 mark)

b) Calculate the percentage of energy in the grasshoppers that is transferred to the mice. Show your working.

....

....

.... %

(2 marks)

c) Describe two ways in which energy is lost within a level of a food chain.

1. ....

2. ....

(2 marks)

d) Explain why food chains rarely have more than four trophic levels.

....

....

....

(1 mark)

6

5 Asif did an experiment on the effect of temperature on the action of the enzyme amylase. The method Asif used is shown below.

1. Add a set quantity of starch solution to a test tube and the same quantity of amylase solution to another.
2. Place the test tubes in a water bath at 10 °C.
3. Allow the starch and amylase solutions to reach the temperature of the water bath, then mix them together and return the mixture to the water bath.
4. Take a small sample of the mixture every minute and test for starch.
5. Stop the experiment when starch is no longer present in the sample, or after 30 minutes (whichever is sooner).
6. Repeat the experiment at different temperatures.

a) What happens to the solution of starch during the experiment?

....

(1 mark)

The graph below shows Asif's results.

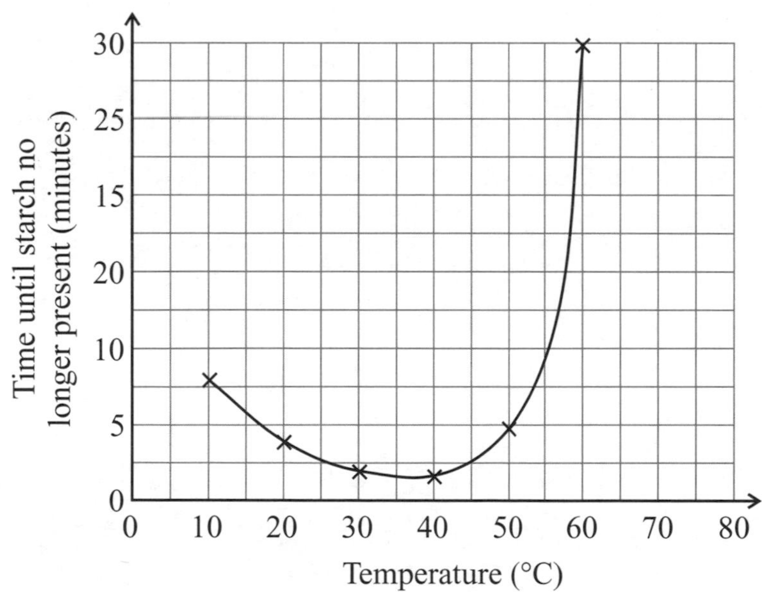

b) Use the graph to estimate the optimum temperature for this enzyme.

....

(1 mark)

Question 5 continues on the next page

Turn over➤

c) Explain the results between 50 °C and 60 °C.

....

....

....

(2 marks)

d) Explain why it is important that the pH of the solution is constant throughout Asif's experiments.

....

....

(1 mark)

5

6 Read this extract from a report by a lifeboat crew member, then answer the questions that follow.

> "We were very concerned when we received news of a man lost overboard tonight because the sea is extremely cold at this time of year. Fortunately, we found him quickly and were able to rescue him before he suffered any serious ill effects. His skin was very cold when we picked him up, but his core body temperature was normal."

a) What is the normal core body temperature of a human?

....

(1 mark)

b) Describe how the brain obtains information about the body's core temperature and skin temperature.

....

....

....

(3 marks)

c) Explain two ways in which the man's body may have helped prevent his core temperature from falling whilst he was in the sea.

....

....

....

....

(4 marks)

$\overline{}$
8

Turn over for the next question

Turn over➤

7 Gregor Mendel proposed the idea of separate 'hereditary units'. In one experiment he investigated the inheritance of round or wrinkled seed coats in pea plants. The allele for round seed coats (R) is dominant over the allele for wrinkled seed coats (r).

Mendel first crossed pure-breeding round seed plants (RR) with pure-breeding wrinkled seed plants (rr). All the offspring had round seeds.

a) Explain how the experiment shows that the allele for round seeds is dominant.

....

....

(2 marks)

b) He then crossed the offspring together.

i) Draw a genetic diagram to show the predicted results of this cross.

(3 marks)

ii) When Mendel crossed the offspring, 7324 plants were produced. 5474 of these had round seed coats and the other 1850 had wrinkled seed coats.

Calculate the ratio of round to wrinkled seed coats in Mendel's results.

....

(1 mark)

iii) Explain why this ratio does not exactly match the ratio predicted by your genetic diagram.

....

....

(1 mark)

c) Suggest one reason why Mendel's proposal was not recognised by scientists until after his death.

....

....

(1 mark)

8

END OF TEST

General Certificate of Secondary Education

AQA GCSE Biology

Set A

Unit Biology 3

Higher Tier

Centre name					
Centre number					
Candidate number					

Time allowed: 45 minutes.

Surname	
Other names	
Candidate signature	

Instructions to candidates

- Write your name and other details in the spaces provided above.
- Answer all questions in the spaces provided.
- Do all rough work on this question paper.
- Write your answers in black or blue ink or ball-point pen.

Information for candidates

- The marks available are given in brackets at the end of each question or part-question.
- In calculations show clearly how you worked out your answers.
- You may use a calculator.
- There are 8 questions in this paper.
- The maximum mark for this paper is 45.

Advice to candidates

- Work steadily through the paper.
- Don't spend too long on one question.
- If you have time at the end, go back and check your answers.

Answer **all** questions in the spaces provided.

1 The diagram below shows an alveolus and a blood capillary.

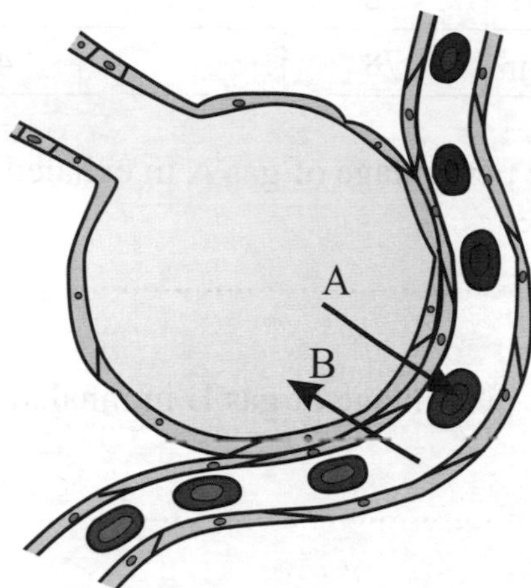

a) The arrows on the diagram show the net movement of two gases, A and B.

i) Name gas A.

....
(1 mark)

ii) Name gas B.

....
(1 mark)

b) Explain how alveoli are adapted for gas exchange.

....

....

....
(3 marks)

Question 1 continues on the next page

Turn over➤

c) The table below shows the approximate composition of inhaled and exhaled air.

	% composition			
	Nitrogen	Gas A	Gas B	Other gases
Inhaled air	78	21		0.96
Exhaled air	78		4.04	0.96

i) Calculate the percentage of gas A in exhaled air.

....

(1 mark)

ii) Calculate the percentage of gas B in inhaled air.

....

(1 mark)

—
7

2 The diagram shows a model of the human circulatory system.

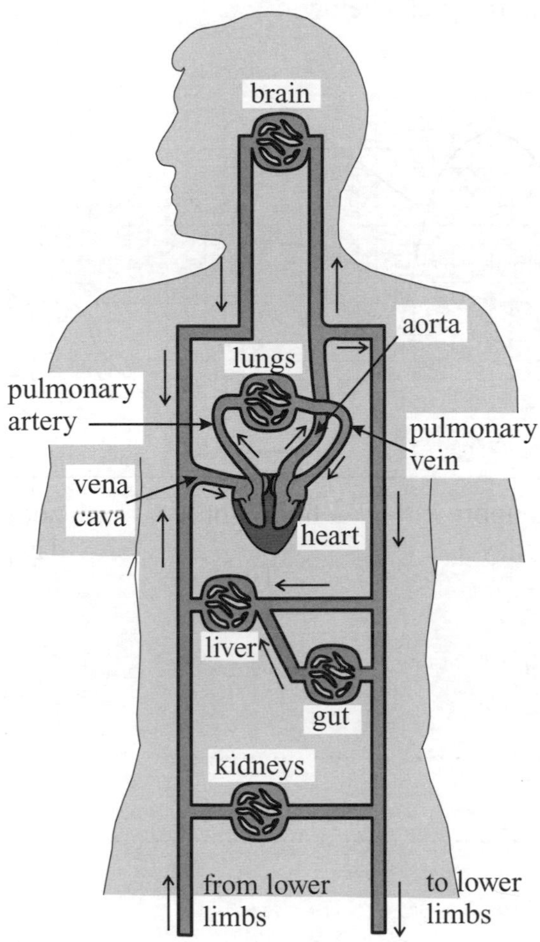

a) Complete the sentences about the circulatory system.

Blood is carried away from the heart in ....

These split off into thousands of ....

.... carry the blood back to the heart.

(3 marks)

b) Blood plasma transports carbon dioxide from the organs to the lungs. Name two other substances transported by blood plasma and say where these substances are transported from and to.

....

....

....

(2 marks)

5

Turn over➤

3 A scientist measured the rate of transpiration from a plant over 48 hours.
The results are shown in the graph below.

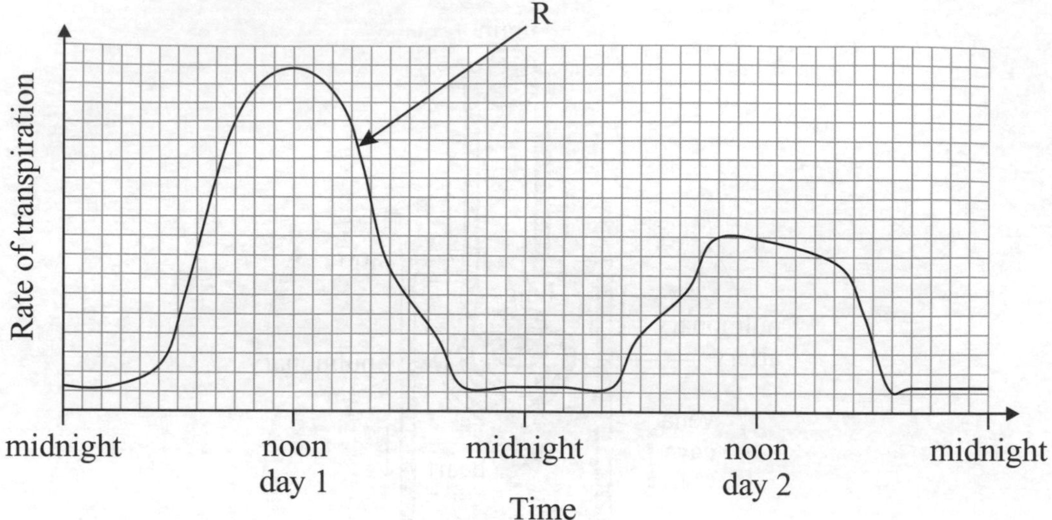

a) What is transpiration?

....

....
(1 mark)

b) At what time was the rate of transpiration highest on day 1?

....
(1 mark)

c) The rate of transpiration was slower on day 2 than on day 1.
Suggest one explanation for this.

....

....

....
(2 marks)

d) At time R on the graph, the plant was wilting.
Suggest one explanation for this.

....

....
(1 mark)

5

Turn over for the next question

Turn over➤

4 The kidneys play a crucial role in filtering the blood.
The diagram shows a kidney nephron and the blood vessels associated with it.

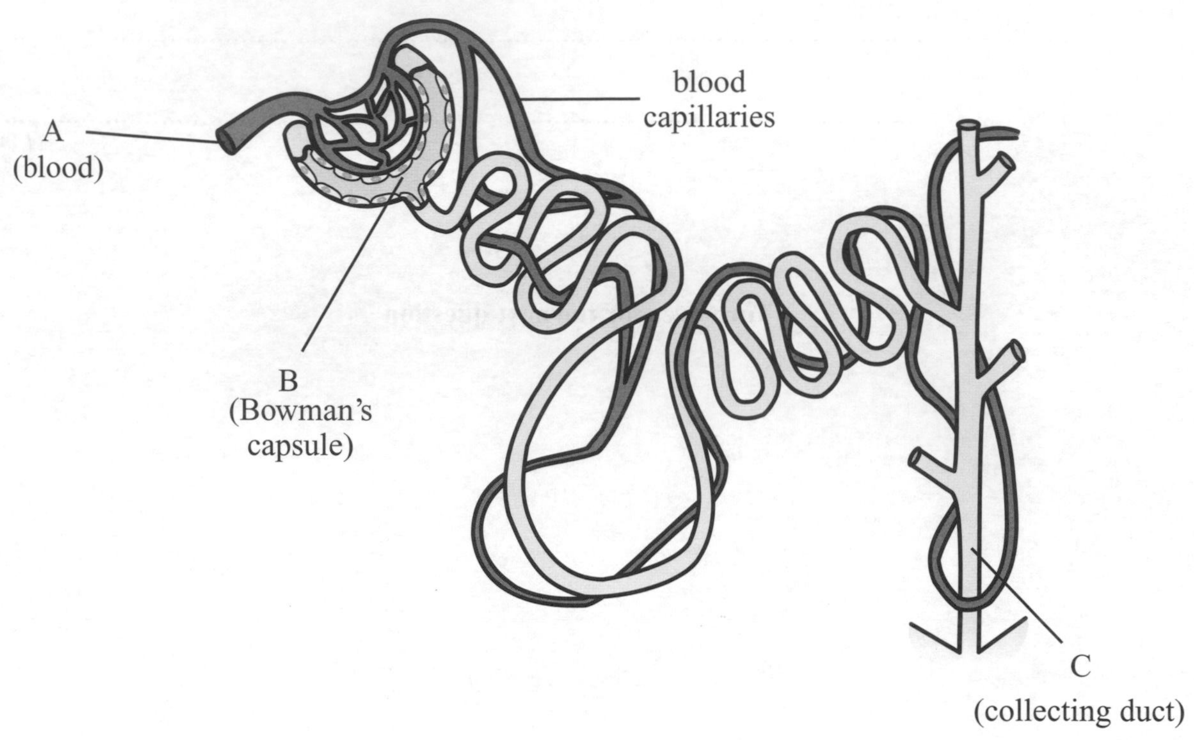

a) Many different proteins are found in the blood at point A but hardly any are found in the Bowman's capsule at point B.

i) Explain why there is almost no protein at point B.

....

....

(1 mark)

ii) Name one other component of the blood that would be present at point A but not at point B.

....

(1 mark)

b) The concentration of urea is greatest at point C. Explain why.

....

....

....

(1 mark)

c) How would you expect the concentration of sugar at point C to compare to the concentration at point B? Explain your answer.

....

....

(1 mark)

d) Kidney cells contain a large number of mitochondria.
Suggest an explanation for this.

....

....

....

....

(2 marks)

6

Turn over for the next question

Turn over➤

5 Read the information below about the work of Louis Pasteur.

Louis Pasteur carried out a series of experiments to disprove the then popular theory of spontaneous generation. In his experiments he poured a nutrient broth into two flasks and then bent the necks of the flasks into an S shape (called a swan-neck). He then boiled the two flasks to kill all the microorganisms before snapping the neck of one of the flasks, as shown in the diagram below.

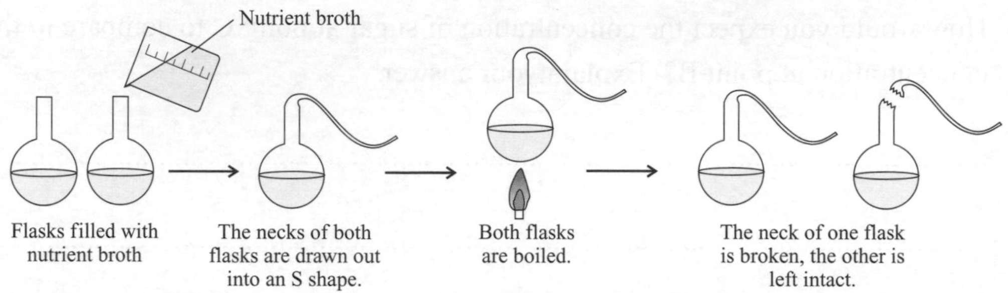

Pasteur believed that even though the intact swan-neck flask was open to the air, the swan-neck would prevent microorganisms from entering the flask.

He discovered that the broth in the flask with the broken neck quickly went cloudy. The broth in the flask with the intact swan-neck stayed fresh.

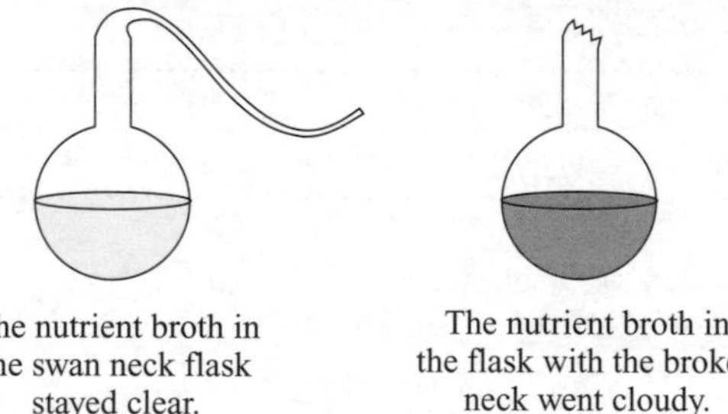

After some weeks, Pasteur broke the swan-neck of the flask.
A few days later, the broth went bad.

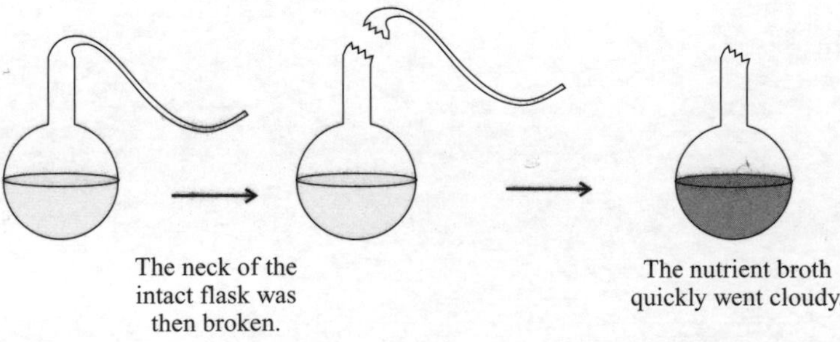

a) Pasteur's experiments were involved in the development of the theory of biogenesis.

What is the theory of **biogenesis**?

....

....

(1 mark)

b) In Pasteur's experiment, explain the reasons for the following:

i) drawing out the neck of the flask into a long tube.

....

....

(1 mark)

ii) keeping the swan-neck open to the air.

....

....

(1 mark)

iii) breaking the neck of one flask and leaving the other intact.

....

....

(2 marks)

c) Explain how Pasteur could have checked that there were no microorganisms in a sample of broth.

....

(1 mark)

d) Explain why it is important that other scientists are able to repeat Pasteur's experiment.

....

(1 mark)

$\overline{}$ 7

Turn over➤

6 The diagram shows a fermenter used in the production of penicillin.

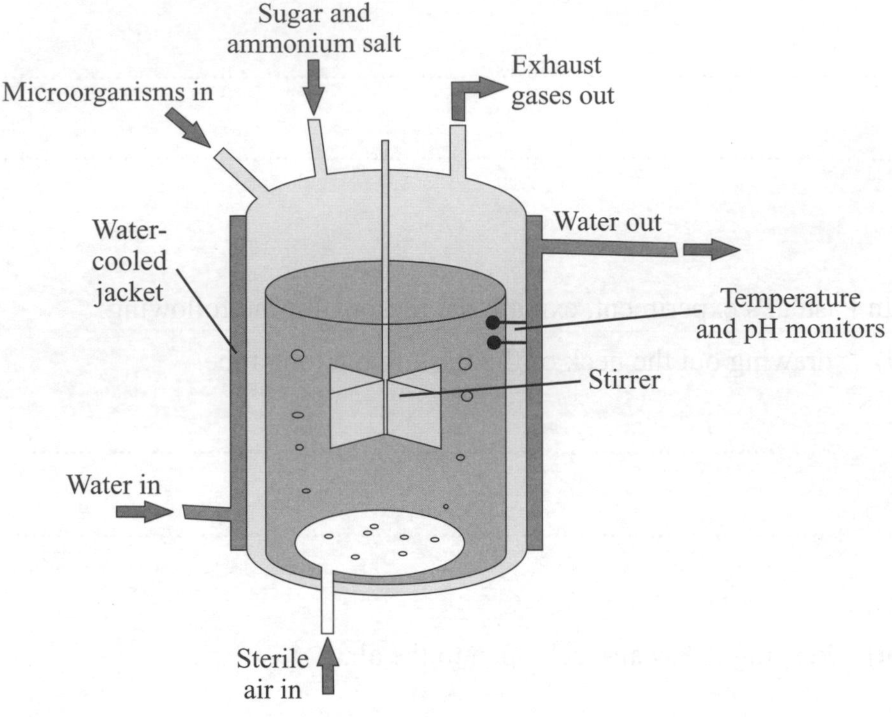

a) Name the microorganism used in penicillin production.

....

(1 mark)

b) Microorganisms produce heat during respiration.
Describe how the fermenter helps to keep a constant temperature.

....

....

....

....

(2 marks)

c) Sugar and ammonium salt are only added at the start of the reaction.
Suggest a reason why they are not added continuously.

....

....
(1 mark)

4

Turn over for the next question

Turn over➤

7 Nancy is a cyclist. A sports physiologist has produced a graph to show how the concentration of lactic acid in her blood changes with different work rates.

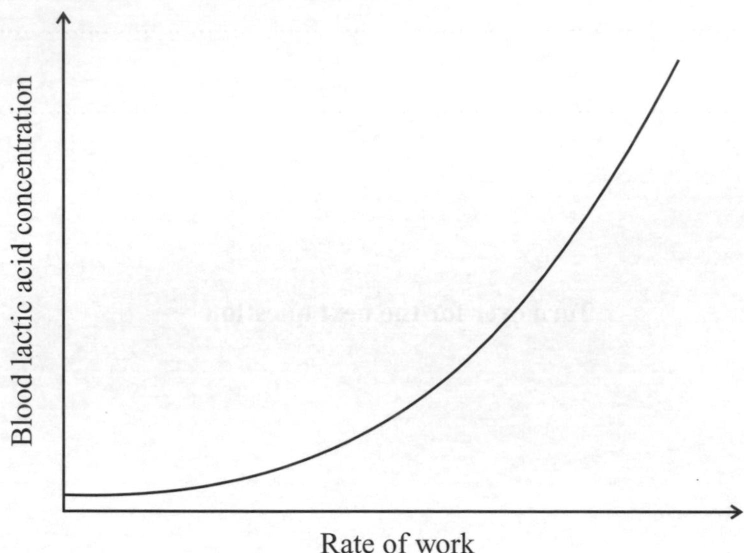

a) i) Describe the trend shown by the graph.

....

....

(1 mark)

ii) Suggest a reason for the trend you have described above.

....

....

....

....

(3 marks)

b) After a sprint race, Nancy's pulse rate and breathing rate remained high. Explain why.

....

....

(2 marks)

$\overline{}$ 6

8 Stomata are found on the underside of leaves.
The diagram shows a stoma on a plant at 10 am and at 11 pm on the same day.

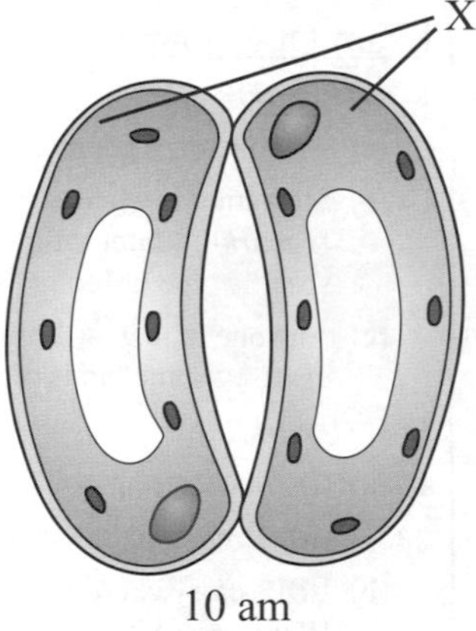

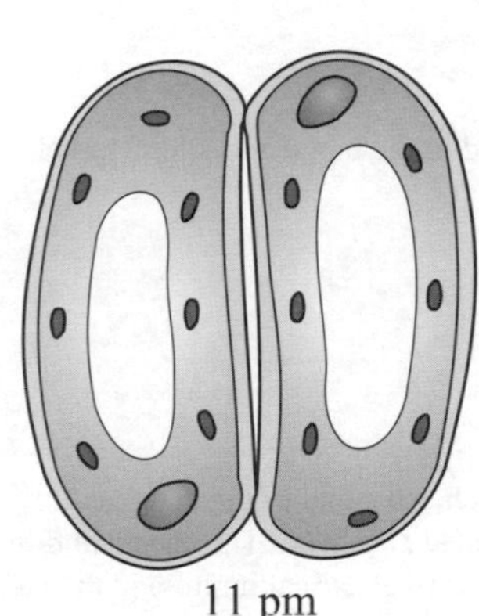

a) i) Name the cells labelled X.

....
(1 mark)

ii) Describe how these cells control the size of the stomata.

....

....
(2 marks)

b) What is the function of the stomata?

....

....
(1 mark)

c) Give one reason why the stomata are closed at 11 pm.

....

....
(1 mark)

5

END OF TEST

Page 13

Warm-Up Questions

1) eyes, ears, nose, tongue, skin
2) It receives information from the sense organs and coordinates responses.
3) as electrical impulses
4) a synapse
5) A chemical messenger that is carried in the blood and affects target cells.
6) the pancreas

Exam Questions

1 (a) reflex action ***(1 mark)***
(b) (i) B ***(1 mark)***
(ii)D ***(1 mark)***
(c) When the electrical impulse reaches the end of the neurone, it stimulates the release of a chemical ***(1 mark)***. The chemical diffuses across the gap/synapse to activate an electrical impulse in the next neurone ***(1 mark)***.
(d) Any one of, they minimise damage to the body (because they are so quick) / they help to prevent injury ***(1 mark)***.

2 B ***(1 mark)***

Page 19

Warm-Up Questions

1) Day 1 is when the bleeding starts because the uterus lining breaks down.
2) Hormones are given to a female to stimulate egg production. Eggs are collected and fertilised in a laboratory using the male's sperm. The eggs are grown into embryos, which are then transplanted into the female.
3) The maintenance of a constant internal environment.
4) E.g. water / ions / temperature / blood glucose levels.
5) Any three of, in sweat / in breathing out / in urine / in faeces.
6) This is the optimal temperature for most enzymes in the body.

Exam Questions

1 B ***(1 mark)***

2 (a) It inhibits it ***(1 mark)***.
(b) FSH ***(1 mark)***
(c) day 14 ***(1 mark)***

3 C ***(1 mark)***

4 Any two of, e.g. abdominal pain / vomiting / dehydration / increased risk of cancer ***(1 mark for each)***.

There are risks associated with most medical treatments, and IVF is no exception. People who decide to undergo IVF treatment should know and understand the risks, but if it's the only way they can have a child, then perhaps the benefits outweigh those risks.

5 (a) kidney ***(1 mark)***.
(b) brain ***(1 mark)***
(c) insulin ***(1 mark)***

Page 24

Warm-Up Questions

1) E.g. to keep food moving smoothly through the digestive system / to avoid constipation.
2) E.g. unbalanced diet, over eating, not enough exercise.
3) Any three of, e.g. slow growth in children / fatigue / poor resistance to infection / irregular periods in women.
4) high blood pressure (hypertension)
5) Cholesterol deposits narrow the lumen of the arteries and can cause blood clots.
6) the liver

Exam Questions

1 C ***(1 mark)***

2 (a) Any one of, e.g. protein / fibre / minerals ***(1 mark)***.
(b) Starvation is where a person doesn't get enough food of any sort ***(1 mark)***. Malnutrition is where a person lacks of one or more specific type of food ***(1 mark)***
(c) Any one of, e.g. arthritis / diabetes / high blood pressure / heart disease / some kinds of cancer ***(1 mark)***.

3 C ***(1 mark)***

4 (a) (i) increased blood cholesterol levels ***(1 mark)***
(ii) decreased blood cholesterol levels ***(1 mark)***
(b) LDLs carry cholesterol from the liver to the body cells ***(1 mark)***. HDLs carry cholesterol that isn't needed from the body cells back to the liver for removal from the body ***(1 mark)***.

Page 31

Warm-Up Questions

1) A substance that alters chemical reactions in the body.
2) Substances that can cause cancer.
3) E.g. emphysema, bronchitis.
4) Any one of, e.g. caffeine, alcohol, nicotine.
5) E.g. the effects of cannabis create a desire to try harder drugs / cannabis use brings people into contact with drug dealers / certain people are more likely to take drugs generally, so cannabis users will also try other drugs.
6) E.g. where has the health claim been published? Was the research carried out by a qualified person? Was a large enough sample used? Have the results been backed up by other findings?

Exam Questions

1 (a) Tar damages the cilia in the tubes of the lungs and windpipe. It also makes chest infections more likely ***(1 mark)***.
(b) Carbon monoxide reduces the oxygen carrying capacity of haemoglobin in the blood/red blood cells ***(1 mark)***.
(c) Nicotine is addictive ***(1 mark)***.

2 (a) Alcohol reduces the activity of the nervous system, making reactions slower ***(1 mark)***. It can also lead to impaired judgement, poor balance and coordination and false confidence ***(1 mark)***.
(b) Any two of, e.g. damage to brain cells/reduction in brain function / liver disease/damage / increased risk of stroke/heart attack ***(1 mark for each)***.
(c) Any two of, e.g. increased crime/violence / costs to the NHS / costs to economy through lost working days. ***(1 mark for each)***

3 (a) Computer models, testing on human tissues, testing on live animals, clinical trials on human volunteers ***(4 marks)***.
(b) (i) E.g. it stunted the growth of fetuses' arms and legs ***(1 mark)***.
(ii) E.g. leprosy / AIDS / certain cancers ***(1 mark)***

Page 37

Warm-Up Questions

1) A disease-causing organism.
2) Viruses replicate by invading your cells and using the cell machinery to produce many copies of themselves. Then they cause the cell to break open, releasing new viruses into your body.

3) Unique molecules which are present on the surface of cells/pathogens/ microorganisms.
4) To kill / harm pathogenic bacteria without killing your own body cells.
5) Any two of, e.g. polio / measles / whooping cough / rubella / mumps / tetanus.
6) Any one of, e.g. a swelling / fever / seizure.
7) It's when a disease spreads all over the world.

Exam Questions

1 4, 3, 1, 5, 2 ***(1 mark)***

2 (a) Flu is caused by a virus ***(1 mark)*** and antibiotics are not effective against viruses ***(1 mark)***.

(b) Inappropriate use of antibiotics increases the chances of antibiotic-resistant strains of bacteria emerging ***(1 mark)***.

3 White blood cells consume pathogens ***(1 mark)***, produce antibodies that kill pathogens ***(1 mark)*** and produce antitoxins that counteract the pathogenic toxins ***(1 mark)***.

Page 38

Revision Summary for Biology 1a

7) (a) A

(b) B

14) professional runner, builder, waitress, secretary

21) (a) 6 pm

(b) 8 pm

(c) no

Page 43

Warm-Up Questions

1) Keeping the surface area to volume ratio to a minimum reduces heat loss.
2) Bright warning colours to scare predators away, and a poisonous sting.
3) Competition, disease and predation.

Exam Questions

1 A — 2 ***(1 mark)***

B — 3 ***(1 mark)***

C — 4 ***(1 mark)***

D — 1 ***(1 mark)***

2 Any three of, e.g. has spines instead of leaves to reduce water loss / small surface area compared to volume reduces water loss from evaporation / storing water in its stem / extensive shallow root system to absorb water over a wide area / deep roots to access underground water ***(1 mark each)***.

3 (a) In a woodland area ***(1 mark)***.

(b) (i) competition ***(1 mark)***

(ii) The population of Species A is likely to decrease ***(1 mark)***, because the number of beetles available to eat will decrease ***(1 mark)*** as Species B will be feeding on them too ***(1 mark)***.

Page 48

Warm-Up Questions

1) a) eye colour

b) scar

c) weight

2) the nucleus
3) Alleles are different versions of the same gene.
4) one parent

Exam Questions

1 (a) sperm ***(1 mark)*** and egg ***(1 mark)***

(b) 23 ***(1 mark)***

(c) 46 ***(1 mark)***

(d) half ***(1 mark)***

2 (a) Ruth and Mark have (inherited) different eye-colour genes ***(1 mark)***.

(b) During sexual reproduction, an individual receives a mixture of genes/chromosomes from both parents ***(1 mark)***. The combination that it receives determines what features it inherits ***(1 mark)***.

(c) B ***(1 mark)***

Page 53

Warm-Up Questions

1) A few plant cells are put in a growth medium with hormones, and they then grow into new plants that are clones of the parent plant.
2) By taking cuttings.
3) E.g. hundreds of "ideal" offspring can be produced each year.
4) A reduced gene pool is where there are fewer alleles in a population.
5) Gene splicing is using enzymes to cut an organism's chromosome, and insert a useful gene from another organism into it.

Exam Questions

1 (a) E.g. to cut the gene out of the donor organism's chromosome ***(1 mark)***.
To cut the DNA of the recipient organism's chromosome ***(1 mark)***.
To insert the gene into the recipient organism's chromosome ***(1 mark)***.

(b) Any one of, e.g. to give resistance to viruses / to give resistance to herbicides / to produce long-life fruit/vegetables / to give increased yields / to give crops with added nutrients ***(1 mark)***.

(c) E.g. to produce milk containing substances (e.g. drugs) that can be used to treat human diseases. ***(1 mark)***.

(d) Any two of, e.g. they could affect the numbers of other plants around the crop, reducing biodiversity / they could increase the risk of food allergies / they might not be safe / transplanted genes could transfer to other plants / super-weeds could develop. ***(1 mark each)***

Make sure you can explain the pros and cons of genetic engineering because it's a really controversial issue — and it could easily come up in the exam.

2 (a) The nucleus was removed from a sheep egg cell ***(1 mark)***. A complete set of chromosomes from an adult body cell (from a sheep) was inserted into the empty egg cell ***(1 mark)***. This grew into an embryo which was implanted into a surrogate mother ***(1 mark)***.

(b) (i) A cloned embryo that is genetically identical to the sufferer could be produced ***(1 mark)*** and embryonic stem cells extracted from it (to grow new cells or organs) ***(1 mark)***.

(ii) E.g. some people think it's unethical because embryos are destroyed ***(1 mark)***.

Page 56

Warm-Up Questions

1) Fossils provide us with evidence about an animal or plant that lived ages ago. They can tell us about the organism itself, its diet, habitat and how long ago it lived.

2) Gaps exist in the fossil record because few organisms turn into fossils when they die. Most decay completely.
3) A species that doesn't exist anymore.
4) A change in an organism's DNA.
5) Evolution is the gradual change/adaptation of a population of organisms over time. Natural selection is the process by which evolution can occur.

Exam Questions

1 C ***(1 mark)***

2 (a) Fossils ***(1 mark)***

(b) By estimating the age of the layer of rock where the fossil was found (e.g. based on known ages of other rocks or fossils nearby) ***(1 mark)***.

(c) Any one of, e.g. dietary information/what kind of food it ate / roughly how old the individual stegosaurus was when it died. ***(1 mark)***

(d) Gaps in the fossil record mean that you might not be able to find evidence of a common ancestor. / Fossils of the ancestor may not have formed/survived. ***(1 mark)***

3 (a) Some individuals are better adapted to their environment than others ***(1 mark)***. These individuals will be more likely to survive and reproduce ***(1 mark)***, passing on their characteristics to the next generation ***(1 mark)***. Over generations, the 'good' characteristics (that lead to a better chance of survival) will become more common in the population ***(1 mark)***.

Remember, individuals in a species are naturally selected for but individuals cannot evolve — only a species as a whole can evolve.

(b) E.g. he could not explain how characteristics could be inherited / it went against may people's religious beliefs ***(1 mark)***.

Page 65-66

Warm-Up Questions

1) E.g. modern farming methods have reduced the number of people dying from starvation / modern medicine has reduced the numbers dying from disease.
2) Many people around the world are demanding a better standard of living, so more energy is used to produce the various products that they want. More waste/pollution is also produced by manufacturing these products. Also accept: people tend to travel more nowadays, e.g. for work and for holidays, which burns a lot of fuel and causes pollution.
3) (a) Any one of, e.g. burning fuels produces carbon dioxide (a greenhouse gas that causes global warming) / sulfur dioxide (causes acid rain).

(b) Any one of, e.g. household waste is buried in landfill sites / nuclear waste is buried underground / chemicals (e.g. herbicides and pesticides) are used on farmland.

(c) Any one of, e.g. sewage is released into lakes, rivers and oceans / toxic chemicals from industry can pollute waterways / chemicals used on farmland can be washed into waterways.

4) The greenhouse effect is the process in which certain gases trap reflected heat and prevent it leaving the atmosphere.
5) Carbon dioxide and methane.
6) E.g. as the sea gets warmer it expands, which could cause flooding in low-lying areas / there would be changes in the weather — e.g. hurricanes form over water that's warmer than 27 °C, so with more warm water about you could expect more hurricanes / higher temperatures melt ice, causing the sea level to rise even more / other changes to weather patterns and the climate could mean some important agricultural areas may no longer be suitable for growing food.

Recent documentaries have shown footage of polar bears swimming for miles as their normal habitat disappears into the sea. But it's not just polar bears that will suffer due to climate change. Species all over the world, including humans, will have to adapt if their climate and habitat change — many could die out altogether.

7) Sustainable development is development that meets the needs of today's population without harming the ability of future generations to meet their own needs.
8) E.g. lichen.

Exam Questions

1 (a) (i) The concentration stayed about the same ***(1 mark)***.

(ii) The concentration rose sharply ***(1 mark)***.

(b) Any two of, e.g. deforestation / using cars/planes/other transport / burning fuel in power stations / burning more fuel to heat our homes / industrial processes ***(1 mark each)***.

2 (a) Melting ice on land runs into the sea / the sea water becomes warmer and expands ***(1 mark)***.

(b) Hurricanes can only form over water when it is above 27 °C — there is likely to be more water above this temperature as a result of global warming ***(1 mark)***.

3 (a) There would be fewer trees to carry out photosynthesis ***(1 mark)***, which absorbs/removes the greenhouse gas carbon dioxide from the air ***(1 mark)***.
Also accept: The trees might be burned/broken down by microorganisms ***(1 mark)***, which would release the greenhouse gas carbon dioxide ***(1 mark)***.

(b) Using the trees as fuel would contribute more to global warming ***(1 mark)***, because combustion releases the carbon in the wood as carbon dioxide ***(1 mark)***.

4 (a) The two sets of data show the same pattern/increase at the same time ***(1 mark)***.

(b) Any one of, e.g. a relationship between two things doesn't necessarily prove that one causes another / it could be a coincidence / some other factor may have caused both increases ***(1 mark)***.

5 (a) Biodiversity is the variety of different species in an area ***(1 mark)***.

(b) E.g. species may be able to provide useful products such as medicines / loss of some species may unbalance the ecosystem ***(1 mark each)***.

(c) (i) Bacteria in the water increase in numbers and use up oxygen, meaning the water becomes deoxygenated, killing off some of the species ***(1 mark)***.

(ii) Some species (like mayfly larvae) can only live in clean water, so their presence indicates a lack of pollution ***(1 mark)***.

Page 67

Revision Summary for Biology 1b

22) The fact that one glacier is melting doesn't mean that all glaciers are melting. One glacier melting doesn't mean that the average global temperature is rising. You'd need to collect a lot more data from around the whole world over a long period of time.

23) (a) As the world population increases the number of extinct species increases.

(b) E.g. more humans means more animals are hunted and more habitats are destroyed to make way for farming, living etc.

Page 75

Warm-Up Questions

1) Plant cells have a rigid cell wall, they have a permanent vacuole and they contain chloroplasts.
2) (a) To carry oxygen.

(b) Any two of, e.g. concave shape gives the red blood cells a large surface area for absorbing oxygen / concave shape helps the red blood cells pass through capillaries to body cells / no nucleus maximises the space for haemoglobin.

3) Diffusion is the passive movement of particles from an area of high concentration to an area of low concentration.
4) Water will move out of the animal cell by osmosis from an area of high water concentration to an area of low water concentration.
5) A partially permeable membrane only allows small molecules (e.g. water) to diffuse through it.

Exam Questions

1 (a) C ***(1 mark)***

(b) Chlorophyll ***(1 mark)***

(c) It has an tall shape/a large surface area for absorbing carbon dioxide ***(1 mark)***. Palisade cells have a thin shape so that they can be packed in at the top of a leaf where most light falls ***(1 mark)***.

2 (a) The potato cylinder in tube D ***(1 mark)***, because this tube contains the most concentrated sugar solution so this cylinder will have lost the most water by osmosis ***(1 mark)***.

(b) Tube A contained distilled water, so some of the water moved by osmosis into the potato cylinder ***(1 mark)*** from an area of high water concentration to an area of low water concentration ***(1 mark)***.

Page 80

Warm-Up Questions

1) Carbon dioxide, water, (sun)light, chlorophyll.
2) A limiting factor is something that stops photosynthesis from happening any faster.
3)

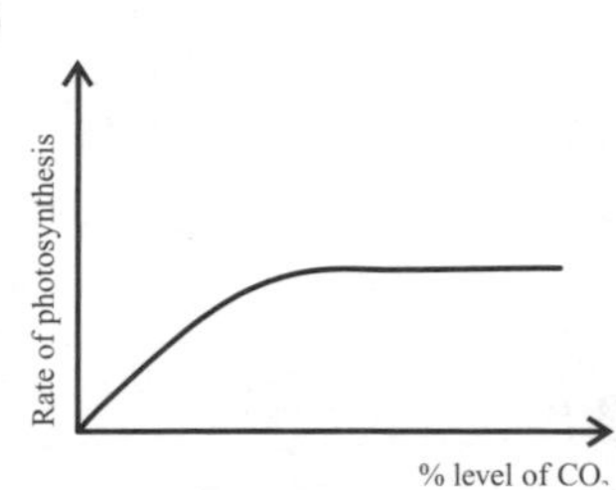

Exam Questions

1 (a) (i) At 20 °C the molecules/enzymes work more rapidly, so the rate of photosynthesis is quicker ***(1 mark)***.

(ii) At 50 °C the enzymes are denatured/the plant dies. ***(1 mark)***

(b) In the experiment the rate was highest at this temperature ***(1 mark)***, but the optimum could actually be anywhere between 30 °C and 50 °C (where no measurements were made) ***(1 mark)***.

2 (a) By counting the number of bubbles produced/measuring the volume of gas produced, in a given time/at regular intervals ***(1 mark)***.

(b) (i) The rate of photosynthesis/number of bubbles/volume of gas ***(1 mark)***.

(ii) The light intensity ***(1 mark)***.

(c) E.g. carbon dioxide concentration in the water / temperature / the plant being used ***(1 mark)***.

3 (a) A label anywhere on the sloping part of the graph, before it levels off ***(1 mark)***.

(b) E.g. carbon dioxide concentration / temperature / amount of chlorophyll ***(1 mark)***.

Page 83

Warm-Up Questions

1) respiration
2) glucose and fructose
3) Because starch is insoluble, which makes it much better for storing, as it doesn't bloat the storage cells by osmosis like glucose would.
4) the roots
5) All the plants are the same crop, so they need the same minerals. This means the soil becomes deficient in the minerals which that crop uses lots of.

Exam Questions

1 Making cell walls — cellulose ***(1 mark)***
Making enzymes — amino acids ***(1 mark)***
Making fruit sweet — sucrose ***(1 mark)***
Storing energy — starch ***(1 mark)***

2

Mineral	Function
magnesium	needed for making chlorophyll
nitrate	**needed for proteins / growth**

(1 mark for each)

3 (a) magnesium ***(1 mark)***

(b) nitrate ***(1 mark)***

Page 90-91

Warm-Up Questions

1) A feeding level in a food chain or web.
2) Because material and energy are lost at every stage in a food chain, so it takes a lot of animals to support each carnivore.
3) Biomass is basically the mass of living material at a trophic level — how much it weighs.
4) A community where the materials taken out of the soil and used are balanced by those that are put back in.
5) Any three of, e.g. the crowded conditions on factory farms can aid the spread of disease / intensively farmed animals are given antibiotics so, as a result of eating their meat, antibiotics may be less effective in humans / keeping intensively farmed animals warm uses extra fossil fuels / intensively farmed animals may be forced to eat sources of food they wouldn't naturally eat.

Exam Questions

1 (a) A ***(1 mark)***

(b) C ***(1 mark)***

(c) The mass of the organisms decreases at each trophic level as shown by this pyramid ***(1 mark)***.

(d) Their energy initially comes from the Sun ***(1 mark)***.

2 3, 4, 5, 1, 6, 2 ***(1 mark)***.

3 (a) Materials in living organisms are returned to the environment either in waste materials ***(1 mark)*** or when they die and decay ***(1 mark)***. Microorganisms break down the materials, returning them to the environment to be taken up again by organisms ***(1 mark)***.

(b) Any two of, e.g. warm / good oxygen supply / lots of decomposers ***(1 mark for each)***

4 C is the most efficient ***(1 mark)*** because there are fewer steps in this food chain so less energy is lost ***(1 mark)***.

5 (a) To prevent disease (which may be more likely in the warm, crowded conditions) ***(1 mark)***.

(b) The disease organisms may develop resistance to the antibiotics, which makes the disease harder to treat ***(1 mark)***.

(c) This reduces the energy the cattle lose as heat ***(1 mark)***. Keeping them inside means they use less energy because they move less, and using less energy means they'll need less food and so cost less money ***(1 mark)***.

6 (a) A = decay / respiration, B = photosynthesis, C = respiration ***(1 mark each)***.
(b) There would be less photosynthesis and so more carbon dioxide in the atmosphere/less carbon dioxide removed from the atmosphere ***(1 mark)***.
(c) photosynthesis ***(1 mark)***

Page 92

Revision Summary for Biology 2(i)

10 (a) 40 units
(b) Any two of, e.g. temperature / light / water.

Page 96

Warm-Up Questions

1) A catalyst is a substance that increases the speed of a reaction, without being changed or used up in the reaction.
2)

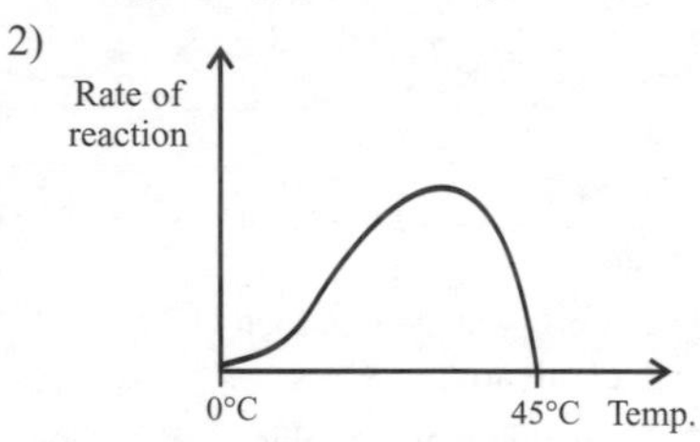

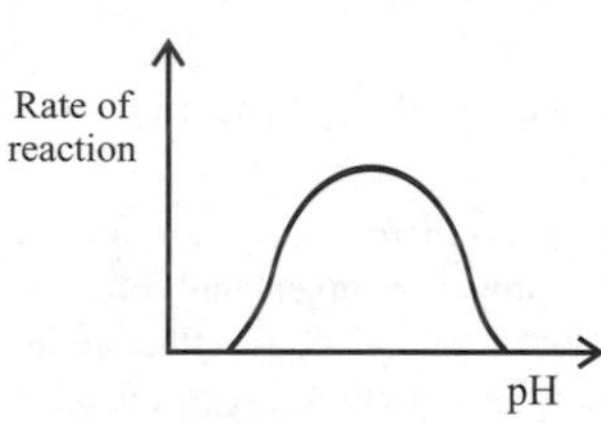

3) The optimum temperature or pH is the temperature or pH at which the enzyme works best.
4) Respiration is the process of breaking down glucose to release energy, which happens in every cell.
5) glucose + oxygen → carbon dioxide + water + energy

Exam Questions

1 (a) Accept answers between 38 °C and 40 °C ***(1 mark)***.
(b) Enzyme B ***(1 mark)***, because it has an unusually high optimum temperature which it would need to work in the hot vent ***(1 mark)***.
(c) It would break down the proteins in stains such as blood and grass on clothing ***(1 mark)***. It would not be denatured by high-temperature washes ***(1 mark)***.
2 (a) The enzyme has a specific shape which will only fit with one type of substance ***(1 mark)***.
(b) In the wrong conditions (e.g. high temperatures), the bonds in the enzyme are broken/the enzyme changes shape, so the substance can no longer fit into it/the enzyme won't work anymore ***(1 mark)***.
If you heat a substance you supply it with energy and it moves about more. This helps things to react faster. But if you heat an enzyme too much, it jiggles about such a lot that it ends up breaking some of the bonds that hold it together and it loses its shape. A similar thing happens with pH — the wrong pH disrupts the bonds and the shape is changed.
3 A ***(1 mark)***

Page 100

Warm-Up Questions

1) They break down big molecules into smaller ones.
2) (a) amylase
(b) protease
(c) lipase
Proteases break down proteins, and lipases break down lipids (fats).
3) (a) maltose and simple sugars
(b) amino acids
(c) glycerol and fatty acids
4) Bile emulsifies fats and neutralises the hydrochloric acid from the stomach.
5) Because they're protein-digesting and fat-digesting enzymes that break down animal and plant matter, so they're ideal for removing stains like food or blood.
6) Proteases are used to pre-digest the protein in some baby foods so it's easier for a baby to digest.
7) Advantages — any two of, e.g. they're specific, so they only catalyse the reaction you want them to / using lower temperatures and pressures means a lower cost and it saves energy / enzymes work for a long time, so after the initial cost of buying them you can continually use them / they're biodegradable and so cause less environmental pollution.
Disadvantages — e.g. enzymes can be denatured by even a small increase in temperature so conditions must be tightly controlled / contamination of the enzyme with other substances can affect the reaction.

Exam Questions

1

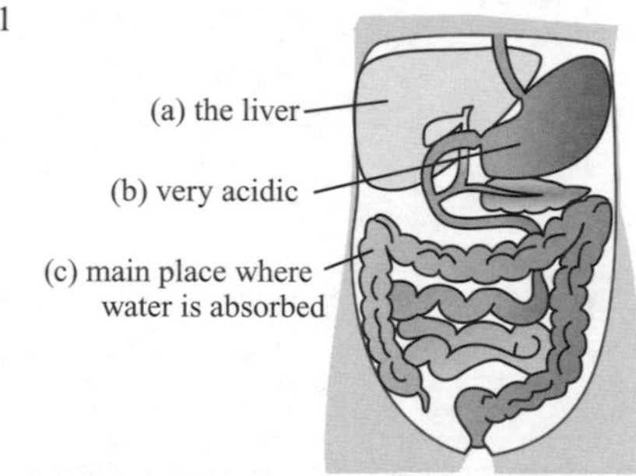

(1 mark for each)
The acidic part is the stomach. The large intestine absorbs most of the water.
2 (a) It stores bile until it is ready to be released ***(1 mark)***.
(b) It produces/releases digestive enzymes ***(1 mark)***.
(c) It produces bile ***(1 mark)***.
3 (a) amylase/carbohydrase ***(1 mark)***
(b) Any three of, e.g. temperature / volume of solution / concentration of starch solution / concentration of enzyme solution ***(1 mark for each)***.
(c) At pH 8 ***(1 mark)***, because this is the pH in the part of the gut where this enzyme works/because most enzymes work best at around a neutral pH ***(1 mark)***.

Page 105

Warm-Up Questions

1) E.g. carbon dioxide and urea
2) thermoregulatory centre
3) It contains receptors that are sensitive to the temperature of the blood flowing through the brain. It also receives impulses from the skin, giving information about skin temperature.

4) E.g. hairs lie flat / sweat is produced by sweat glands and evaporates from the skin, which removes heat / the blood vessels supplying the skin dilate, so more blood flows close to the skin's surface, making it easier for heat to be lost to the environment.
5) They remove urea from the blood, adjust the blood's ion content and make sure blood contains the right amount of water.

Exam Questions

1 E.g. hairs stand on end, which traps a layer of warm air next to the skin / sweat production stops / blood vessels constrict to close off the skin's blood supply ***(1 mark for each)***.

2 X = ureter, Y = bladder, Z = urethra ***(1 mark for each)***

3 (a) Urea, ions, and water ***(1 mark)***.

(b) Excess salt has to be removed from the body by the kidneys ***(1 mark)***. Reducing the amount of salt in the diet reduces the amount of work that the kidneys have to do / this reduces the chance of a dangerous build up of salt between dialysis sessions ***(1 mark)***.

4 B ***(1 mark)***

Page 110

Warm-Up Questions

1) food / drink
2) the pancreas
3) It's a disorder where the pancreas doesn't produce enough insulin so a person's blood sugar level can get too high.
4) Using a glucose-monitoring device — they prick a finger to get a drop of blood, which the handheld machine checks.

Exam Questions

1 (a) (i) pancreas ***(1 mark)***

(ii) liver ***(1 mark)***

(b) (i) E.g. after eating a meal containing carbohydrate/sugar ***(1 mark)***.

(ii) cellular metabolism / respiration ***(1 mark)***

(iii) E.g. vigorous exercise ***(1 mark)***

2 (a) Any two of, large amounts can be regularly produced / there's less chance of allergic reactions / it is 'human' insulin and therefore more effective ***(1 mark for each)***.

(b) Advantage — any one of, e.g. it's a permanent cure/there's no need for any more injections / the person can have a more normal diet / the person avoids all of the risks associated with diabetes that isn't properly controlled ***(1 mark)***.

Disadvantage — any one of, e.g. there's a possibility of rejection / the person will need to take immunosuppressive drugs / it involves surgery, which always carries some risk ***(1 mark)***.

Page 111

Revision Summary for Biology 2(ii)

4) a) 1.65

b) the stomach

Page 116

Warm-Up Questions

1) deoxyribose nucleic acid
2) mitosis
3) ovaries and testes / reproductive organs
4) 46
5) 23

Exam Questions

1 Before the cell starts to divide, the DNA is duplicated ***(1 mark)***. The cell then divides twice, during which the chromosomes line up in pairs and are pulled apart ***(1 mark)***. Four gametes are produced, each with a single set of chromosomes ***(1 mark)***.

2 (a) Yes ***(1 mark)***, because his DNA profile has the same pattern as the DNA profile from the blood at the crime scene ***(1 mark)***.

(b) It is true that usually everyone's DNA is unique ***(1 mark)***, but identical twins have the same DNA and so would have identical genetic fingerprints ***(1 mark)***.

3 (a) (i) Each cell should contain only three chromatids ***(1 mark)***, and there should be one of each type ***(1 mark)*** as shown:

Remember that there are two divisions in meiosis. In the first division, one chromosome from each pair goes into each of two new cells. In the second division, both those cells divide again, with one half of each chromosome going into each of the new cells.

(ii) They contain half the genetic material that the original cell contained ***(1 mark)***.

(b) Any three of, e.g. it involves two divisions, instead of one / it halves the chromosome number, rather than keeping it constant / it produces genetically different cells, not genetically identical cells / it produces sex cells/gametes, not body cells ***(1 mark for each)***.

Page 121

Warm-Up Questions

1) E.g. white blood cell / red blood cell
2) It's the process by which a cell changes to become specialised for its job.
3) Any two of, e.g. paralysis / diabetes / heart disease.
4) a) XY

b) XX

Exam Questions

1 (a) They are undifferentiated cells ***(1 mark)*** that can develop into different types of/specialised cells ***(1 mark)***.

(b) They could be grown into a particular type of cell, which can then be used to replace faulty cells ***(1 mark)***.

(c) Any one of, embryonic stems cells have the potential to develop into any kind of cell, adult stem cells can only develop into certain types of cell / embryonic stem cells are more versatile than adult stem cells ***(1 mark)***.

(d) E.g. bone marrow ***(1 mark)***.

(e) For, e.g. curing patients who are suffering is more important than the rights of an embryo ***(1 mark)***.

Against, e.g. they feel that embryos shouldn't be used for experiments since each one is a potential life / it is not ethical that one person should benefit from another person's suffering ***(1 mark)***.

This is a place where you need to make sure that you know about both sides of the argument.

2 C ***(1 mark)***

Page 128-129

Warm-Up Questions

1) They're different versions of the same gene.
2) The allele which causes cystic fibrosis is a recessive allele, so people can have one copy of the allele and not have the disorder/show any symptoms.
3) It's a genetic disorder of the nervous system.
4) A cell is removed from the embryo and its genes are analysed so that genetic disorders can be detected.
5) 1:1

Exam Questions

1 (a) No ***(1 mark)***, because colour-blindness isn't a significant health issue / embryos are only screened for serious genetic disorders ***(1 mark)***.

(b) Certain types of gene increase the risk of cancer, but they aren't a definite indication that the person will develop cancer ***(1 mark)***. Also some types of cancer can be treated successfully ***(1 mark)***. It can be argued that it isn't right to destroy an embryo because it might develop a disease which could be treatable ***(1 mark)***.

(c) An alternative is prenatal testing ***(1 mark)***. This is when a couple conceive naturally and the fetus is tested when it is in the mother's womb ***(1 mark)***.

Extracts can be a bit scary — all that scientific information in a big wodge. Try reading the extract once, then reading the questions and then reading the extract again, underlining any useful bits. The extract's there to help you with the questions — so use it.

2 (a) White flowers ***(1 mark)***

(b) (i) FF ***(1 mark)***

(ii) ff ***(1 mark)***

(iii) Ff ***(1 mark)***

(c) E.g. they are smaller / easier to keep and breed / grow more quickly ***(1 mark)***.

3 (a)

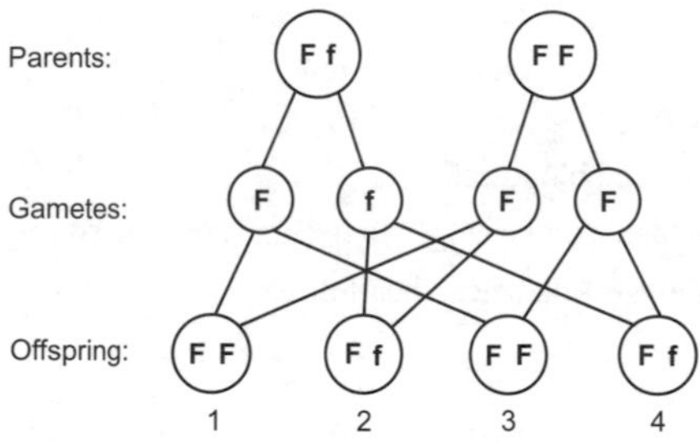

(1 mark for gametes correct, 1 mark for offspring correct)

(b) They will all be unaffected ***(1 mark)***.

(c) (i) 1 in 2 / 50% ***(1 mark)***

(ii) 2 and 4 ***(1 mark)***

Page 130

Revision Summary for Biology 2(iii)

12) 50%

19) BB and bb

Page 136

Warm-Up Questions

1) Through the stomata.
2) The intercostal muscles and diaphragm relax. The volume of the thorax decreases and air is forced out .
3) alveoli
4) Active transport involves moving substances from an area of lower concentration to an area of higher concentration — diffusion can only move substances the other way (down a concentration gradient).

   Active transport needs energy from respiration and diffusion does not.

Exam Questions

1 Answer should be similar to: The diaphragm contracts ***(1 mark)***, and the intercostal muscles contract ***(1 mark)***. This increases the volume of the thorax ***(1 mark)***, and so decreases the pressure in the thorax, drawing air in ***(1 mark)***.

2 (a) The products of digestion move by diffusion down their concentration gradients into the blood ***(1 mark)***, and by active transport, against their concentration gradient ***(1 mark)***.

(b) E.g. they increase the surface area to maximise absorption ***(1 mark)***. They have a thin wall to reduce the distance across which diffusion occurs ***(1 mark)***. They have a good blood supply for the uptake of substances ***(1 mark)***.

3 (a) It has a hair-like shape that sticks out into the soil, creating a large surface area for diffusion/active transport ***(1 mark)***.

(b) The concentration of mineral ions is higher inside the root hair cell than in the soil around it ***(1 mark)***. So mineral ions are absorbed by active transport ***(1 mark)*** against a concentration gradient/using energy from respiration ***(1 mark)***.

Page 141

Warm-Up Questions

1) It carries deoxygenated blood.
2) The heart has two sides, which each pump blood to different areas of the body.
3) Any four of, e.g. red blood cells / white blood cells / platelets / glucose / amino acids / carbon dioxide / urea / hormones / antibodies / antitoxins.
4) Any three of, e.g. the heart rate increases / the breathing rate increases / respiration rate increases / more energy is released in the muscles / anaerobic respiration may begin.
5) glycogen

Exam Questions

1 D ***(1 mark)***

2 (a) During vigorous exercise the body can't supply enough oxygen to the muscles ***(1 mark)***. It uses anaerobic respiration to provide energy without using oxygen, which keeps the muscles going for longer ***(1 mark)***.

(b) glucose → lactic acid + energy ***(1 mark)***.

(c) It causes a build up of lactic acid, which is painful ***(1 mark)*** and it doesn't release as much energy as aerobic respiration ***(1 mark)***.

3 (a) During exercise the muscles need more energy from respiration, and this respiration requires oxygen. So the rate of respiration increases and so does the rate of oxygen use ***(1 mark)***.

(b)

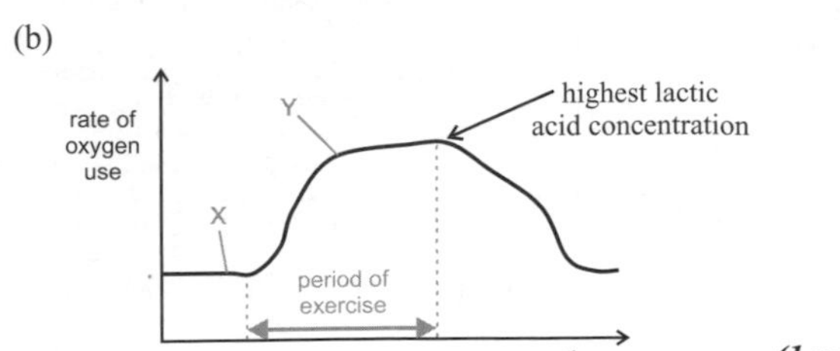

(1 mark)

This isn't a question that involves simply repeating facts you have learned, so don't worry if you found it difficult. You should know that lactic acid builds up when there isn't enough oxygen for aerobic respiration, and then hopefully you can work out that this would happen when oxygen consumption was at its peak (and when the person had been exercising for the longest).

(c) Because there is an oxygen debt / oxygen is needed to break down the lactic acid that has built up ***(1 mark)***.

20) a)

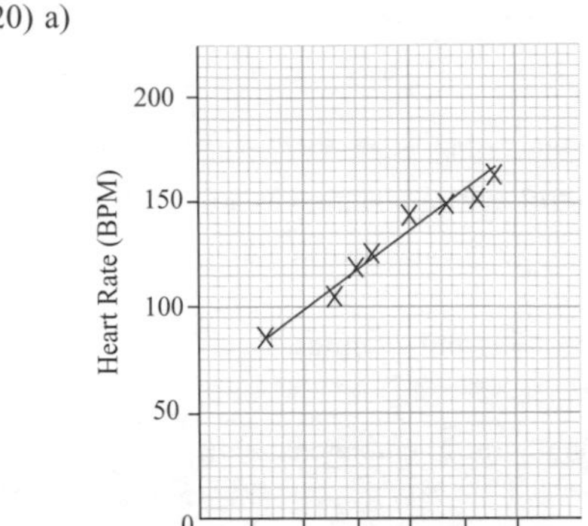

b) It shows that oxygen consumption increases as heart rate increases.

c) When the athlete exercises their muscles consume more oxygen (because they need more energy to contract faster). The heart rate needs to increase in order to supply more oxygen.

Page 145

Warm-Up Questions

1) Part of the kidney, where the blood is filtered and purified.
2) active transport
3) Wastes substances build up in the blood and that person will lose their ability to control the levels of ions and water in their body. It could result in death.

Exam Questions

1 5, 2, 4, 3, 1 ***(1 mark)***

2 (a) Glucose is reabsorbed back into the blood ***(1 mark)***.

(b) The membranes between the blood and the capsule act like filters ***(1 mark)***, and protein molecules are too big to fit through ***(1 mark)***.

3 (a) (i) The urea diffuses out through the dialysis membrane ***(1 mark)***, because the concentration of urea in the blood is more than in the dialysis fluid/because the dialysis fluid contains no urea ***(1 mark)***.

(ii) The dialysis fluid contains the same concentration of glucose as healthy blood ***(1 mark)***, so there is no concentration gradient and glucose ***(1 mark)***.

(b) E.g. She will not have to have dialysis sessions three times every week for hours each time ***(1 mark)***.

Page 146

Revision Summary for Biology 3(i)

18) a) The athlete's body will make more red blood cells to compensate for the lower oxygen levels at night. The increased number of red blood cells will allow the athlete to get more oxygen to his or her muscle cells for respiration, meaning more energy is released. This may improve their performance.

b) Live/sleep at a high altitude, e.g. up a mountain.

Page 152

Warm-Up Questions

1) It's the theory that living things are created from other living organisms.
2) The milk is heat treated first to kill off any bacteria that may be in it, then cooled. A starter culture of bacteria is then added. The bacteria ferment the lactose sugar in the milk to lactic acid. The acid causes the milk to clot and solidify into yoghurt.
3) Barley grains are allowed to germinate for a few days, during which the starch in the grains is broken down into sugar by enzymes. Then the grains are dried in a kiln.
4) *Fusarium*

Exam Questions

1 (a) X = cell wall ***(1 mark)***

Y = nucleus ***(1 mark)***

This yeast cell looks a bit odd but the bits you have to identify are still the same as any other cell.

(b) (i) The yeast ferments (respires anaerobically) the sugar in the grape juice ***(1 mark)***, converting it to ethanol/alcohol ***(1 mark)***.

(ii) To prevent the yeast from respiring aerobically, which will not produce ethanol ***(1 mark)***.

(iii) glucose $\rightarrow$ ethanol + carbon dioxide + energy ***(1 mark)***

(c) Any one of, e.g. bread / beer ***(1 mark)***.

2 (a) It's used to make meat substitutes for vegetarian meals ***(1 mark)***.

(b) Because the fungus produces heat energy as it respires ***(1 mark)***. Too much heat will denature its enzymes and too low a temperature will be less efficient ***(1 mark)***.

(c) Any two of, e.g. pH / concentration of nutrients / concentration of oxygen / concentration of carbon dioxide/waste products ***(1 mark for each)***.

Page 157

Warm-Up Questions

1) Yeast break down glucose into ethanol by anaerobic respiration.
2) It's a mixture of ethanol and petrol that can be used as a fuel for vehicles.
3) An inlet for waste material, an outlet for the digested material and an outlet for the biogas.
4) Carbohydrates, mineral ions, proteins and vitamins.
5) E.g. petri dishes, inoculating loops.
6) To reduce the chance of growing harmful pathogens.

Exam Questions

1 (a) methane ***(1 mark)***

(b) Advantage — any one of, e.g. they are mechanically loaded and emptied, this has to be done manually in batch generators / they don't have to be continuously cleaned / they produce biogas all the time ***(1 mark)***.

Disadvantage — e.g. they are more expensive to set up than batch generators ***(1 mark)***.

(c) The rate of biogas production is faster at higher temperatures. Nigeria and Brazil have higher average temperatures than England and Denmark ***(1 mark)***.

2 (a) Biological waste (e.g. sewage / food scraps / animal dung / remains of plants) ***(1 mark)***.

(b) (i) Because of the unpleasant smell / possibility of harmful bacteria in the waste ***(1 mark)***.

It's really just common sense that something which is busy fermenting poo and rubbish will smell. Don't be afraid to give common sense answers — examiners like to see that you can relate science to real life.

(ii) So it is convenient for adding animal/plant waste ***(1 mark)***.

(c) Any two of, e.g. it is carbon neutral / it produces less sulfur/nitrogen oxides/acid rain / harmful methane is burned away / it is cheap/ readily available / the digested material can be used as a fertiliser / (potentially harmful) waste is disposed of / it saves the damaging effects of mining the coal ***(1 mark for each)***.

Page 158

Revision Summary for Biology 3(ii)

8) Heating yeast to 90 °C for 2 hours kills it. Keeping yeast at 0 °C doesn't kill it. You could repeat your experiment to check if you get the same results.

14) a) Biogas is suitable because waste from the goats and cows can be used in the biogas generator.

Advantages — villagers won't have to spend time collecting wood, digested material could be used to fertilise soil, and waste would be disposed of, reducing disease.

Disadvantages — biogas production slows down in cold conditions, so they might need an alternative fuel source in winter.

b) Their conclusion isn't valid. Possible reasons: the amounts spread on the ground might have been different, the weather in the two places might have been different, the species of crop might have been different etc.

15) a)

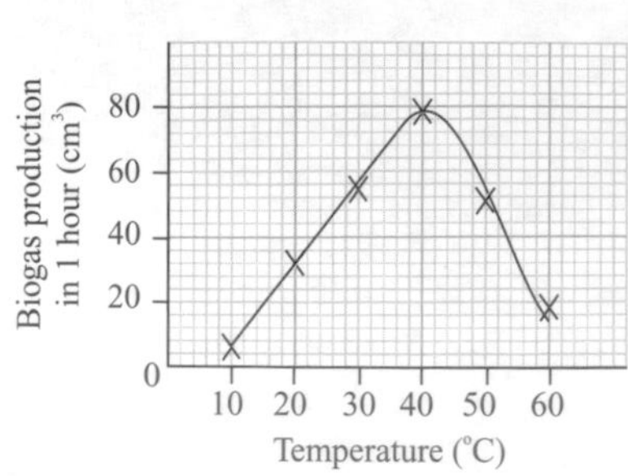

b) 40 °C

c) 44 cm³ in 1 hour so it's 44 x 24 = 1056 cm³ in 24 hours.

PRACTICE EXAM PAPER ANSWERS

Unit Biology 1a — Human Biology (p.165)

1 A 2 ***(1 mark)*** *Patient A fits the bill.*
B 1 ***(1 mark)*** *People with diabetes can't control their blood sugar level very well so it's likely to be high.*
C 4 ***(1 mark)*** *The heaviest smoker is most likely to get lung cancer.*
D 3 ***(1 mark)*** *High blood pressure, smoking and obesity all increase the chance of getting heart disease.*

2 A 2 ***(1 mark)***
B 4 ***(1 mark)*** *It's a choice between 2 and 4, but ions aren't lost in breath so it must be 4.*
C 3 ***(1 mark)***
D 1 ***(1 mark)***

3 A 4 ***(1 mark)*** *Hormones always travel in the blood.*
B 1 ***(1 mark)*** *IVF doesn't guarantee having twins and you can't choose what colour eyes the baby will have.*
C 2 ***(1 mark)***
D 3 ***(1 mark)*** *The introduction states that they can cause abdominal pain and dehydration.*

4 A 1 ***(1 mark)*** *It's the one that causes the biggest clear patch around the disc (where the antibiotic has killed the bacteria).*
B 4 ***(1 mark)*** *The dependent variable is the thing that you measure.*
C 3 ***(1 mark)***
D 2 ***(1 mark)*** *If the bacteria have developed resistance the antibiotic wouldn't kill them.*

5 A 3 ***(1 mark)***
B 1 ***(1 mark)*** *The graph only shows data for people of one weight (75 kg) so it can't be 1.*
C 2 ***(1 mark)***
D 2 ***(1 mark)*** *The graph only shows data for one type of wine, some may contain far more alcohol.*

6 A 4 ***(1 mark)***
B 3 ***(1 mark)*** *(7 × 30) + (14 × 10) = 350 kJ*
C 3 ***(1 mark)*** *760 ÷ 40 = 19*
D 4 ***(1 mark)*** *He'll put on weight but his diet could cause deficiency diseases too (it's unbalanced).*

7 A 4 ***(1 mark)***
B 4 ***(1 mark)*** *With these kind of questions look for anything that could also affect the thing you're looking at.*
C 1 ***(1 mark)***
D 4 ***(1 mark)*** *It's not just the heart it affects, it's the blood vessels too.*

8 A 3 ***(1 mark)*** *18 became immune so two didn't. Only seven suffered side effects, which isn't the majority or near 50%.*
B 1 ***(1 mark)***
C 2 ***(1 mark)***
D 4 ***(1 mark)***

9 A 2 ***(1 mark)*** *A stimulus is a change in environment, e.g. someone poking your neck.*
B 2 ***(1 mark)*** *Reflexes are automatic, if you have to think about what response to give then it's not a reflex action.*
C 3 ***(1 mark)*** *The more you repeat an experiment the more reliable your result becomes.*
D 2 ***(1 mark)***

Unit Biology 1b — Evolution and the Environment (p.180)

1 A 3 ***(1 mark)*** *Plants remove carbon dioxide from the air for photosynthesis.*
B 2 ***(1 mark)*** *Cattle release methane gas, which enters the atmosphere.*
C 4 ***(1 mark)*** *Excess fertiliser can be washed into rivers and streams, causing pollution.*
D 1 ***(1 mark)*** *Carbon dioxide is produced when petrol or diesel is burnt.*

2 A 2 ***(1 mark)*** *This is the only site with lichen that need clean air to survive, so it must be unpolluted.*
B 1 ***(1 mark)*** *There is a high number of sulfur tolerant lichen Y, so it must be an area polluted with sulfur dioxide.*
C 3 ***(1 mark)*** *This area is polluted with ozone as there are more of Lichen X in this area than anywhere else.*
D 4 ***(1 mark)***

3 A 1 ***(1 mark)***
B 2 ***(1 mark)*** *The starting mass doesn't matter because you measure % increase in mass.*
C 1 ***(1 mark)***
D 2 ***(1 mark)*** *There may be no allele in the population to give resistance to a new disease — the plants could be killed.*

4 A 2 ***(1 mark)*** *Organisms that are less well adapted to the environment have a reduced chance of survival.*
B 4 ***(1 mark)***
C 1 ***(1 mark)***
D 4 ***(1 mark)***

5 A 1 ***(1 mark)***
B 3 ***(1 mark)***
C 2 ***(1 mark)*** *Some people may believe that it is fine to interfere with natural processes, so it is only an opinion.*
D 1 ***(1 mark)***

6 A 3 ***(1 mark)*** *300 − 25 = 275*
B 1 ***(1 mark)***
C 3 ***(1 mark)*** *Be careful — the other three options may be likely, but you can't tell from the graph.*
D 2 ***(1 mark)*** *Look for the point on the graph where the lines cross.*

7 A 3 ***(1 mark)*** *Look for where the line on the graph falls suddenly — it must be after point 8.*
B 1 ***(1 mark)***
C 3 ***(1 mark)***
D 1 ***(1 mark)*** *Read across the graph from 5 mg/l and see which points fall under this level.*

8 A 1 ***(1 mark)*** *Genes control a person's characteristics.*
B 3 ***(1 mark)***
C 2 ***(1 mark)***
D 3 ***(1 mark)*** *Carlo and Louis have an identical gene pool to pass on, so their children will share similar characteristics.*

9 A 2 ***(1 mark)***
B 3 ***(1 mark)*** *Natural selection always starts with a variation in genetic material, giving rise to new characteristics.*
C 2 ***(1 mark)***
D 2 ***(1 mark)***

Unit Biology 2 (p.195)

1 (a) Nitrogen is needed for the synthesis of amino acids/proteins ***(1 mark)***, which are essential for growth ***(1 mark)***.
(b) They would have yellow leaves ***(1 mark)*** because without magnesium the plants can't make chlorophyll, which gives plants their green colour ***(1 mark)***.
(c) *Any one of*, e.g. the amount of light shining on each beaker / the level of other substances in the mineral solution / the size of the beakers / the amount of air available / the amount of water available ***(1 mark)***.
(d) E.g. plants grow at a faster rate with both magnesium and nitrates ***(1 mark)***.

2 (a) alleles ***(1 mark)***
(b) (i) Because a person's DNA is unique ***(1 mark)***, so if the suspect's DNA matches a sample from the crime scene it shows they were probably there ***(1 mark)***.
Everyone has unique DNA, except identical twins.
(ii) Identical twins have the same DNA so it isn't possible to distinguish between them ***(1 mark)***.
(iii) *Any one of*, e.g. people think it is an invasion of privacy / the information could be used to find out about a physical characteristics/health / a mistake could mean an innocent person was accused of a crime / it could be expensive to set up / the information could be leaked to other people who might misuse it ***(1 mark)***.

3 (a) oxygen ***(1 mark)***
Remember, plants give off oxygen when they photosynthesise.
(b) It would decrease ***(1 mark)***, because the decrease in light intensity would decrease the rate of photosynthesis ***(1 mark)***.
(c) It is absorbed by chlorophyll in the chloroplasts of the cells ***(1 mark)***.
(d) It is used to convert carbon dioxide and water into glucose / for photosynthesis ***(1 mark)***.
(e) Carbon dioxide is needed for photosynthesis ***(1 mark)***, so adding it to the water ensures that the rate of photosynthesis is not limited by a lack of carbon dioxide ***(1 mark)***.

4 (a) The Sun ***(1 mark)***.
(b) (130 ÷ 1100) × 100% = 11.8% ***(2 marks for correct answer, otherwise 1 mark for correct working)***
It's always a good idea to show your working — if you don't get the right answer you could still pick up some marks if you were on the right tracks.
(c) *Any two of*, e.g. energy is used for respiration/movement/growth / energy is lost in waste materials/as heat ***(1 mark for each correct answer)***.
(d) So much energy is lost at each stage of a food chain, that there isn't enough energy to support another trophic level after about four stages ***(1 mark)***.

5 (a) It is broken down into sugars ***(1 mark)***.
(b) Approximately 37 °C (accept values between 35 °C and 40 °C) ***(1 mark)***.
(c) The increasing temperature causes the enzyme to change shape/ denature ***(1 mark)***. This means that it no longer matches the shape of the starch, so cannot catalyse its breakdown, so the time taken for the reaction to be complete increases ***(1 mark)***.
(d) The pH must be kept constant to ensure it is a fair test, because the rate at which the enzyme works also depends on the pH of the solution ***(1 mark)***.

6 (a) 37 °C ***(1 mark)***
(b) The thermoregulatory centre of the brain ***(1 mark)*** contains receptors that monitor the temperature of blood flowing past them ***(1 mark)*** and receive information from temperature receptors in the skin ***(1 mark)***.
(c) Blood vessels close to the surface of the skin would have constricted ***(1 mark)*** to reduce the amount of heat lost from the skin ***(1 mark)***. His muscles would also have contracted causing shivering ***(1 mark)***, which generates heat ***(1 mark)***.

7 (a) Each new plant would have inherited one allele for round seed coats and one allele for wrinkled seed coats ***(1 mark)***. Since all the offspring had round seed coats, this allele must be dominant ***(1 mark)***.
(b) (i)

(1 mark for each correct level)
(ii) 5474 ÷ 1850 = 2.96 (to 2 d.p.), so the ratio is 2.96:1 ***(1 mark)***
(iii) Because fertilisation is a random process / the genetic diagram only shows the probability ***(1 mark)***
(c) E.g. because scientists in Mendel's time had no knowledge of genes or DNA, so they did not understand the significance of his work ***(1 mark)***.

Unit Biology 3 (p.208)

1 (a) (i) oxygen ***(1 mark)***

(ii) carbon dioxide ***(1 mark)***

A fairly easy one to get you started, the job of the lungs is to transfer oxygen to the blood and remove waste carbon dioxide from it.

(b) *Any three of,* they provide a large surface area for diffusion to occur across / they have thin walls, which decreases the distance for diffusion to occur across / they have a good blood supply to maintain a high concentration gradient / they have a moist lining for dissolving gases, which aids diffusion ***(1 mark for each correct answer)***.

(c) (i) 100 – 78 – 4.04 – 0.96 = 17% ***(1 mark)***

(ii)100 – 78 – 21 – 0.96 = 0.04% ***(1 mark)***

2 (a) arteries ***(1 mark)***, capillaries ***(1 mark)***, veins ***(1 mark)***.

(b) *Any two of,* e.g. products of digestion/digested food (or named food substance, such as glucose) from the intestine to the liver/respiring cells / urea from the liver to the kidneys / hormones (or a named hormone such as insulin) from an endocrine gland to its target organ ***(1 mark for each correct answer)***.

3 (a) Loss of water vapour from the surface of plant leaves ***(1 mark)***.

(b) noon ***(1 mark)***

(c) *Any one of, e.g.* day 2 was colder, so the water evaporated/diffused slower. / Day 2 was less windy, so the water vapour was carried away slower. / Day 2 was wetter/more humid, so there was a smaller diffusion gradient ***(1 mark for reason, 1 mark for explanation)***.

(d) The plant has lost too much water/has lost water faster than it could be replaced through the roots ***(1 mark)***.

4 (a) (i) The blood is filtered at Bowman's capsule and proteins are too big to pass through the membrane ***(1 mark)***.

(ii) E.g. red blood cells ***(1 mark)***.

Proteins and red blood cells are too large to be filtered out of the blood into the Bowman's capsule.

(b) Urea is not reabsorbed into the blood, so its concentration increases through the nephron as sufficient water is reabsorbed ***(1 mark)***.

(c) The concentration of sugar at point B would be high, there would be no sugar at point C, as all sugar is reabsorbed back into the blood in the first part of the nephron ***(1 mark)***.

(d) The cells need extra energy to actively transport sugars, ions and amino acids back into the blood ***(1 mark)***. This extra energy is provided by the large number of mitochondria ***(1 mark)***.

5 (a) The theory that living organisms can only develop from other living ` organisms ***(1 mark)***.

(b) (i) The swan-necked flask prevented the entry of microorganisms into the broth ***(1 mark)***.

(ii) To show that it was not the absence of air that prevented microorganisms from forming ***(1 mark)***.

(iii) The neck of the flask was broken in one flask to act as a control ***(1 mark)***, to show that microorganisms could grow in the nutrient broth if they could reach it ***(1 mark)***.

(c) By examining it with a microscope ***(1 mark)***.

(d) To show that Pasteur's results were reliable ***(1 mark)***.

They might just throw in a couple of how science works questions like this one in the exam. Make sure you know all about what makes results reliable and how to spot bias.

6 (a) *Penicillium* ***(1 mark)***

(b) *Any two of,* water-cooled jacket removes heat produced by microorganisms / the paddles of the stirrer even out the heat ***(1 mark for each correct answer)***.

It doesn't matter if you don't know a single thing about penicillin production — all the information you need to answer this question is in the diagram.

(c) Because the microorganism used in penicillin production doesn't begin to produce penicillin until most of the nutrients have been used up ***(1 mark)***.

7 (a) (i) As the rate of work increases Nancy's blood lactic acid concentration also increases ***(1 mark)***.

(ii) During vigorous exercise the body can't supply enough oxygen to the muscles so they start to respire anaerobically as well as aerobically ***(1 mark)***. Anaerobic respiration produces lactic acid ***(1 mark)***. The harder the muscles work, the more they'll resort to anaerobic respiration and the more lactic acid they'll produce ***(1 mark)***.

(b) After vigorous exercise the body has an oxygen debt ***(1 mark)***. Nancy's pulse rate and breathing rate remain high to help oxidise the lactic acid that has built up ***(1 mark)***.

8 (a) (i) guard cells ***(1 mark)***

(ii) When the plant has plenty of water they become turgid, which makes the stoma open ***(1 mark)***. When the plant loses water they becomes flaccid, which makes the stoma close ***(1 mark)***.

(b) To allow entry of carbon dioxide (for photosynthesis) ***(1 mark)***.

(c) E.g. the guard cells are sensitive to light and close when it's dark ***(1 mark)***.

Index

A

accuracy of results 162
acid rain 155
active transport 131, 135
acupuncture 26
adaptation 39, 40
adult cell cloning 50
aerobic respiration 95, 149, 151
agar jelly 156
AIDS 25
alcohol 27, 149
alginate beads 99
alleles 45, 123
allergies 99
alveoli 133, 134
amino acids 93, 94, 97, 112
amylase 97, 98
anaerobic respiration 95, 140, 149, 153
angina 22
animal cells 68
animal embryos 51
anomalies 161, 163
antibiotic resistance 35
antibiotics 35, 36, 88
antibodies 33
antigens 33
antiseptic solution 36
antitoxins 138
antiviral drugs 35, 36
applying scientific knowledge 159
arctic animals 39
armour 40
arteries 137, 139
arthritis 21
asexual reproduction 46, 114, 115
Atkins diet 29
averages 5, 161

B

baby foods 99
bacteria 32, 33, 35, 36, 148, 153, 154
balanced diet 20
Banting, Frederick 108, 109
batch generators 153-155
beer 149
Best, Charles 108, 109
bias 5
bile 97, 98
biodegradable 99
biodiversity 63, 64
biofuels 155
biogas 153
biogas generators 153-155
biogenesis 147
biological catalysts 93, 94
biological detergents 99
biomass 84, 85
blood
  circulation 137, 138
  in homeostasis 103
  plasma 11, 17
  sugar levels 17, 106-109
  vessels 22, 26, 102
body temperature 18, 102
bone marrow 117
bone marrow transplants 7, 118
Bowman's capsule 142
brain 8, 18
bread 149
breathing 133
breathing rate 139, 140
bronchi 133
bronchioles 133
bronchitis 26

C

cacti 40
caffeine 25
camels 39
Canadian pondweed 77
cancer 16, 21, 25, 26
cannabis 28, 30
capillaries 137, 138
carbohydrase 99, 153
carbohydrates 20, 106, 107, 156
carbon cycle 89
carbon dioxide 59, 60, 76, 101, 132-134, 137-140, 153, 155
carbon monoxide 26
carriers 124
catalysts 93, 94
categoric variables 162
cattle rearing 60
cell fibres 114
cell membranes 68, 82, 124, 134
cells 68, 69
cell sap 68
cellulose 68, 81
cell walls 68, 81
central nervous system 8
cheese 148
chemical messengers 11
chemical reactions 93
chest infections 26
chlorophyll 68, 76, 82
chloroplasts 68, 70, 76
cholesterol 22, 23
chromosomes 45, 112, 114, 115, 119
cilia 26
circulation system 137
climate change 6, 61, 62
clinical trials 25
clones 46, 49, 113
cloning 49, 50
cocaine 25, 28
competition 41, 42
compost heaps 86
concentration gradients 135
conclusions 164
contamination 156
continuous data 162
continuous generators 153-155
contraception 16
control groups 160, 164
controlled experiments 3
correlations 163
culture medium 156
cuttings 49
cystic fibrosis 124
cytoplasm 68, 114

D

Darwin, Charles 55
data 21
decay 86
deficiency diseases
  humans 20
  plants 82
dependent variables 160
desert animals 39
desert plants 40
detritus feeders 89
diabetes 17, 21, 107-109, 118
dialysis machines 143
diaphragm 133
diet 20
differentiation 117
diffusion 72, 73, 131, 134
digester 153
digestion 97, 98
discrete data 162
disease 36, 41
distillation 153
DNA 45, 82, 112-115, 122
DNA fingerprinting 113
Dolly the sheep 50
dominant alleles 122-124, 126, 127
double circulation system 137
drugs 25-30, 35

E

effectors 8, 9
egg cells 14, 71, 115, 119
embryonic screening 7, 125
embryonic stem cells 117, 118
embryos 16, 117, 118
embryo transplants (animals) 49
emphysema 26
emulsifiers 97, 98
energy 20, 95, 135, 139
energy transfer 85
environment 57, 58
environmental variation 44
enzymes 51, 93-95, 97-99
  denatured 94
  in industry 99
ethanol 149, 153
ethical questions 6, 7
evidence 1-4
evolution 54, 55
exchange surfaces 131, 132
exercise 20, 139, 140
experiment questions 160-164
experiments 1-3
extinction 54

F

faeces 98
fair tests 3, 78
family tree 54

Index

fatigue 21
fats 97
fatty acids 97
fermentation 149, 153
fermenters 150, 151
fertilisation 115
fertiliser 82, 155
fertility 16
fertility clinics 118
fibre 20
fish stocks 88
follicle-stimulating hormone (FSH) 15, 16
food chains 84-86
food groups 20
food scares 29
forensic science 113
fossil fuels 88
fossils 54
fructose 81
fruits 81
fuels 153-155
fungi 149, 151
Fusarium 151
fusion cell cloning 50

G

gall bladder 97, 98
gametes 115, 120
gas exchange 70, 131-134
gasohol 153
gateway drug 28
genes 45, 112, 122-124
gene therapy 51
genetics 112-130
  genetic diagrams 120, 123-127
  genetic disorders 51, 124, 125
  genetic engineering 51, 52, 109
  genetic experiments 122
genetically modified (GM) crops 52
genetic variation 44, 47
glands 11, 98
global warming 6, 59, 155
glucose 17, 76, 81, 95, 106, 107, 139
glycerol 97
glycogen 139
greenhouse effect 59, 60
greenhouse gases 155
greenhouses 78, 79
grey squirrels 42
growth medium 156
guard cells 70, 132
gullet 98
gut 97, 98, 135

H

haemoglobin 26, 71, 138
hamsters 123
health claims 29, 30
heart 26, 137
heart attack 22, 26
heart disease 21, 22, 30, 118
heart rate 139, 140
heroin 25, 28
hypnosis 26
high blood pressure 21, 22
high density lipoproteins (HDLs) 23
homeostasis 17, 18, 101-104
hops 149
hormonal responses 12
hormones 11, 12, 15, 16, 106
human impact (on the environment) 57, 58, 64
Huntington's 124
hygiene 36
hypertension 22
hypotheses 1, 2

I

identical twins 113
immune system 33
immunisation 34
immunity 36, 88
independent variables 160
indicator species 64
infectious disease 41
inoculating loops 156
insulin 17, 51, 106-109, 118
intercostal muscles 133
in vitro fertilisation (IVF) 16, 125
ion content 17, 101, 104
ions 17, 103, 104, 142, 143
isomerase 99

K

kidneys 17, 103, 104, 142-144
  kidney dialysis 143
  kidney failure 143, 144
  kidney transplant 144
  kidney tubules 135

L

lab experiments 4
lactic acid 140
large intestine 98
leprosy 25
light meter 77
limiting factors 77-79
limits of science 6
line of best fit 163
lipase 97-99
lipids 81
lipoproteins 23
liver 22, 27, 97, 98, 107, 139
low density lipoproteins (LDLs) 23
lung cancer 26
lungs 26, 133, 137, 140
luteinising hormone (LH) 15, 16

M

magnesium 82
maize starch 153
malnutrition 20, 21
managing food production 88
mean (or average) 161
measles 34, 36
medical drug testing 25
meiosis 115
Mendel, Gregor 122
menstrual cycle 14, 15
metabolic rate 20
metabolism 17, 20, 106
methane 59, 60, 153, 155
microorganisms 34, 86, 89, 99, 147-156
minerals 20, 81, 82
  deficiency symptoms 82
mitochondria 68, 71
mitosis 114, 115
MMR vaccine 34
monoculture 82
monounsaturated fats 23
moral questions 6
motor neurones 8, 9
mould 151
MRSA (methicillin-resistant *Staphylococcus aureus*) 35, 36
mucus 26, 33
mumps 34, 36
muscles 139
mutations 55
mycoprotein 151

N

natural selection 35, 55
negative correlations 163
nephrons 142
nerves 12
nervous system 8, 27, 124
NHS (National Health Service) 21, 27
nicotine 25, 26
nitrates 82
nitrogen oxides 155
nucleus 45, 68, 112, 114
nutrients 89

O

obesity 21
ocean currents 62
oesophagus 98
oestrogen 15, 16
offspring 122-127
ordered variable 162
organic farming 88
organs 69
osmosis 73, 74, 131
ovaries 11, 15, 115
oxygen 76, 77, 95, 132-134, 137-139
oxygen debt 140
oxyhaemoglobin 138

P

painkillers 35
palisade leaf cells 70
pancreas 11, 97, 98, 106-109, 124
  transplant 109
pandemic 36
paraffin heaters 79
partially permeable membranes 73

Index

partridges 84
Pasteur, Louis 147
paternity testing 113
pathogens 32, 156
pea plants 122
penicillin 151
Penicillium chrysogenum 151
pepsin 94, 97, 98
petri dishes 156
pH 94, 98, 99
phosphates 82
photosynthesis 70, 76-79, 89
pituitary gland 11, 15
plant cells 68
plasma 138
platelets 33, 138
poisons 40
polio 36
polyunsaturated fats 23
populations 41, 42
positive correlations 163, 164
potassium 82
potatoes 74
precision of results 162
predation 41
predictions 1, 2
primary consumers 84
processed foods 22, 23
producers 84
progesterone 16
protease 97-99
protein 20
protein coat 32
proteins 81, 93-95, 97, 99, 112, 156
protein synthesis 94, 95
pulmonary artery 137
pulmonary vein 137
pyramids of biomass 84, 85
pyramids of number 84

R

random errors 161
range 161
raw materials 57
reabsorption 142
receptors 8
recessive alleles 122-124, 126, 127
recreational drugs 28
rectum 98
red blood cells 71, 117, 138
red squirrels 42
reduced gene pools 49
reflex arcs 9, 10
reflexes 9, 10
relay neurones 9
reliability of results 3, 4
repeating experiments 161
representative samples 3
reproducing results 2, 3
reproduction 46, 47, 71
reproductive organs 115
respiration 81, 85, 89, 95
respiratory system 133
ribcage 133
ribosomes 68
rice growing 60
risk factors 22
root hair cells 135
rubella 34, 36

S

saliva 98
salivary glands 97, 98
salt 22
satellites 62
saturated fats 23
scattergrams 163
scepticism 2
Schwann, Theodor 147
scientific studies 29
scientific theories 1, 2
secondary consumers 84
seeds 81
Semmelweiss, Ignaz 36
sense organs 8
sexually transmitted diseases 16
sexual reproduction 47, 115
shivering 102
sickle cell anaemia 118, 127
silica gel 99
small intestine 97, 98, 134
smallpox 36
smoking 26, 27
sodium 22, 104
solute exchange 131, 132
Spallanzani, Lazzaro 147
specialised cells 69, 70, 71, 117
sperm 71, 115, 119
starch 81, 97, 149
starvation 20, 21
statins 30
statistical correlation 26
stem cells 117, 118
sterilisation 156
stimuli 8
stomach 97, 98
stomata 70, 132
strokes 26
sugar cane juices 153
sugars 95, 97
sulfur dioxide 155
sunlight 76, 77
sustainable development 63, 64
sweat 18, 102, 104
synapses 10
systematic errors 161

T

tar 26
temperature 77-79, 94, 101
testes 11, 115
tetanus 36
thalidomide 25
thermoregulatory centre 102
thorax 133
tissue culture 49
tissue fluid 17, 74
tissues 69
tobacco 27
toxins 32
trachea 133
transpiration 132
trophic levels 84, 85
tobacco 26

U

ultrafiltration 142
unanswerable questions 6
urea 103, 142, 143
urine 17, 18, 103, 104, 142
uterus 14

V

vaccines 34, 36
vacuole 68
validity of results 4
variables 3, 4, 162, 164
variation 44
veins 137
villi 134
viruses 32, 35, 36
vitamins 20, 156

W

warning colours 40
waste products 86, 101
water 18, 73, 74, 76, 104
water bath 78
water content 101, 103, 104
water vapour 132
weather 61, 62
weight problems 21
white blood cells 33
whooping cough 36
wine 149
withdrawal symptoms 25

X

X chromosomes 119, 120

Y

Y chromosomes 119, 120
yeast 149, 153
yoghurt 148